brief contents

v

contents

foreword

The mobile phone and portable device handset are currently undergoing a transformation caused by several different factors. For one, portable devices are getting more powerful and capable of performing tasks that would have been hard to imagine a few short years ago. Many of us carry a portable device that is capable of everything from using the World Wide Web to watching movies to playing 3D games–and it can even make phone calls! For another, consumers are becoming more savvy and demanding about what they want such a device to do. A third part of the convergence is that portable devices now form a bigger market for software and applications developers than larger computing platforms, and delivery of applications to those devices is often easier and more streamlined than to larger ones.

The next generation of phones already includes hardware graphics acceleration, wireless connectivity, data access plans, GPS, hardware expansion and connectivity, touch screens, and so on. Operating systems and applications are being written to take advantage of these new capabilities and the delivery of these applications is undergoing a quiet revolution by putting consumers in control of what their device will do, and connecting developers and consumers with a minimum of fuss and overhead. Consumers get the software they want, and developers get access to a potentially enormous market for their products.

Underlying this transformation is a trend toward more openness. Openness in the capabilities of the devices and how they can be harnessed, openness for the applications that can be developed and brought to market, openness in the collaboration among handset manufacturers, network carriers and software providers. Granted, there is still room for improvement, but I believe no next-generation mobile platform embodies this spirit of openness more than Android.

Android is an operating system born of an alliance of 30 organizations from across the mobile devices industry—hardware manufacturers, carriers, and software companies—committed to bringing a better mobile phone to market. The result is an operating system and application development environment capable of running on multiple devices, providing a consistent and feature rich environment for developers. The larger Android ecosystem will eventually include multiple handsets, myriad applications and components to harness or build on, and multiple distribution channels (including the already available Android marketplace).

Writing applications for Android is in some ways akin to enterprise- or container-based development. Instead of a view of the world where your application runs and at some point quits, Android provides a way for your application to integrate itself into the larger Android environment. This environment is based on Java tools and skills, shortening the learning curve and bringing the ease and security of development in a managed language. Android lets you run services in the background, and provides components and data services that can share or be shared with other applications.

In short, Android is a great environment for application developers and this book will help you take full advantage of it. The authors skillfully guide you—from the development tools, through the architecture, basic and advanced APIs—and on to advanced topics like native application development. *Unlocking Android* is a valuable and useful guide to developing your own applications for this new and exciting open platform.

DICK WALL, SOFTWARE ENGINEER,
FORMER ANDROID ADVOCATE FOR GOOGLE,
AND JAVA POSSE CO-HOST

preface

The first mobile applications I had the opportunity to work with were inventory control programs used in retail and manufacturing settings. The "terminals," as we called them at the time, were heavy and expensive. They had big antennas, lots of clunky keys, grayscale LCD displays, and they looked like they came straight from the set of a science fiction movie.

From that austere beginning, my mobile horizons expanded when the Palm Pilot™ became the craze in the mid to late 1990s. My first significant PalmOS™ project was to develop an IrDA™ communications library for an application which printed Calendars, Contacts, and Task-lists. Back then the "hip" printers had an IrDA™ port and it was cool to "beam" your business card to someone. Ironically, I always enjoyed designing and writing the software more than using the devices themselves.

Fast forward ten years, and I have had the privilege of working on some very challenging and engaging mobile software projects for numerous clients along the way. Much of my career to date can be traced back to relationships stemming from my early mobile development experiences—and what a blessing it has been for me. I just love the question, "would it be possible to…?" And more often than not, the answer has been "Yes!" What I particularly enjoy is helping change the way a business operates or the way problems are solved through the application of mobile software. Mobile technology can and will continue to change the way we live, work and play…and this brings me to Android and this book.

In the fall of 2007 I was speaking with my friend Troy Mott, who happens to also be an editor for Manning, the publisher of this book. Troy and I were discussing the mobile marketplace, something we have done for years. We started kicking around the idea of writing a book on Android. The challenge was that Android didn't really exist. Yet. We knew from some of the preliminary information that the platform promised to be open, capable, and popular. We felt that those ingredients could make for an interesting and valuable topic, so we began thinking about what that book might look like, taking it on faith that the platform would actually come to fruition.

Before long we convinced ourselves (and Manning) that this was a good idea and the work began in early 2008. Beyond the usual challenges of putting a book together, we had the additional obstacle that our subject matter has been in a steady, though unpredictable, state of change over the past year. In essence we've written this book two times because the SDK has been changed multiple times and Android-equipped phones have become available, accelerating the interest and demand for the platform. Every time a significant change occurred, we went back and revisited portions of the book, sometimes rewriting entire chapters to accommodate the latest developments in the Android platform.

I say "we" because in the process of writing this book, Troy and I decided to share the fun and brought in two experienced authors to contribute their expertise and enthusiasm for this platform. It has been a pleasure getting to know and working with both Charlie Collins and Robi Sen.

While I focused on the first and third parts of the book, Charlie and Robi wrote part 2 which covers the important fundamentals of writing Android applications. Thanks to their contributions I enjoyed the freedom to express my vision of what Android means to the mobile space in the first part of the book and then to work on a couple of more advanced applications at the end of the book.

We hope that you enjoy reading this book and that it proves to be a valuable resource for years to come as together we contribute to the future of the Android platform.

FRANK ABLESON

acknowledgments

Naïvely, we thought this book would be completed a year ago. Boy, did we learn a thing or two about what it takes to write a technical book! There were some tense times during the writing of this book, particularly during the conference calls when we were trying to decide how to navigate the numerous SDK updates and indefinite timelines of Android releases. Thankfully those decisions were made, and made well, by the team at Manning.

In particular we'd like to acknowledge and thank those at Manning who helped bring this book about. First, Troy Mott, our acquisitions editor, who was there from the beginning, from the "what if" stages, through helping push us over the goal line; Tom Cirtin, our book editor, who provided input on structure and content; Karen Tegtmeyer, who did all the big and little things to bring the project together; and Marjan Bace, our publisher, whose influence is felt in many places in the book. Marjan always wanted to hear what reviewers didn't like in the book—so we could make it better and satisfy our readers. It wasn't easy, but together, we got it done.

Once the book was "done," the next round of work began and special thanks need to go to three individuals: Linda Recktenwald, our copyeditor who made our content readable in cases where it went either "too geek" or where the geek in us tried to be "too literary;" Elizabeth Martin, our proofreader who added the common sense to the project as well as a terrific sense of humor and encouraging attitude; and Jesse Dailey, our technical proofreader who jumped in and validated our technical work, balanced out the xml indentations, and made the text more readable. Of course there were many more folks behind the scenes at Manning who did the heavy lifting to bring this book to print, and we are indebted to each and every one of them.

Thanks also to Dick Wall, who played the dual role of reviewing our work and writing the foreword. And special thanks to the other reviewers who took time out of their busy schedules to read our manuscript at different times during its development: Bruno Lowagie, Hannu Terävä, Maxim Yudin, Dierk König, Michael Martin, Charles Hudson, Gabor Paller, Scott Webster, Aleksey Nudelman, Horaci Macias, Andrew Oswald, Kevin P. Galligan, Chris Gray, and Tyson S. Maxwell.

Lastly, we want to thank the thoughtful and encouraging MEAP subscribers who provided feedback along the way; the book is better thanks to their contributions.

FRANK ABLESON

I would like to thank Charlie Collins, Robi Sen, and Troy Mott for their contributions, collaboration, and endurance on this project! And to my wife Nikki and children, Julia, Tristan, Natalie, Aidan and Liam—it's done! In particular, I want to thank my son Tristan who was a steady source of encouragement throughout this process, enthusiastically asking how it was going and spurring me toward the finish. Lastly, I would like to thank Barry Quiner and Michael Petrin for their consistent encouragement and friendship.

CHARLIE COLLINS

To begin, I would like to thank my coauthors, Frank Ableson and Robi Sen, who worked diligently on this project from the start, and who welcomed me into the fold. It's finally a book, guys; thanks, and congratulations. Additionally, I would like to reiterate my gratitude to everyone at Manning.

I would also like to thank the Open Handset Alliance, and the entire Android team. Having an open, yet concise and focused, mobile platform such as Android is a huge plus for the technological world, and for users. It's not perfect, yet, but it's a long race and the approach and collaboration can't be underestimated. Along the same lines I would like to thank all of the other contributors to the open tools I used to work on this project, including: Ubuntu Linux, OpenOffice, Eclipse, Subversion, GIMP, and Java.

I also want to thank my friends and family, who once again put up with my taking huge amounts of time away from our shared activities to work on a "tech" book. Many of the people I care about the most will probably read this book up to about, well, here—if they ever pick it up at all. If you are one of those people, thanks. Specifically, my wife Erin, and my daughters Skylar and Delaney, were always supportive and even feigned excitement at the right times to keep me going. My parents Earl and Margaret Farmer were instrumental as always. My mountain biking/fishing/engine building buddy Mike Beringson put up with more than his share of "Sorry, I can't make it" phone calls. And, my neighbors in the cul-de-sac crew also helped get me through it: the Cheathams, the Thomspons, the Crowders, and the Haffs—thanks again to everyone.

Robi Sen

I would like to thank Troy Mott and the team—and everyone at Manning Publications—for their hard work making this book something worth reading. I would like to thank my coauthors, Frank and Charlie, who were great to work with and very understanding when I was the one holding things up. I would also like to thank Jesse Dailey for his technical edits on this book but for assistance with the OpenGL ES samples in chapter 9.

Finally I would like to thank my family who, more of than I liked, had to do without me while I worked on my chapters.

about this book

Unlocking Android doesn't fit nicely into the camp of "introductory text," nor is it a highly detailed reference manual. The text has something to offer for both the complete Android novice and the experienced developer who is looking to sell his or her application in the Android Market. This book covers important beginner topics such as "What is Android" and installing and using the development environment. The text then advances to practical working examples of core programming topics any developer will be happy to have at the ready on the reference shelf. The final part of the book presents a pair of advanced application topics including a field service application with a web-based server side. The final chapter presents an out-of- the-box Native C application discussion and example.

The book is meant to be read from start to finish—and doing so will be of great value, as the chapters are laid out to build upon one another. However, if you are looking for a collection of practical, working samples, this title will also provide great value to you, particularly in part 2, where major subsystems and topics are broken down with practical examples.

The Audience

Unlocking Android is written for professional programmers and hobbyists alike. Many of the concepts can be absorbed without specific Java language knowledge, though the most value will be found by readers with Java programming skills because Android application programming requires them. A reader with C, C++, or C# programming knowledge will be able to follow the examples.

Prior Eclipse experience is helpful, but not required. There are a number of good resources available on Java and Eclipse to augment the content of this book.

Roadmap

This book is divided into three parts. Part 1 contains introductory material about the platform and development environment. Part 2 takes a close look at the fundamental skills required for building Android applications. Part 3 presents a larger scope application and a Native C Android application.

PART 1: THE ESSENTIALS

Part 1 introduces the Android platform including the architecture and setting up the development environment.

Chapter 1 delves into the background and positioning of the Android platform, including comparisons to other popular platforms such as BlackBerry, iPhone, and Windows Mobile. After an introduction to the platform, the balance of the first chapter introduces the high-level architecture of Android applications and the operating system environment.

Chapter 2 takes you on a step-by-step development exercise teaching you the ropes of using the Android development environment, including the key tools and concepts for building an application. If you have never used Eclipse or have never written an Android application, this chapter will prepare you for the next part of the book.

PART 2: THE PROGRAMMING ENVIRONMENT

Part 2 includes an extensive survey of key programming topics in the Android environment.

Chapter 3 covers the fundamental Android UI components, including View and Layout. We also review the Activity in further detail. These are the basic building blocks of screens and applications on the Android platform. Along the way we also touch on other basic concepts such as handling external resources, dealing with events, and the lifecycle of an Android application.

Chapter 4 expands on the concepts we learned in chapter 3 and we delve into the Android Intent to demonstrate interaction between screens, activities, and entire applications. Also we introduce and utilize the Service, which brings background processes into the fold.

Chapter 5 incorporates methods and strategies for storing and retrieving data locally. The chapter examines use of the filesystem, databases, the SD card, and Android specific entities such as the SharedPreferences and ContentProvider classes. At this point we begin combining fundamental concepts with more real-world details, such as handling application state, using a database for persistent storage, and working with SQL.

Chapter 6 deals with storing and retrieving data over the network. Here we include a networking primer before delving into using raw networking concepts such as sockets on Android. From there we progress to using HTTP, and even exploring web services (such as REST and SOAP).

Chapter 7 covers telephony on the Android platform. We touch on basics such as originating and receiving phone calls, as well as more involved topics such as working with SMS. Along the way we also cover telephony properties and helper classes.

Chapter 8 looks at how to work with Notifications and Alarms. In this chapter we look at how to notify users of various events such as receiving a SMS message as well as how to manage and set alarms.

Chapter 9 deals with the basics of Androids Graphics API as well as more advanced concepts such as working with the OpenGL ES library for creating sophisticated 2D and 3D graphics. We will also touch upon animation.

Chapter 10 looks at Androids support for multimedia and we will cover both playing multimedia as well as using the camera and microphone to record our own multimedia files.

Chapter 11 introduces `Location`-based services as we look at an example that combines many of the concepts from the earlier parts of the book in a mapping application. Here we learn about using the mapping APIs on Android, including different location providers and properties that are available, how to build and manipulate map related screens, and how to work with location related concepts within the emulator.

PART 3: BRINGING IT ALL TOGETHER

Part 3 contains two chapters, both of which build upon knowledge from earlier in the text with a focus on bringing a larger application to fruition.

Chapter 12 demonstrates an end-to-end Field Service Application. The application includes server communications, persistent storage, multiple Activity navigation, menus, and signature capture.

Chapter 13 explores the world of native C language applications. The Android SDK is limited to the Java language although native applications may be written for Android. This chapter walks you through examples of building C language applications for Android including the use of built-in libraries and TCP socket communications as a Java application connects to our C application.

THE APPENDICES

The appendices contain additional information which didn't fit with the flow of the main text. Appendix A is a step-by-step guide to installing the development environment. This appendix, along with chapter 2, provides all the information needed to build an Android application. Appendix B demonstrates how to create an application for the Android Market—an important topic for anyone looking to sell an application commercially.

Code Conventions

All source code in the book is in a `fixed-width font like this`, which sets it off from the surrounding text. For most listings, the code is annotated to point out the key concepts, and numbered bullets are sometimes used in the text to provide additional information about the code. We have tried to format the code so that it fits within the available page space in the book by adding line breaks and using indentation carefully. Sometimes, however, very long lines will include line-continuation markers.

Source code for all the working examples is available from www.manning.com/ UnlockingAndroid or http://www.manning.com/ableson. A readme.txt file is provided in the root folder and also in each chapter folder; the files provide details on how to install and run the code. Code examples appear throughout this book. Longer listings will appear under clear listing headers while shorter listings will appear between lines of text. All code is set in a special font to clearly differentiate it.

Software Requirements

Developing applications for Android may be done from the Windows XP/Vista environment, a Mac OS X (Intel only) environment or a Linux environment. Appendix A includes a detailed description of setting up the Eclipse environment along with the Android Developer Tools plug-in for Eclipse.

Author Online

Purchase of *Unlocking Android* includes free access to a private web forum run by Manning Publications where you can make comments about the book, ask technical questions, and receive help from the authors and from other users. To access the forum and subscribe to it, point your web browser to www.manning.com/UnlockingAndroid or www.manning.com/ableson. This page provides information on how to get on the forum once you're registered, what kind of help is available, and the rules of conduct on the forum.

Manning's commitment to our readers is to provide a venue where a meaningful dialog between individual readers and between readers and the authors can take place. It's not a commitment to any specific amount of participation on the part of the authors, whose contribution to the AO remains voluntary (and unpaid). We suggest you try asking the authors some challenging questions lest their interest stray!

The Author Online forum and the archives of previous discussions will be accessible from the publisher's website as long as the book is in print.

about the cover illustration

The illustration on the cover of *Unlocking Android* is taken from a French book of dress customs, *Encyclopedie des Voyages* by J. G. St. Saveur, published in 1796. Travel for pleasure was a relatively new phenomenon at the time and illustrated guides such as this one were popular, introducing both the tourist as well as the armchair traveler to the inhabitants of other regions of the world, as well as to the regional costumes and uniforms of France.

The diversity of the drawings in the *Encyclopedie des Voyages* speaks vividly of the uniqueness and individuality of the world's countries and regions just 200 years ago. This was a time when the dress codes of two regions separated by a few dozen miles identified people uniquely as belonging to one or the other, and when members of a social class or a trade or a tribe could be easily distinguished by what they were wearing. This was also a time when people were fascinated by foreign lands and faraway places, even though they could not travel to these exotic destinations themselves.

Dress codes have changed since then and the diversity by region and tribe, so rich at the time, has faded away. It is now often hard to tell the inhabitant of one continent from another. Perhaps, trying to view it optimistically, we have traded a world of cultural and visual diversity for a more varied personal life. Or a more varied and interesting intellectual and technical life.

We at Manning celebrate the inventiveness, the initiative, and the fun of the computer business with book covers based on native and tribal costumes from two centuries ago brought back to life by the pictures from this travel guide.

Part 1

What is Android?
—The Big Picture

Android promises to be a market-moving technology platform—not just because of the functionality available in the platform but because of how the platform has come to market. Part 1 of this book brings you into the picture as a developer of the open source Android platform.

We begin with a look at the Android platform and the impact it has on each of the major "stakeholders" in the mobile marketplace (chapter 1). We then bring you on board to developing applications for Android with a hands-on tour of the Android development environment (chapter 2).

Targeting Android 1

This chapter covers:

- Examining Android, the open source mobile platform
- Activating Android
- Rapidly changing smartphones

You've heard about Android. You've read about Android. Now it is time to begin *Unlocking Android*.

Android is the software platform from Google and the Open Handset Alliance that has the potential to revolutionize the global cell phone market. This chapter introduces Android—what it is, and importantly, what it is not. After reading this chapter you will have an understanding of how Android is constructed, how it compares with other offerings in the market and its foundational technologies, plus you'll get a preview of Android application architecture. The chapter concludes with a simple Android application to get things started quickly.

This introductory chapter answers basic questions about what Android is and where it fits. While there are code examples in this chapter, they are not very indepth—just enough to get a taste for Android application development and to convey the key concepts introduced. Aside from some context-setting discussion in the introductory chapter, this book is about understanding Android's capabilities and will hopefully inspire you to join the effort to unlock the latent potential in the cell phone of the future.

1.1   *Introducing Android*

Android is the first open source mobile application platform that has the potential to make significant inroads in many markets. When examining Android there are a number of technical and market-related dimensions to consider. This first section introduces the platform and provides context to help you better understand Android and where it fits in the global cell phone scene.

Android is the product of primarily Google, but more appropriately the Open Handset Alliance. Open Handset Alliance is an alliance of approximately 30 organizations committed to bringing a "better" and "open" mobile phone to market. A quote taken from its website says it best: "Android was built from the ground up with the explicit goal to be the first open, complete, and free platform created specifically for mobile devices." As discussed in this section, open is good, complete is good; "free" may turn out to be an ambitious goal. There are many examples of "free" in the computing market that are free from licensing, but there is a cost of ownership when taking support and hardware costs into account. And of course, "free" cell phones come tethered to two-year contracts, plus tax. No matter the way some of the details play out, the introduction of Android is a market-moving event, and Android is likely to prove an important player in the mobile software landscape.

With this background of who is behind Android and the basic ambition of the Open Handset Alliance, it is time to understand the platform itself and how it fits in the mobile marketplace.

1.1.1   *The Android platform*

Android is a software environment built for mobile devices. It is *not* a hardware platform. Android includes a Linux kernel-based OS, a rich UI, end-user applications, code libraries, application frameworks, multimedia support, and much more. And, yes, even telephone functionality is included! While components of the underlying OS are written in C or C++, user applications are built for Android in Java. Even the built-in applications are written in Java. With the exception of some Linux exploratory exercises in chapter 13, all of the code examples in this book are written in Java using the Android SDK.

One feature of the Android platform is that there is no difference between the built-in applications and applications created with the SDK. This means that powerful applications can be written to tap into the resources available on the device. Figure 1.1 demonstrates the relationship between Android and the hardware it runs on. The most notable feature of Android may be that it is an open source platform; missing elements can and will be provided by the global developer community. Android's Linux kernel–based OS does not come with a sophisticated shell environment, but because the platform is open, shells can be written and installed on a device. Likewise, multimedia codecs can be supplied by third-party developers and do not need to rely on Google or anyone else to provide new functionality. That is the power of an open source platform brought to the mobile market.

The mobile market is a rapidly changing landscape with many players with diverging goals. Consider the often-at-odds relationship among mobile operators, mobile device manufacturers, and software vendors. Mobile operators want to lock down their networks, controlling and metering traffic. Device manufacturers want to differentiate themselves with features, reliability, and price points. Software vendors want unfettered access to the metal to deliver cutting-edge applications. Layer onto that a demanding user base, both consumer and corporate, that has become addicted to the "free phone" and operators who reward churn but not customer loyalty. The mobile market becomes not only a confusing array of choices but also a dangerous fiscal exercise for the participants, such as the cell phone

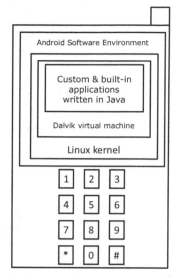

Figure 1.1 Android is software only. Leveraging its Linux kernel to interface with the hardware, you can expect Android to run on many different devices from multiple cell phone manufacturers. Applications are written in Java.

retailer who sees the underbelly of the industry and just wants to stay alive in an endless sea of change. What users come to expect on a mobile phone has evolved rapidly. Figure 1.2 provides a glimpse of the way we view mobile technology and how it has matured in a few short years.

Platform vs. device

Throughout the book, wherever code must be tested or exercised on a device, a software-based emulator is employed. See chapter 2 for information on how to set up and use the Android Emulator.

The term *platform* refers to Android itself—the software—including all of the binaries, code libraries, and tool chains. This book is focused on the Android platform. The Android emulators available in the SDK are simply one of many components of the Android platform.

With all of that as a backdrop, creating a successful mobile platform is clearly a nontrivial task involving numerous players. Android is an ambitious undertaking, even for Google, a company of seemingly boundless resources and moxie. If anyone has the clout to move the mobile market, it is Google and its entrant into the mobile marketplace, Android.

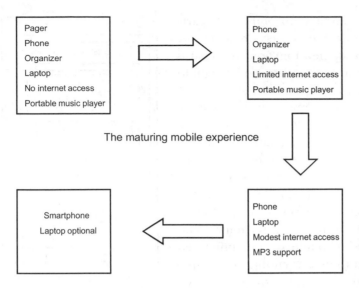

Figure 1.2   **The mobile worker can be pleased with the reduction in the number of devices that need to be toted. Mobile device functionality has converged at a very rapid pace. The laptop computer is becoming an optional piece of travel equipment.**

The next section begins and ends the "why and where of Android" to provide some context and set the perspective for Android's introduction to the marketplace. After that, it's on to exploring and exploiting the platform itself!

1.1.2   *In the market for an Android?*

Android promises to have something for everyone. Android looks to support a variety of hardware devices, not just high-end ones typically associated with expensive "smartphones." Of course, Android will run better on a more powerful device, particularly considering it is sporting a comprehensive set of computing features. The real question is how well Android can scale up and down to a variety of markets and gain market and mind share. This section provides conjecture on Android from the perspective of a few existing players in the marketplace. When talking about the cellular market, the place to start is at the top, with the carriers, or as they are sometimes referred to, mobile operators.

MOBILE OPERATORS

Mobile operators are in the business, first and foremost, of selling subscriptions to their services. Shareholders want a return on their investment, and it is hard to imagine an industry where there is a larger investment than in a network that spans such broad geographic territory. To the mobile operator, cell phones are—at the same time—a conduit for services, a drug to entice subscribers, and an annoyance to support and lock down.

The optimistic view of the mobile operator's response to Android is that it is embraced with open arms as a platform to drive new data services across the excess capacity operators have built into their networks. Data services represent high premium services and high-margin revenues for the operator. If Android can help drive those revenues for the mobile operator, all the better.

The pessimistic view of the mobile operator's response to Android is that the operator feels threatened by Google and the potential of "free wireless," driven by advertising revenues and an upheaval of the market. Another challenge with mobile operators is that they want the final say on what services are enabled across their network. Historically, one of the complaints of handset manufacturers is that their devices are handicapped and not exercising all of the features designed into them because of the mobile operator's lack of capability or lack of willingness to support those features. An encouraging sign is that there are mobile operators involved in the Open Handset Alliance.

Enough conjecture; let's move on to a comparison of Android and existing cell phones on the market today.

ANDROID VS. THE FEATURE PHONES

The overwhelming majority of cell phones on the market are the consumer flip phones and feature phones. These are the phones consumers get when they walk into the retailer and ask what can be had for "free"; these are the "I just want a phone" customers. Their primary interest is a phone for voice communications and perhaps an address book. They might even want a camera. Many of these phones have additional capabilities such as mobile web browsing, but because of a relatively poor user experience, these features are not employed heavily. The one exception is text messaging, which is a dominant application no matter the classification of device. Another increasingly in-demand category is location-based services, or as it is typically known, GPS.

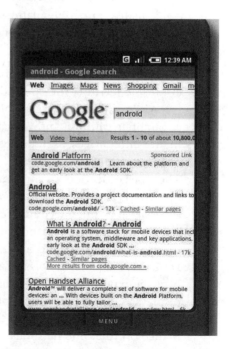

Android's challenge is to scale down to this market. Some of the bells and whistles in Android can be left out to fit into lower-end hardware. One of the big functionality gaps on these lower-end phones is the web experience. Part of this is due to screen size, but equally challenging is the browser technology itself, which often struggles to match the rich web experience of the desktop computer. Android features the market-leading WebKit browser engine, which brings desktop compatible browsing to the mobile arena. Figure 1.3 demonstrates the WebKit in action on Android. If this can be effectively scaled down to the feature phones, it would go a long way toward penetrating this end of the market.

Figure 1.3　Android's built-in browser technology is based on Webkit's browser engine.

NOTE   The WebKit (http://www.webkit.org) browser engine is an open source project that powers the browser found in Macs (Safari) and is the engine behind Mobile Safari, the browser found on the iPhone. It is not a stretch to say that the browser experience is what makes the iPhone popular, so its inclusion in Android is a strong plus for Android's architecture.

Software at this end of the market generally falls into one of two camps:

- *Qualcomm's BREW environment*—BREW stands for Binary Runtime Environment for Wireless. For a high-volume example of BREW technology, consider Verizon's Get It Now–capable devices, which run on this platform. The challenge to the software developer desiring to gain access to this market is that the bar to get an application on this platform is very high because everything is managed by the mobile operator, with expensive testing and revenue-sharing fee structures. The upside to this platform is that the mobile operator collects the money and disburses it to the developer after the sale, and often these sales are recurring monthly. Just about everything else is a challenge to the software developer, however. Android's open application environment is more accessible than BREW.
- *J2ME*, or *Java Micro Edition*, is a very popular platform for this class of device. The barrier to entry is much lower for software developers. J2ME developers will find a "same but different" environment in Android. Android is not strictly a J2ME-compatible platform; however, the Java programming environment found in Android is a plus for J2ME developers. Also, as Android matures, it is very likely that J2ME support will be added in some fashion.

Gaming, a better browser, and anything to do with texting or social applications present fertile territory for Android at this end of the market.

While the masses carry the feature phones described in this section, Android's capabilities will put Android-capable devices into the next market segment with the higher-end devices, as discussed next.

ANDROID VS. THE SMARTPHONES

The market leaders in the smartphone race are Windows Mobile/SmartPhone and BlackBerry, with Symbian (huge in non-U.S. markets), iPhone, and Palm rounding out the market. While we could focus on market share and pros versus cons of each of the smartphone platforms, one of the major concerns of this market is a platform's ability to synchronize data and access Enterprise Information Systems for corporate users. Device-management tools are also an important factor in the Enterprise market. The browser experience is better than with the lower-end phones, mainly because of larger displays and more intuitive input methods, such as a touch screen or a jog dial.

Android's opportunity in this market is that it promises to deliver more performance on the same hardware and at a lower software acquisition cost. The challenge Android faces is the same challenge faced by Palm—scaling the Enterprise walls. BlackBerry is dominant because of its intuitive email capabilities, and the Microsoft platforms are compelling because of tight integration to the desktop experience and overall familiarity for Windows users. Finally, the iPhone has enjoyed unprecedented success as an intuitive yet capable consumer device with a tremendous wealth of available software applications.

The next section poses an interesting question: can Android, the open source mobile platform, succeed as an open source project?

ANDROID VS. ITSELF

Perhaps the biggest challenge of all is Android's commitment to open source. Coming from the lineage of Google, Android will likely always be an open source project, but in order to succeed in the mobile market, it must sell millions of units. Android is not the first open source phone, but it is the first from a player with the market-moving weight of Google leading the charge.

Open source is a double-edged sword. On one hand, the power of many talented people and companies working around the globe and around the clock to push the ball up the hill and deliver desirable features is a force to be reckoned with, particularly in comparison with a traditional, commercial approach to software development. This is a trite topic unto itself by now, because the benefits of open source development are well documented. The other side of the open source equation is that, without a centralized code base that has some stability, Android could splinter and not gain the critical mass it needs to penetrate the mobile market. Look at the Linux platform as an alternative to the "incumbent" Windows OS. As a kernel, Linux has enjoyed tremendous success: it is found in many operating systems, appliances such as routers and switches, and a host of embedded and mobile platforms such as Android. Numerous Linux distributions are available for the desktop, and ironically, the plethora of choices has held it back as a desktop alternative to Windows. Linux is arguably the most successful open source project; as a desktop alternative to Windows, it has become splintered and that has hampered its market penetration from a product perspective. As an example of the diluted Linux market, here is an abridged list of Linux distributions:

- Ubuntu
- openSUSE
- Fedora (Red Hat)
- Debian
- Mandriva (formerly Mandrake)
- PCLinuxOS
- MEPIS
- Slackware
- Gentoo
- Knoppix

The list contains a sampling of the most popular Linux desktop software distributions. How many people do you know who use Linux as their primary desktop OS, and if so, do they all use the same version? Open source alone is not enough; Android must stay focused as a product and not get diluted in order to penetrate the market in a meaningful way. This is the classic challenge of the intersection between commercialization and open source. This is Android's challenge, among others, because Android needs to demonstrate staying power and the ability scale from the mobile operator to the software vendor, and even at the grass-roots level to the retailer. Becoming diluted into many distributions is not a recipe for success for such a consumer product as a cell phone.

The licensing model of open source projects can be sticky. Some software licenses are more restrictive than others. Some of those restrictions pose a challenge to the open source label. At the same time, Android licensees need to protect their investment, so licensing is an important topic for the commercialization of Android.

1.1.3   *Licensing Android*

Android is released under two different open source licenses. The Linux kernel is released under the GPL (GNU General Public License), as is required for anyone licensing the open source OS kernel. The Android platform, excluding the kernel, is licensed under the Apache Software License (ASL). While both licensing models are open source–oriented, the major difference is that the Apache license is considered friendlier toward commercial use. Some open source purists may find fault with anything but complete openness, source code sharing, and noncommercialization; the ASL attempts to balance the open source goals with commercial market forces. If there is not a financial incentive to deliver Android-capable devices to the market, devices will never appear in the meaningful volumes required to adequately launch Android.

Selling applications

A mobile platform is ultimately valuable only if there are applications to use and enjoy on that platform. To that end, the topic of buying and selling applications for Android is important and gives us an opportunity to highlight a key difference between Android and the iPhone. The Apple AppStore contains software titles for the iPhone. However, Apple's somewhat draconian grip on the iPhone software market requires that all applications be sold through its venue. This results in a challenging environment for software developers who might prefer to make their application available through multiple channels.

Contrast Apple's approach to application distribution with the freedom an Android developer enjoys to ship applications via traditional venues such as freeware and shareware and commercially through various marketplaces, including a developer's very own website! For software publishers desiring the focus of an on-device shopping experience, Google has launched the Android Market. For software developers who already have titles for other platforms such as Windows Mobile, Palm, or BlackBerry, traditional software markets such as Handango (http://www.Handango.com) also support selling Android applications. This is important because consumers new to Android will likely visit sites like Handango because that may be where they first purchased one of their favorite applications for their prior device.

The high-level, touchy-feely portion of the book has now concluded! The remainder of this book is focused on Android application development. Any technical discussion of a software environment must include a review of the layers that compose the environment, sometimes referred to as a *stack* because of the layer-upon-layer construction. The next section begins a high-level breakdown of the components of the Android stack.

1.2 *Stacking up Android*

The Android stack includes an impressive array of features for mobile applications. In fact, looking at the architecture alone, without the context of Android being a platform designed for mobile environments, it would be easy to confuse Android with a general computing environment. All of the major components of a computing platform are here and read like a Who's Who of the open source community. Here is a quick run-down of some of the prominent components of the Android stack:

- A Linux kernel provides a foundational hardware abstraction layer as well as core services such as process, memory, and file-system management. The kernel is where hardware-specific drivers are implemented—capabilities such as Wi-Fi and Bluetooth are found here. The Android stack is designed to be flexible, with many optional components which largely rely on the availability of specific hardware on a given device. These include features like touch screens, cameras, GPS receivers, and accelerometers.
- Prominent code libraries include:
  - Browser technology from WebKit—the same open source engine powering Mac's Safari and the iPhone's Mobile Safari browser
  - Database support via SQLite an easy-to-use SQL database
  - Advanced graphics support, including 2D, 3D, animation from SGL, and OpenGL ES
  - Audio and video media support from Packet Video's OpenCore
  - SSL capabilities from the Apache project
- An array of managers providing services for:
  - Activities and views
  - Telephony
  - Windows
  - Resources
  - Location-based services
- The Android runtime provides:
  - Core Java packages for a nearly full-featured Java programming environment. Note that this is *not* a J2ME environment.
  - The Dalvik virtual machine employs services of the Linux-based kernel to provide an environment to host Android applications.

Both core applications and third-party applications (such as the ones built in this book) run in the Dalvik virtual machine, atop the components just introduced. The relationship among these layers can be seen in figure 1.4.

| User applications: Contacts, phone, browser, etc. |
| Application managers: windows, content, activities, telephony, location, notifications, etc. |
| Android runtime: Java via Dalvik VM
Libraries: graphics, media, database, communications, browser engine, etc. |
| Linux kernel, including device drivers |
| Hardware device with specific capabilities such as GPS, camera, Bluetooth, etc. |

Figure 1.4 The Android stack offers an impressive array of technologies and capabilities.

TIP Android development requires Java programming skills, without question. To get the most out of this book, please be sure to brush up on your Java programming knowledge. There are many Java references on the internet, and there is no shortage of Java books on the market. An excellent source of Java titles can be found at http://www.manning.com/catalog/java.

Now that the obligatory stack diagram is shown and the layers introduced, let's look further at the runtime technology that underpins Android.

1.2.1 *Probing Android's foundation*

Android is built on a Linux kernel and an advanced, optimized virtual machine for its Java applications. Both technologies are crucial to Android. The Linux kernel component of the Android stack promises agility and portability to take advantage of numerous hardware options for future Android-equipped phones. Android's Java environment is key: it makes Android very accessible to programmers because of both the number of Java software developers and the rich environment that Java programming has to offer. Mobile platforms that have relied on less-accessible programming environments have seen stunted adoption because of a lack of applications as developers have shied away from the platform.

BUILDING ON THE LINUX KERNEL

Why use Linux for a phone? Using a full-featured platform such as the Linux kernel provides tremendous power and capabilities for Android. Using an open source foundation unleashes the capabilities of talented individuals and companies to move the platform forward. This is particularly important in the world of mobile devices, where products change so rapidly. The rate of change in the mobile market makes the general computer market look slow and plodding. And, of course, the Linux kernel is a proven core platform. Reliability is more important than performance when it comes to a mobile phone, because voice communication is the primary use of a phone. All mobile phone users, whether buying for personal use or for a business, demand voice reliability, but they still want cool data features and will purchase a device based on those features. Linux can help meet this requirement.

Speaking to the rapid rate of phone turnover and accessories hitting the market, another advantage of using Linux as the foundation of the Android platform stack is that it provides a hardware abstraction layer, letting the upper levels remain unchanged despite changes in the underlying hardware. Of course, good coding practices demand that user applications fail gracefully in the event a resource is not available, such as a camera not being present in a particular handset model. As new accessories appear on the market, drivers can be written at the Linux level to provide support, just as on other Linux platforms.

User applications, as well as core Android applications, are written in the Java programming language and are compiled into *byte codes*. Byte codes are interpreted at runtime by an interpreter known as a *virtual machine*.

RUNNING IN THE DALVIK VIRTUAL MACHINE

The Dalvik virtual machine is an example of the needs of efficiency, the desire for a rich programming environment, and even some intellectual property constraints colliding, with innovation as a result. Android's Java environment provides a rich application platform and is very accessible because of the popularity of the Java language itself. Also, application performance, particularly in a low-memory setting such as is found in a mobile phone, is paramount for the mobile market. However this is not the only issue at hand.

Android is not a J2ME platform. Without commenting on whether this is ultimately good or bad for Android, there are other forces at play here. There is a matter of Java virtual machine licensing from Sun Microsystems. From a very high level, Android's code environment is Java. Applications are written in Java, which is compiled to Java bytecodes and subsequently translated to a similar but different representation called *dex files*. These files are logically equivalent to Java bytecodes, but they permit Android to run its applications in its own virtual machine that is both (arguably) free from Sun's licensing clutches and an open platform upon which Google, and potentially the open source community, can improve as necessary.

NOTE   It is too early to tell whether there will be a big battle between the Open Handset Alliance and Sun over the use of Java in Android. From the mobile application developer's perspective, Android is a Java environment; however, the runtime is not strictly a Java virtual machine. This accounts for the incompatibilities between Android and "proper" Java environments and libraries.

The important things to know about the Dalvik virtual machine are that Android applications run inside it and that it relies on the Linux kernel for services such as process, memory, and filesystem management.

After this discussion of the foundational technologies in Android, it is time to focus on Android application development. The remainder of this chapter discusses high-level Android application architecture and introduces a simple Android application. If you are not comfortable or ready to begin coding, you might want to jump to chapter 2, where we introduce the development environment step by step.

1.3   *Booting Android development*

This section jumps right into the fray of Android development to focus on an important component of the Android platform, then expands to take a broader view of how Android applications are constructed. An important and recurring theme of Android development is the `Intent`. An `Intent` in Android describes what you want to do. This may look like "I want to look up a contact record," or "Please launch this website," or "Show the Order Confirmation Screen." `Intents` are important because they not only facilitate navigation in an innovative way as discussed next, but they also represent the most important aspect of Android coding. *Understand the `Intent`, understand Android.*

NOTE   Instructions for setting up the Eclipse development environment are found in appendix A. This environment is used for all examples in this book. Chapter 2 goes into more detail on setting up and using the development tools.

   The code examples in this chapter are primarily for illustrative purposes. Classes are referenced and introduced without necessarily naming specific Java packages. Subsequent chapters take a more rigorous approach to introducing Android-specific packages and classes.

The next section provides foundational information about why `Intents` are important, then describes how `Intents` work. Beyond the introduction of the `Intent`, the remainder of this chapter describes the major elements of Android application development leading up to and including the first complete application.

1.3.1   *Android's good Intent-ions*

The power of Android's application framework lies in the way in which it brings a web mindset to mobile applications. This doesn't mean the platform has a powerful browser and is limited to clever JavaScript and server-side resources, but rather it goes to the core of how the Android platform itself works and how the user of the platform interacts with the mobile device. The power of the internet, should one be so bold to reduce it to a single statement, is that everything is just a click away. Those clicks are known to the user as Uniform Resource Locators (URLs), or alternatively, Uniform Resource Identifiers (URIs). The use of effective URIs permits easy and quick access to the information users need and want every day. "Send me the link" says it all.

   Beyond being an effective way to get access to data, why is this URI topic important, and what does it have to do with `Intents`? The answer is a nontechnical but crucial response: *the way in which a mobile user navigates on the platform is crucial to its commercial success*. Platforms that replicate the desktop experience on a mobile device are acceptable to only a small percentage of hard-core power users. Deep menus, multiple taps, and clicks are generally not well received in the mobile market. The mobile application, more than in any other market, demands intuitive ease of use. While a consumer may purchase a device based on cool features enumerated in the marketing materials, instruction manuals are almost never touched. The ease of use of the UI of a computing environment is highly correlated with its market penetration. UIs are also a reflection of the platform's data access model, so if the navigation and data models are clean and intuitive, the UI will follow suit. This section introduces the concept of `Intents` and `IntentFilters`, Android's innovative navigation and triggering mechanism. `Intents` and `IntentFilters` bring the "click on it" paradigm to the core of mobile application use (and development!) for the Android platform.

- An `Intent` is a declaration of need.
- An `IntentFilter` is a declaration of capability and interest in offering assistance to those in need.
- An `Intent` is made up of a number of pieces of information describing the desired action or service. This section examines the requested action and, generically, the data that accompanies the requested action.
- An `IntentFilter` may be generic or specific with respect to which `Intents` it offers to service.

The action attribute of an `Intent` is typically a verb, for example: `VIEW`, `PICK`, or `EDIT`. A number of built-in `Intent` actions are defined as members of the `Intent` class. Application developers can create new actions as well. To view a piece of information, an application would employ the following `Intent` action:

```
android.content.Intent.ACTION_VIEW
```

The data component of an `Intent` is expressed in the form of a URI and can be virtually any piece of information, such as a contact record, a website location, or a reference to a media clip. Table 1.1 lists some URI examples.

Table 1.1   `Intents` employ URIs, and some of the commonly employed URIs in Android are listed here.

Type of Information	URI Data
Contact lookup	content://contacts/people
Map lookup/search	Geo:0,0?q=23+Route+206+Stanhope+NJ
Browser launch to a specific website	http://www.google.com/

The `IntentFilter` defines the relationship between the `Intent` and the application. `IntentFilters` can be specific to the data portion of the `Intent`, the action portion, or both. `IntentFilters` also contain a field known as a *category*. A category helps classify the action. For example, the category named CATEGORY_LAUNCHER instructs Android that the `Activity` containing this `IntentFilter` should be visible in the main application launcher or home screen.

When an `Intent` is dispatched, the system evaluates the available `Activitys`, `Services`, and registered `BroadcastReceivers` (more on these in the next section) and dispatches the `Intent` to the most appropriate recipient. Figure 1.5 depicts this relationship among `Intents`, `IntentFilters`, and `BroadcastReceivers`.

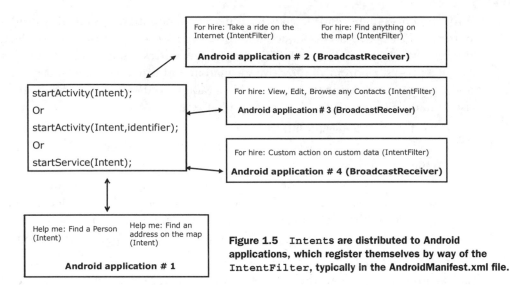

Figure 1.5 `Intents` **are distributed to Android applications, which register themselves by way of the** `IntentFilter`**, typically in the AndroidManifest.xml file.**

`IntentFilters` are often defined in an application's AndroidManifest.xml with the `<intent-filter>` tag. The AndroidManfest.xml file is essentially an application descriptor file, discussed later in this chapter.

A common task on a mobile device is the lookup of a specific contact record for the purpose of initiating a call, sending an SMS (Short Message Service), or looking up a snail-mail address when you are standing in line at the neighborhood pack-and-ship store. A user may desire to view a specific piece of information, say a contact record for user 1234. In this case, the action is `ACTION_VIEW` and the data is a specific contact record identifier. This is accomplished by creating an `Intent` with the action set to `ACTION_VIEW` and a URI that represents the specific person of interest.

Here is an example of the URI for use with the `android.content.Intent.ACTION_VIEW` action:

```
content://contacts/people/1234
```

Here is an example of the URI for obtaining a list of all contacts, the more generalized URI of

```
content://contacts/people
```

Here is a snippet of code demonstrating the `PICK`ing of a contact record:

```
Intent myIntent = new Intent(Intent.ACTION_PICK,Uri.parse("content://contacts/
    people"));
startActivity(myIntent);
```

This `Intent` is evaluated and passed to the most appropriate handler. In this case, the recipient would likely be a built-in `Activity` named `com.google.android.phone.Dialer`. However, the best recipient of this `Intent` may be an `Activity` contained in the same custom Android application (the one you build), a built-in application as in this case, or a third-party application on the device. Applications can leverage existing functionality in other applications by creating and dispatching an Intent requesting existing code to handle the Intent rather than writing code from scratch. One of the great benefits of employing Intents in this manner is that it leads to the same UIs being used frequently, creating familiarity for the user. *This is particularly important for mobile platforms where the user is often neither tech-savvy nor interested in learning multiple ways to accomplish the same task, such as looking up a contact on the phone.*

The Intents we have discussed thus far are known as *implicit* Intents, which rely on the IntentFilter and the Android environment to dispatch the Intent to the appropriate recipient. There are also *explicit* Intents, where we can specify the exact class we desire to handle the Intent. This is helpful when we know exactly which Activity we want to handle the Intent and do not want to leave anything up to chance in terms of what code is executed. To create an explicit Intent, use the overloaded Intent constructor, which takes a class as an argument, as shown here:

```
public void onClick(View v) {
try {
startActivityForResult(new Intent(v.getContext(),RefreshJobs.class),0);
} catch (Exception e) {
. . .
}
}
```

These examples show how an Android application creates an Intent and asks for it to be handled. Similarly, an Android application can be deployed with an IntentFilter, indicating that it responds to Intents already created on the system, thereby publishing new functionality for the platform. This facet alone should bring joy to independent software vendors (ISVs) who have made a living by offering better contact manager and to-do list management software titles for other mobile platforms.

Intent resolution, or *dispatching*, takes place at runtime, as opposed to when the application is compiled, so specific Intent-handling features can be added to a device, which may provide an upgraded or more desirable set of functionality than the original shipping software. This runtime dispatching is also referred to as *late binding*.

The power and the complexity of Intents

It is not hard to imagine that an absolutely unique user experience is possible with Android because of the variety of Activitys with specific IntentFilters installed on any given device. It is architecturally feasible to upgrade various aspects of an Android installation to provide sophisticated functionality and customization. While this may be a desirable characteristic for the user, it can be a bit troublesome for someone providing tech support and having to navigate a number of components and applications to troubleshoot a problem.

Because of this potential for added complexity, this approach of ad hoc system patching to upgrade specific functionality should be entertained cautiously and with one's eyes wide open to the potential pitfalls associated with this approach.

Thus far this discussion of `Intents` has focused on the variety of `Intents` that cause UI elements to be displayed. There are also `Intents` that are more event driven than task-oriented, as the earlier contact record example described. For example, the `Intent` class is also used to notify applications that a text message has arrived. `Intents` are a very central element to Android and will be revisited on more than one occasion.

Now that `Intents` have been introduced as the catalyst for navigation and event flow on Android, let's jump to a broader view and discuss the Android application lifecycle and the key components that make Android tick. The `Intent` will come into better focus as we further explore Android throughout this book.

1.3.2 *Activating Android*

This section builds on the knowledge of the `Intent` and `IntentFilter` classes introduced in the previous section and explores the four primary components of Android applications as well as their relation to the Android process model. Code snippets are included to provide a taste of Android application development. More in-depth examples and discussion are left for later chapters.

NOTE A particular Android application may not contain all of these elements, but it will have at least one of these elements and could in fact have all of them.

ACTIVITY

An application may or may not have a UI. If it has a UI, it will have at least one `Activity`.

The easiest way to think of an Android `Activity` is to relate a visible screen to an `Activity`, as more often than not there is a one-to-one relationship between an `Activity` and a UI screen. An Android application will often contain more than one `Activity`. Each `Activity` displays a UI and responds to system- and user-initiated events. The `Activity` employs one or more `Views` to present the actual UI elements to the user. The `Activity` class is extended by user classes, as shown in listing 1.1.

Listing 1.1 A very basic `Activity` in an Android application

```
package com.msi.manning.chapter1;

import android.app.Activity;          ⟵—❶ Activity class import
import android.os.Bundle;

public class activity1 extends Activity {    ⟵⎤
    @Override                                   ⎥  ❷ Activity class extension
    public void onCreate(Bundle icicle) {          implementation
        super.onCreate(icicle);
        setContentView(R.layout.main);   ⟵—❸ Set up the UI
    }
}
```

The `Activity` class ❶ is part of the `android.app` Java package, found in the Android runtime. The Android runtime is deployed in the android.jar file. The class `activity1` ❷ extends the class `Activity`. For more examples of using an `Activity`, please see chapter 3. One of the primary tasks an `Activity` performs is the display of

UI elements, which are implemented as `Views` and described in XML layout files ❸. Chapter 3 goes into more detail on `Views` and `Resources`.

Moving from one `Activity` to another is accomplished with the `startActivity()` method or the `startActivityForResult()` method when a synchronous call/result paradigm is desired. The argument to these methods is the `Intent`.

You say Intent; I say Intent

The `Intent` class is used in similar sounding but very different scenarios.

There are `Intents` used to assist in navigation from one activity to the next, such as the example given earlier of `VIEW`ing a contact record. Activities are the targets of these kinds of `Intents` used with the `startActivity` or `startActivityForResult` methods.

Services can be started by passing an `Intent` to the `startService` method.

`BroadcastReceivers` receive `Intents` when responding to systemwide events such as the phone ringing or an incoming text message.

The `Activity` represents a very visible application component within Android. With assistance from the `View` class covered in chapter 3, the `Activity` is the most common type of Android application. The next topic of interest is the `Service`, which runs in the background and does not generally present a direct UI.

SERVICE

If an application is to have a long lifecycle, it should be put into a `Service`. For example, a background data synchronization utility running continuously should be implemented as a `Service`.

Like the `Activity`, a `Service` is a class provided in the Android runtime that should be extended, as seen in listing 1.2, which sends a message to the Android log periodically.

Listing 1.2   A simple example of an Android `Service`

```
package com.msi.manning.chapter1;

import android.app.Service;        ←❶ Service import
import android.os.IBinder;
import android.util.Log;           ←❷ Log import

public class service1 extends Service implements Runnable {    ←┐ ❸ Extending the
public static final String tag = "service1";                       Service class
   private int counter = 0;
   @Override                       ❹ Initialization in the
   protected void onCreate() {   ←┘ onCreate method
       super.onCreate();
   Thread aThread = new Thread (this);
       aThread.start();
   }
```

```
public void run() {
    while (true) {
      try {
      Log.i(tag,"service1 firing : # " + counter++);
      Thread.sleep(10000);
      } catch(Exception ee) {
       Log.e(tag,ee.getMessage());
      }
    }
}

@Override
public IBinder onBind(Intent intent)   {      ◄──❺  Binding to the Service
return null;
}

}
```

This example requires that the package android.app.Service ❶ be imported. This
package contains the Service class. This example also demonstrates Android's logging mechanism ❷, which is useful for debugging purposes. Many of the examples in
the book include using the logging facility. Logging is discussed in chapter 2. The
service1 class ❸ extends the Service class. This class also implements the Runnable
interface to perform its main task on a separate thread. The onCreate ❹ method of
the Service class permits the application to perform initialization-type tasks. The
onBind() method ❺ is discussed in further detail in chapter 4 when the topic of inter-
process communication in general is explored.

   Services are started with the startService(Intent) method of the abstract
Context class. Note that, again, the Intent is used to initiate a desired result on the
platform.

   Now that the application has a UI in an Activity and a means to have a long-
running task in a Service, it is time to explore the BroadcastReceiver, another form
of Android application that is dedicated to processing Intents.

BROADCASTRECEIVER

If an application wants to receive and respond to a global event, such as the phone
ringing or an incoming text message, it must register as a BroadcastReceiver. An
application registers to receive Intents in either of two manners:

- The application may implement a <receiver> element in the AndroidMan-
  fest.xml file, which describes the BroadcastReceiver's class name and enumerates its IntentFilters. Remember, the IntentFilter is a descriptor of the
  Intent an application wants to process. If the receiver is registered in the
  AndroidManifest.xml file, it does not have to be running in order to be triggered. When the event occurs, the application is started automatically upon
  notification of the triggering event. All of this housekeeping is managed by the
  Android OS itself.

- An application may register at runtime via the Context class's registerRe-
  ceiver method.

Like `Services`, `BroadcastReceivers` do not have a UI. Of even more importance, the code running in the `onReceive` method of a `BroadcastReceiver` should make no assumptions about persistence or long-running operations. If the `BroadcastReceiver` requires more than a trivial amount of code execution, it is recommended that the code initiate a request to a `Service` to complete the requested functionality.

NOTE The familiar `Intent` class is used in the triggering of `BroadcastReceiv-`
ers; the use of these `Intents` is mutually exclusive from the `Intents` used
to start an `Activity` or a `Service`, as previously discussed.

A `BroadcastReceiver` implements the abstract method `onReceive` to process incoming `Intents`. The arguments to the method are a `Context` and an `Intent`. The method returns `void`, but a handful of methods are useful for passing back results, including `setResult`, which passes back to the invoker an integer return code, a `String` return value, and a `Bundle` value, which can contain any number of objects.

Listing 1.3 is an example of a `BroadcastReceiver` triggering upon an incoming text message.

Listing 1.3 A sample `IntentReceiver`

```
package com.msi.manning.unlockingandroid;

import android.content.Context;
import android.content.Intent;
import android.content.IntentReceiver;
import android.util.Log;

public class MySMSMailBox extends BroadcastReceiver {      ❶ Extending
public static final String tag = "MySMSMailBox";             BroadcastReceiver
                                                           ❷ Tag used in logging
@Override
public void onReceive(Context context, Intent intent) {    ❸ onReceive method
   Log.i(tag,"onReceive");
   if (intent.getAction().equals("android.provider.Telephony.SMS_RECEIVED")) {
      Log.i(tag,"Found our Event!");
   }                                        Write        Check Intent's
}                                        ❺ to log           action ❹
}
```

❶ Extending BroadcastReceiver
❷ Tag used in logging
❸ onReceive method
❹ Check Intent's action
❺ Write to log

Looking at listing 1.3 we find a few items to discuss. The class `MySMSMailBox` extends the `BroadcastReceiver` class ❶. This subclass approach is the most straightforward way to employ a `BroadcastReceiver`. Note the class name `MySMSMailBox`, as it will be used in the AndroidManifest.xml file, shown in listing 1.4. The `tag` variable ❷ is used in conjunction with the logging mechanism to assist in labeling messages sent to the console log on the emulator. Using a tag in the log enables filtering and organizing log messages in the console. Chapter 2 discusses the log mechanism in further detail. The `onReceive` method ❸ is where all of the work takes place in a `BroadcastRe-`
ceiver—this method must be implemented. Note that a given `BroadcastReceiver` can register multiple `IntentFilters` and can therefore be instantiated for an arbitrary number of `Intents`.

It is important to make sure to handle the appropriate `Intent` by checking the action of the incoming `Intent`, as shown in ❹. Once the desired `Intent` is received, carry out the specific functionality required. A common task in an SMS-receiving application would be to parse the message and display it to the user via a Notification Manager display. In this snippet, we simply record the action to the log ❺.

In order for this `BroadcastReceiver` to fire and receive this `Intent`, it must be listed in the AndroidManifest.xml file, as shown in listing 1.4. This listing contains the elements required to respond to an incoming text message.

Listing 1.4   AndroidManifest.xml

```
<?xml version="1.0" encoding="utf-8"?>                    Required permission  ❶
<manifest xmlns:android="http://schemas.android.com/apk/res/android"
  package="com.msi.manning.unlockingandroid">
  <uses-permission android:name="android.permission.RECEIVE_SMS" />
  <application android:icon="@drawable/icon">
    <activity android:name=".chapter1" android:label="@string/app_name">
      <intent-filter>
        <action android:name="android.intent.action.MAIN" />
        <category android:name="android.intent.category.LAUNCHER" />
      </intent-filter>
    </activity>                              ❷ Receiver tag;    ❸ IntentFilter
    <receiver android:name=".MySMSMailBox" >     note the "."      definition
      <intent-filter>
        <action android:name="android.provider.Telephony.SMS_RECEIVED" />
      </intent-filter>
    </receiver>
  </application>
</manifest>
```

Certain tasks within the Android platform require the application to have a designated privilege. To give an application the required permissions, the `<uses-permission>` tag is used ❶. This is discussed in detail later in this chapter in the AndroidManifest.xml section. The `<receiver>` tag contains the class name of the class implementing the `BroadcastReceiver`. In this example the class name is `MySMSMailBox`, from the package `com.msi.manning.unlockingandroid`. Be sure to note the dot that precedes the name ❷. The dot is required. If your application is not behaving as expected, one of the first places to check is your Android.xml file, and look for the dot! The `IntentFilter` is defined in the `<intent-filter>` tag. The desired action in this example is `android.provider.Telephony.SMS_RECEIVED` ❸. The Android SDK enumerates the available actions for the standard `Intents`. In addition, remember that user applications can define their own `Intents` as well as listen for them.

Now that we have introduced `Intents` and the Android classes that process or handle `Intents`, it's time to explore the next major Android application topic, the `ContentProvider`, Android's preferred data-publishing mechanism.

CONTENT PROVIDER

If an application manages data and needs to expose that data to other applications running in the Android environment, a `ContentProvider` should be implemented. Alternatively, if an application component (`Activity`, `Service`, or `Broadcast-Receiver`) needs to access data from another application, the other application's

> ## Testing SMS
>
> The emulator has a built-in set of tools for manipulating certain telephony behavior to simulate a variety of conditions, such as in and out of network coverage and placing phone calls. This section's example demonstrated another feature of the emulator, the receipt of an SMS message.
>
> To send an SMS message to the emulator, telnet to port 5554 (the port # may vary on your system), which will connect to the emulator and issue the following command at the prompt:
>
> ```
> sms send <sender's phone number> <body of text message>
> ```
>
> To learn more about available commands, type `help` from the prompt.
>
> These tools are discussed in more detail in chapter 2.

ContentProvider is used. The ContentProvider implements a standard set of methods to permit an application to access a data store. The access may be for read and/or write operations. A ContentProvider may provide data to an Activity or Service in the same containing application as well as an Activity or Service contained in other applications.

A ContentProvider may use any form of data storage mechanism available on the Android platform, including files, SQLite databases, or even a memory-based hash map if data persistence is not required. In essence, the ContentProvider is a data layer providing data abstraction for its clients and centralizing storage and retrieval routines in a single place.

Directly sharing files or databases is discouraged on the Android platform and is further enforced by the Linux security system, which prevents ad hoc file access from one application space to another without explicitly granted permissions.

Data stored in a ContentProvider may be of traditional data types such as integers and strings. Content providers can also manage binary data such as image data. When binary data is retrieved, suggested practice is to return a string representing the filename containing the binary data. In the event a filename is returned as part of a ContentProvider query, the file should not be accessed directly, but rather you should use the helper class, ContentResolver's openInputStream method, to access the binary data. This approach negates Linux process/security hurdles as well as keeps all data access normalized through the ContentProvider. Figure 1.6 outlines the relationship among ContentProviders, data stores, and their clients.

A ContentProvider's data is accessed through the familiar Content URI. A ContentProvider defines this as a public static final String. For example, an application might have a data store managing material safety data sheets. The Content URI for this ContentProvider might look like this:

```
public static final Uri CONTENT_URI =
Uri.parse("content://com.msi.manning.provider.unlockingandroid/datasheets");
```

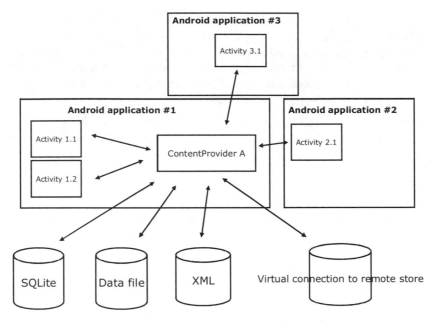

Figure 1.6   The content provider is the data tier for Android applications and is the prescribed manner in which data is accessed and shared on the device.

From this point, accessing a ContentProvider is similar to using Structured Query Language (SQL) in other platforms, though a complete SQL statement is not employed. A query is submitted to the ContentProvider, including the columns desired and optional Where and Order By clauses. For those familiar with parameterized queries in SQL, parameter substitution is even supported. Results are returned in the Cursor class, of course. A detailed ContentProvider example is provided in chapter 5.

NOTE   In many ways, a ContentProvider acts like a database server. While an application could contain only a ContentProvider and in essence be a database server, a ContentProvider is typically a component of a larger Android application that hosts at least one Activity, Service, and/or BroadcastReceiver.

This concludes the brief introduction to the major Android application classes. Gaining an understanding of these classes and how they work together is an important aspect of Android development. Getting application components to work together can be a daunting task. For example, have you ever had a piece of software that just didn't work properly on your computer? Perhaps it was copied and not installed properly. Every software platform has environmental concerns, though they vary by platform. For example, when connecting to a remote resource such as a database server or FTP server, which username and password should you use? What about the necessary libraries to run your application? These are all topics related to software deployment. Each Android application requires a file named

AndroidManifest.xml, which ties together the necessary pieces to run an Android application on a device.

1.3.3 *AndroidManifest.xml*

The previous sections introduced the common elements of an Android application. To restate: an Android application will contain at least one `Activity`, `Service`, `BroadcastReceiver`, or `ContentProvider`. Some of these elements will advertise the `Intents` they are interested in processing via the `IntentFilter` mechanism. All of these pieces of information need to be tied together in order for an Android application to execute. The "glue" mechanism for this task of defining relationships is the AndroidManifest.xml file.

The AndroidManifest.xml file exists in the root of an application directory and contains all of the design-time relationships of a specific application and `Intents`. AndroidManifest.xml files act as deployment descriptors for Android applications. Listing 1.5 is an example of a very simple AndroidManifest.xml file.

Listing 1.5   AndroidManifest.xml file for a very basic Android application

```
<?xml version="1.0" encoding="utf-8"?>
<manifest xmlns:android="http://schemas.android.com/apk/res/android"
    package="com.msi.manning.unlockingandroid">        ❶ Package name
    <application android:icon="@drawable/icon">
        <activity android:name=".chapter1" android:label="@string/app_name">
            <intent-filter>
                <action android:name="android.intent.action.MAIN" />
                <category android:name="android.intent.category.LAUNCHER" />
            </intent-filter>                          IntentFilter definition ❸
        </activity>
    </application>                                      Application name ❷
</manifest>
```

Looking at this simple AndroidManifest.xml, we see that the `manifest` element contains the obligatory namespace as well as the Java package name ❶ containing this application. This application contains a single `Activity`, with a class name of `chapter1` ❷. Note also the `@string` syntax. Anytime an `@` symbol is used in an AndroidManifest.xml file, it is referencing information stored in one of the resource files. In this case, the `label` attribute is obtained from the app_name string resource defined elsewhere in the application. Resources are discussed in further detail later in chapter 3. This application's lone `Activity` contains a single `IntentFilter` definition ❸. The `IntentFilter` used here is the most common `IntentFilter` seen in Android applications. The action `android.intent.action.MAIN` indicates that this is an entry point to the application. The category `android.intent.category.LAUNCHER` places this `Activity` in the launcher window, as shown in figure 1.7. It is possible to have multiple `Activity` elements in a manifest file (and thereby an application), with more than one of them visible in the launcher window.

In addition to the elements used in this sample manifest file, other common tags include:

- The <service> tag represents a Service. The attributes of the service tag include its class and label. A Service may also include the <intent-filter> tag.
- The <receiver> tag represents a BroadcastReceiver, which may or may not have an explicit <intent-filter> tag.
- The <uses-permission> tag tells Android that this application requires certain security privileges. For example, if an application requires access to the contacts on a device, it requires the following tag in its AndroidManifest.xml file:

```
<uses-permission android:name=
"android.permission.READ_CONTACTS" />
```

We revisit the AndroidManifest.xml file a number of times throughout the book because we need to add more detail for certain elements.

Now that you have a basic understanding of the Android application and the AndroidManifest.xml file, which describes its components, it's time to discuss how and where it actually executes. The next section discusses the relationship between an Android application and its Linux and Dalvik virtual machine runtime.

Figure 1.7   Applications are listed in the launcher based on their IntentFilter. In this example, the application "Where Do You Live" is available in the LAUNCHER category.

1.3.4 *Mapping applications to processes*

Android applications each run in a single Linux process. Android relies on Linux for process management, and the application itself runs in an instance of the Dalvik virtual machine. The OS may need to unload, or even kill, an application from time to time to accommodate resource allocation demands. There is a hierarchy or sequence the system uses to select the victim of a resource shortage. In general, the rules are as follows:

- Visible, running activities have top priority.
- Visible, nonrunning activities are important, because they are recently paused and are likely to be resumed shortly.
- A running service is next in priority.
- The most likely candidates for termination are processes that are empty (loaded perhaps for performance-caching purposes) or processes that have dormant Activitys.

It's time to wrap up this chapter with a simple Android application.

ps -a

The Linux environment is complete, including process management. It is possible to launch and kill applications directly from the shell on the Android platform. However, this is largely a developer's debugging task, not something the average Android handset user is likely to be carrying out. It is nice to have for troubleshooting application issues. It is unheard of on commercially available mobile phones to "touch the metal" in this fashion. For more in-depth exploration of the Linux foundations of Android, see chapter 13.

1.4 An Android application

This section presents a simple Android application demonstrating a single `Activity`, with one `View`. The `Activity` collects data, a street address to be specific, and creates an `Intent` to find this address. The `Intent` is ultimately dispatched to Google Maps. Figure 1.8 is a screen shot of the application running on the emulator. The name of the application is Where Do You Live.

Figure 1.8 This Android application demonstrates a simple `Activity` and `Intent`.

As previously introduced, the AndroidManifest.xml file contains the descriptors for the high-level classes of the application. This application contains a single `Activity` named AWhereDoYouLive. The application's AndroidManifest.xml file is shown in listing 1.6.

Listing 1.6   AndroidManifest.xml for the Where Do You Live application

```xml
<?xml version="1.0" encoding="utf-8"?>
<manifest xmlns:android="http://schemas.android.com/apk/res/android"
   package="com.msi.manning.unlockingandroid">
   <application android:icon="@drawable/icon">
     <activity android:name=".AWhereDoYouLive" android:label="@string/
     app_name">
        <intent-filter>
           <action android:name="android.intent.action.MAIN" />
           <category android:name="android.intent.category.LAUNCHER" />
        </intent-filter>
     </activity>
   </application>
</manifest>
```

The sole `Activity` is implemented in the file AWhereDoYouLive.java, presented in listing 1.7.

Listing 1.7   Implementing the Android `Activity` in AWhereDoYouLive.java

```java
package com.msi.manning.unlockingandroid;

// imports omitted for brevity

public class AWhereDoYouLive extends Activity {
   @Override
   public void onCreate(Bundle icicle) {
      super.onCreate(icicle);                         ❶ Set up GUI
      setContentView(R.layout.main);
      final EditText addressfield = (EditText) findViewById(R.id.address);
      final Button button = (Button) findViewById(R.id.launchmap);
      button.setOnClickListener(new Button.OnClickListener()  {
         public void onClick(View view) {
         try {
         String address = addressfield.getText().toString();
         address = address.replace(' ', '+');
         Intent geoIntent = new Intent(android.content.Intent.ACTION_VIEW,
Uri.parse("geo:0,0?q=" + address));
            startActivity(geoIntent);
         } catch (Exception e) {
         ...
         }
      }
   });
   }
}
```

❷ Reference Edit field

❸ Reference button

❹ Get address

❺ Prepare Intent

❻ Initiate lookup

In this example application, the `setContentView` method ❶ creates the primary UI, which is a layout defined in main.xml in the /res/layout directory. The `EditText` view collects information, which is in this case an address. The EditText view is a text box or edit box in generic programming parlance. The findViewById method ❷ connects the resource identified by R.id.address to an instance of the EditText class.

A Button object is connected to the launchmap UI element, again using the find-ViewById method ❸. When this button is clicked, the application obtains the entered address by invoking the getText method of the associated EditText ❹.

Once the address has been retrieved from the UI, we need to create an Intent to find the entered address. The Intent has a VIEW action, and the data portion represents a geographic search query, as seen in ❺.

Finally, the application asks Android to perform the Intent, which ultimately results in the mapping application displaying the chosen address. This is accomplished with a call to the startActivity method ❻.

Resources are precompiled into a special class known as the R class, as shown in listing 1.8. The final members of this class represent UI elements. Note that you should never modify the R.java file manually, as it is automatically built every time the underlying resources change.

> **Listing 1.8   R.java contains the R class, which has UI element identifiers**

```
/* AUTO-GENERATED FILE.  DO NOT MODIFY.
 *
 * This class was automatically generated by the
 * aapt tool from the resource data it found.  It
 * should not be modified by hand.
 */

package com.msi.manning.unlockingandroid;

public final class R {
   public static final class attr {
   }
   public static final class drawable {
      public static final int icon=0x7f020000;
   }
   public static final class id {
      public static final int address=0x7f050000;
      public static final int launchmap=0x7f050001;
   }
   public static final class layout {
      public static final int main=0x7f030000;
   }
   public static final class string {
      public static final int app_name=0x7f040000;
   }
}
```

Android resources are covered in greater depth in chapter 3.

The primary screen of this application is defined as a LinearLayout view, as shown in listing 1.9. It is a single layout containing one label, one text entry element, and one button control.

Listing 1.9   Main.xml defines the UI elements for our sample application

```xml
<?xml version="1.0" encoding="utf-8"?>
<LinearLayout xmlns:android="http://schemas.android.com/apk/res/android"
   android:orientation="vertical"
   android:layout_width="fill_parent"
   android:layout_height="fill_parent"
   >
<TextView
   android:layout_width="wrap_content"
   android:layout_height="wrap_content"
   android:text="Please enter your home address."
   />
<EditText
   android:id="@+id/address"
   android:layout_width="fill_parent"
   android:layout_height="wrap_content"
android:autoText="true"
/>
<Button
   android:id="@+id/launchmap"
   android:layout_width="wrap_content"
   android:layout_height="wrap_content"
   android:text="Show Map"
   />
<TextView
   android:layout_width="wrap_content"
   android:layout_height="wrap_content"
   android:text="Unlocking Android, Chapter 1."
   />
</LinearLayout>
```

❶ ID assignment for EditText

❷ ID assignment for Button

Note the use of the @ symbol in this resource's id attribute ❶ and ❷. This causes the appropriate entries to be made in the R class via the automatically generated R.java file. These R class members are used in the calls to findViewById(), as shown previously, to tie the UI elements to an instance of the appropriate class.

A strings file and icon round out the resources in this simple application. The strings.xml for this application is shown in listing 1.10. The strings.xml file is used to localize string content.

Listing 1.10   strings.xml

```xml
<?xml version="1.0" encoding="utf-8"?>
<resources>
   <string name="app_name">Where Do You Live</string>
</resources>
```

This concludes our first Android application.

1.5   *Summary*

This chapter has introduced the Android platform and briefly touched on market positioning, including what Android is up against as a newcomer to the mobile marketplace. Android is such a new platform that there are sure to be changes and announcements as it matures and more and varied hardware hits the market. New platforms need to be adopted and flexed to identify the strengths and expose the weaknesses so they can be improved. Perhaps the biggest challenge for Android is to navigate the world of the mobile operators and convince them that Android is good for business. Fortunately with Google behind it, Android should have some ability to flex its muscles, and we'll see significant inroads with device manufacturers and carriers alike.

In this chapter we examined the Android stack and discussed its relationship with Linux and Java. With Linux at its core, Android is a formidable platform, especially for the mobile space. While Android development is done in the Java programming language, the runtime is executed in the Dalvik virtual machine, as an alternative to the Java virtual machine from Sun. Regardless of the VM, Java coding skills are an important aspect of Android development. The bigger issue is the degree to which existing Java libraries can be leveraged.

We also examined the Android Intent class. The Intent is what makes Android tick. It is responsible for how events flow and which code handles them, and it provides a mechanism for delivering specific functionality to the platform, enabling third-party developers to deliver innovative solutions and products for Android. The main application classes of Activity, Service, ContentProvider, and BroadcastReceiver were all introduced with a simple code snippet example for each. Each of these application classes interacts with Intents in a slightly different manner, but the core facility of using Intents and using content URIs to access functionality and data combine to create the innovative and flexible Android environment. Intents and their relationship with these application classes are unpacked and unlocked as we progress through this book.

The AndroidManifest.xml descriptor file ties all of the details together for an Android application. It includes all of the information necessary for the application to run, what Intents it can handle, and what permissions the application requires. Throughout this book, the AndroidManifest.xml file will be a familiar companion as new elements are added and explained.

Finally, this chapter provided a taste of Android application development with a very simple example tying a simple UI, an Intent, and Google Maps into one seamless user experience. This is just scratching the surface of what Android can do. The next chapter takes a deeper look into the Android SDK to learn more about what is in the toolbox to assist in *Unlocking Android*.

Development environment

2

This chapter covers:

- Installing the Android SDK
- Using Eclipse for Android development
- Fitting it together with the Android Emulator
- Running and debugging an Android application

This chapter introduces the Android Development Tools chain and provides a hands-on guide to using them as we walk through creating, testing, and debugging a sample application. Upon completing this chapter, you will be familiar with using Eclipse and the Android Development Tools plug-in, navigating the Android SDK and its tools, running Android applications in the emulator, and debugging your application. With these skills in hand, we will look at the Java packages provided in the SDK to better equip you to embrace the development topics introduced later in this book as you prepare to develop your own Android applications.

The core task for a developer when embracing a new platform is getting an understanding of the SDK with its various components. Let's start by examining the core components of the Android SDK, then transition into using the included tools to build and debug an application.

2.1 *The Android SDK*

The Android SDK is a freely available download from Google. The first thing you should do before going any further in this chapter is make sure you have the Android SDK installed along with Eclipse and the Android plug-in for Eclipse, also known as the Android Development Tools, or simply ADT. The Android SDK is required to build Android applications, and Eclipse is the preferred development environment for this book. You can download the Android SDK from http://code.google.com/android/download.html.

> **TIP** The Android download page has instructions for installing the SDK, or you can refer to appendix A of this book for detailed information on installing the required development tools.

As in any development environment, becoming familiar with the class structures is helpful, so having the documentation at hand as a reference is a good idea. The Android SDK includes HTML-based documentation, which primarily consists of Javadoc-formatted pages describing the available packages and classes. The Android SDK documentation is found in the /doc directory under your SDK installation. Because of the rapidly changing nature of this new platform, you may want to keep an eye out for any changes to the SDK. The most up-to-date Android SDK documentation is available at http://code.google.com/android/documentation.html.

2.1.1 *The application programming interface*

The Java environment of Android can be broken down into a handful of key sections. Once you have an understanding of each of these areas, the Javadoc reference material that ships with the SDK becomes a real tool and not just a pile of seemingly unrelated material. You may recall that Android is not a strictly J2ME software environment; however, there is some commonality between the Android platforms and other Java development platforms. The next few sections review some of the Java packages in the Android SDK and where they can be used. The remaining chapters provide a deeper look into using many of these programming interfaces.

2.1.2 *Core Android packages*

If you have developed in Java previously, you will recognize many familiar Java packages for core functionality. These include packages such as:

- java.lang—Core Java language classes.
- java.io—Input/output capabilities.
- java.net—Network connections.
- java.util—Utility classes. This package includes the Log class used to write to the LogCat.
- java.text—Text-handling utilities.
- java.math—Math and number-manipulation classes.
- javax.net—Network classes.

- `javax.security`—Security-related classes.
- `javax.xml`—DOM-based XML classes.
- `org.apache.*`—HTTP-related classes.
- `org.xml`—SAX-based XML classes.

There are additional Java classes. Generally speaking, there is minimal focus in this book on core packages listed here, because our primary concern is Android development. With that in mind, let's look at the Android-specific functionality found in the Android SDK.

Android-specific packages are very easy to identify because they start with `android` in the package name. Some of the more important packages include:

- `android.app`—Android application model access
- `android.content`—Accessing and publishing data in Android
- `android.net`—Contains the `Uri` class, used for accessing various content
- `android.graphics`—Graphics primitives
- `android.opengl`—OpenGL classes
- `android.os`—System-level access to the Android environment
- `android.provider`—`ContentProvider`-related classes
- `android.telephony`—Telephony capability access
- `android.text`—Text layout
- `android.util`—Collection of utilities for text manipulation, including XML
- `android.view`—UI elements
- `android.webkit`—Browser functionality
- `android.widget`—More UI elements

Some of these packages are absolutely core to Android application development, including `android.app`, `android.view`, and `android.content`. Other packages are used to varying degrees depending on the type of applications being constructed.

2.1.3 *Optional packages*

Not every Android device will have the same hardware and mobile connectivity capabilities, so some elements of the Android SDK are optional. Some devices will support these features, and others not. It is important that an application degrade gracefully if a feature is not available on a specific handset. Java packages to pay special attention to include those that rely on specific, underlying hardware and network characteristics, such as location-based services including GPS and wireless technologies such as Bluetooth, IrDA, and Wi-Fi (802.11).

This quick introduction to the Android SDK's programming interfaces is just that—quick and at a glance. Upcoming chapters go into the class libraries in further detail, so we'll focus now on the tools required to build Android applications.

Before building an actual Android application, let's examine how the Android SDK and its components fit into the Eclipse environment.

2.2 *Fitting the pieces together*

After installing the Android SDK along with the ADT plug-in for Eclipse, we're ready to explore the development environment. Figure 2.1 depicts the typical Android development environment, including both real hardware and the useful Android Emulator. While not the exclusive tool required for Android development, Eclipse can play a big role in Android development not only because it provides a rich Java compilation and debugging environment, but also because with the ADTs under Eclipse, we can manage and control virtually all aspects of testing our Android applications directly from the Eclipse IDE.

The key features of the Eclipse environment as it pertains to Android application development include:

- Rich Java development environment including Java source compilation, class autocompletion, and integrated Javadoc
- Source-level debugging
- Android Emulator profile management and launch
- The Dalvik Debug Monitoring Service (DDMS)
  - Thread and heap views
  - Emulator filesystem management
  - Data and voice network control
  - Emulator control
  - System and application logging

Eclipse supports the concept of perspectives, where the layout of the screen has a set of related windows and tools. The windows and tools included in an Eclipse perspective are known as views. When developing Android applications, there are two Eclipse

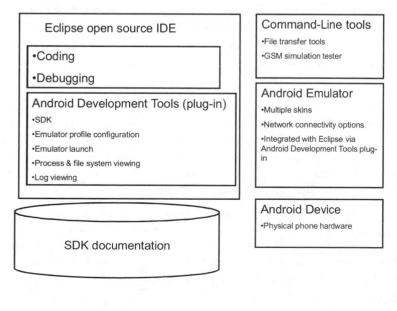

**Figure 2.1
The development environment for building Android applications, including the popular open source Eclipse IDE**

perspectives of primary interest to us: the Java Perspective and the Dalvik Debug Monitoring Service Perspective. Beyond those two, the Debug Perspective is also available and useful when debugging an Android application. To switch between the available perspectives in Eclipse, use the Open Perspective menu, found under the Window menu in the Eclipse IDE. Let's examine the features of the Java and DDMS Perspectives and how they can be leveraged for Android development.

2.2.1 Java Perspective

The Java Perspective is where you will spend most of your time while developing Android applications. The Java Perspective boasts a number of convenient views for assisting in the development process. The Package Explorer view allows us to see the Java projects in our Eclipse Workspace. Figure 2.2 shows the Package Explorer listing some of the sample projects for this book.

The Java Perspective is where you will edit your Java source code. Every time your source file is saved, it is automatically compiled by Eclipse's Java Developer Tools (JDT) in the background. You need not worry about the specifics of the JDT; the important thing to know is that it is functioning in the background to make your Java experience as seamless as possible. If there is an error in your source code, the details will show up in the Problems view of the Java Perspective. Figure 2.3 has an intentional error in the source code to demonstrate the functionality of the Problems view. You can also put your mouse over the red *x* to the left of the line containing the error for a tool-tip explanation of the problem.

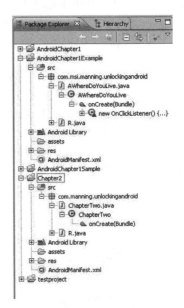

Figure 2.2   The Package Explorer allows us to browse the elements of our Android projects.

One of the very powerful features of the Java Perspective in Eclipse is the integration between the source code and the Javadoc view. The Javadoc view updates automatically to provide any available documentation about a currently selected Java class or method, as shown in figure 2.4, where the Javadoc view displays information about the `Activity` class.

TIPS   This chapter just scratches the surface in introducing the powerful Eclipse environment. If you want to learn more about Eclipse, you might consider reading *Eclipse in Action A Guide for Java Developers,* by David Gallardo, Ed Burnette, and Robert McGovern, published by Manning and available online at http://www.manning.com/.

It is easy to get the views in the current perspective into a layout that may not be desirable. If this occurs, you have a couple of choices to restore the perspective to a more useful state. The first option is to use the Show View menu under the Window menu to display a specific view. Alternatively, you can select the Reset Perspective menu to restore the perspective to its default settings.

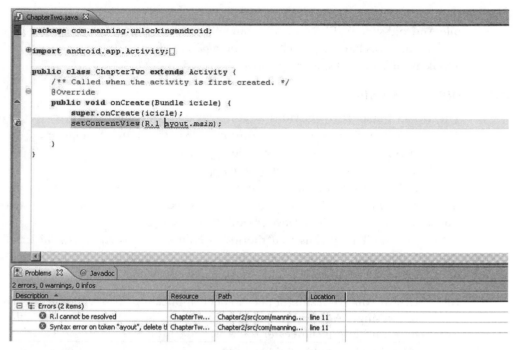

Figure 2.3 The Problems view shows any errors in your source code.

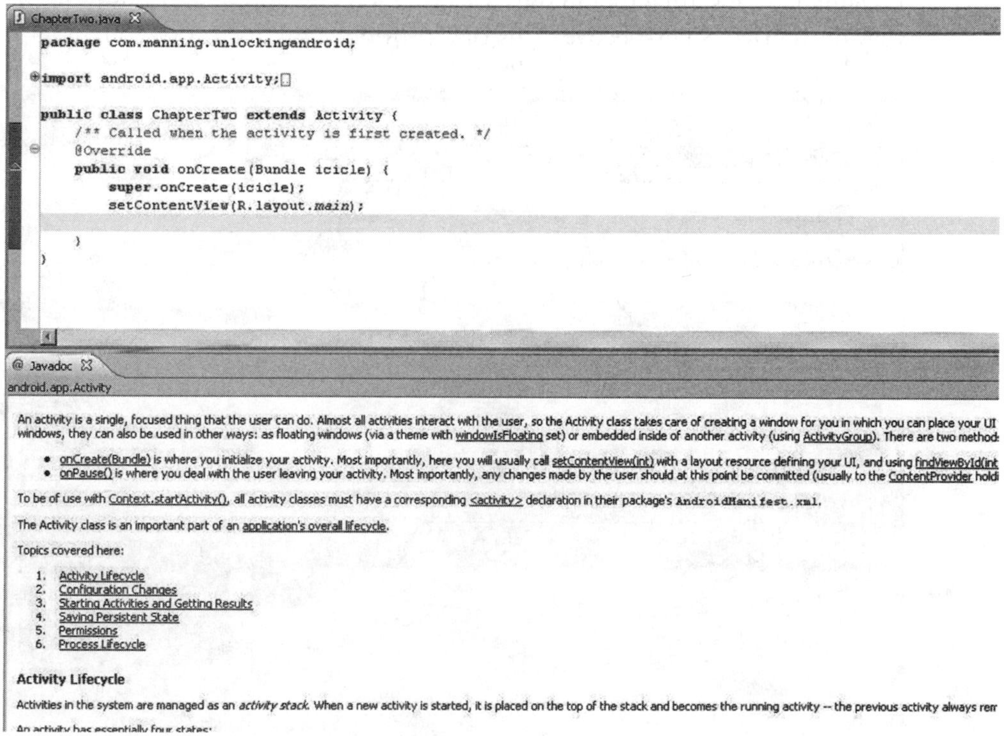

Figure 2.4 The Javadoc view provides context-sensitive documentation, in this case for the `Activity` class.

In addition to the JDT, which compiles Java source files, the ADTs automatically compile Android-specific files such as layout and resource files. We'll learn more about the underlying tools later in this chapter and again in chapter 3, but now it's time to have a look at the Android-specific perspective found in the DDMS.

2.2.2   *DDMS Perspective*

The DDMS Perspective provides a dashboard-like view into the heart of a running Android device, or in our case, a running Android Emulator. Figure 2.5 shows the emulator running the Chapter2 sample application.

We'll walk through the details of the application, including how to build the application and how to start it running in the Android Emulator, but first let's see what we can learn from the DDMS to continue the discussion of the tools available to us for Android development. The Devices view shows a single emulator session, titled `emulator-tcp-5555`. This means that there is a connection to the Android Emulator at TCP/IP port 5555. Within this emulator session, five processes are running. The one of interest to us is `com.manning.unlockingandroid`, with a process id of `616`.

TIP   Unless you are testing a peer-to-peer application, you will typically have only a single Android Emulator session running at a time. It is possible to have multiple instances of the Android Emulator running concurrently on a single development machine.

Logging is an essential tool in software development, and that brings us to the LogCat view of the DDMS Perspective. This view provides a glimpse at system and application

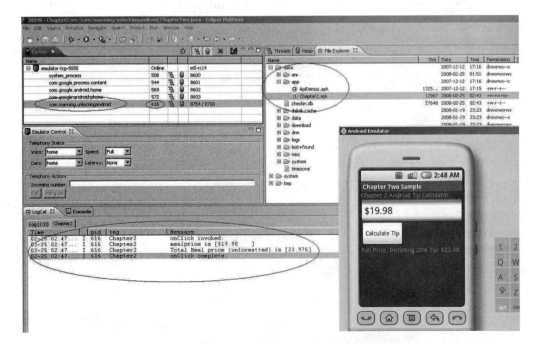

Figure 2.5   Perspective with an application running in the Android Emulator

logging taking place in the Android Emulator. In figure 2.5, a filter has been set up for looking at entries with a `tag` of Chapter2. Using a filter on the LogCat is a helpful practice, because it can reduce the noise of all the logging entries and allow us to focus on our own application's entries. In this case, there are four entries in the list matching our filter criteria. We'll look at the source code soon to see how we get our messages into the log. Note that these log entries have a column showing the process `id`, or PID, of the application contributing the log entry. As expected, the PID for our log entries is 616, matching our running application instance in the emulator.

The File Explorer view is shown in the upper right of figure 2.5. User applications, that is, the ones you and I write, are deployed with a file extension of .apk and are stored in the /data/app directory of the Android device. The File Explorer view also permits filesystem operations such as copying files to and from the Android Emulator as well as removing files from the emulator's filesystem. Figure 2.6 shows the process of deleting a user application from the /data/app directory.

Obviously, being able to casually browse the filesystem of our mobile phone is a great convenience. This is a nice feature to have for mobile development, where we are often relying on cryptic pop-up messages to help us along in the application development and debugging process. With easy access to the filesystem, we can work with files and readily copy them to and from our development computer platform as necessary.

In addition to exploring a running application, the DDMS Perspective provides tools for controlling the emulated environment. For example, the Emulator Control view allows the testing of various connectivity characteristics for both voice and data networks, such as simulating a phone call or receiving an incoming SMS. Figure 2.7 demonstrates sending an SMS message to the Android Emulator.

The DDMS provides quite a bit of visibility into, and control over, the Android Emulator and is a handy tool for evaluating our Android applications. Before we move on to building and testing Android applications, it is helpful to understand what is happening behind the scenes and enabling the functionality of the DDMS.

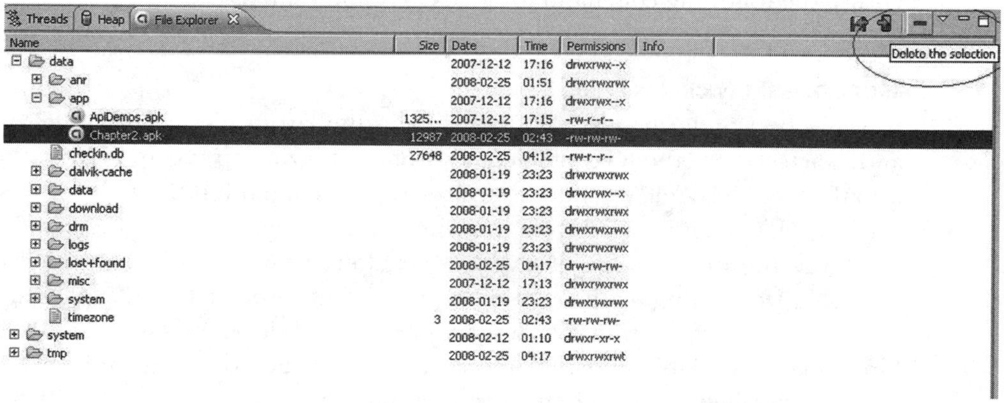

Figure 2.6 Deleting applications from the emulator by highlighting the application file and clicking the delete button

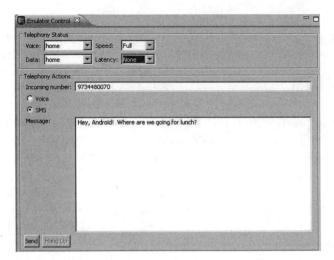

Figure 2.7   Sending a test SMS to the Android Emulator

2.2.3   *Command-Line tools*

The Android SDK ships with a collection of command-line tools, which are located in the tools subdirectory of your Android SDK installation. While Eclipse and the ADTs provide a great deal of control over our Android development environment, sometimes it is nice to exercise greater control, particularly when considering the power and convenience that scripting can bring to a development platform. We are going to explore two of the command-line tools found in the Android SDK.

TIP   It is a good idea to add the tools directory to your search path. For example, if your Android SDK is installed to c:\software\google\androidsdk, you can add the Android SDK to your path by performing the following operation in a command window on your Windows computer:

```
set path=%path%;c:\software\google\androidsdk\tools;
```

Or use the following command for Mac OS X and Linux:

```
export PATH=$PATH:/path_to_Android_SDK_directory/tools
```

ANDROID ASSET PACKAGING TOOL

You may be wondering just how files such as the layout file main.xml get processed and exactly where the R.java file comes from. Who zips up the application file for us into the apk file? Well, you may have already guessed, but it is the Android Asset Packaging Tool, or as it is called from the command line, aapt. This is a versatile tool that combines the functionality of pkzip or jar along with an Android-specific resource compiler. Depending on the command-line options provided to it, aapt wears a number of hats and assists with our design-time Android development tasks. To learn the functionality available in aapt, simply run it from the command line with no arguments. A detailed usage message is written to the screen.

While aapt helps with design-time tasks, another tool, the Android Debug Bridge, assists us at runtime to interact with the Android Emulator.

ANDROID DEBUG BRIDGE

The Android Debug Bridge (adb) utility permits us to interact with the Android Emulator directly from the command line or script. Have you ever wished you could navigate the filesystem on your smartphone? Well, now you can with the adb! The adb works as a client/server TCP-based application. While there are a couple of background processes that run on the development machine and the emulator to enable our functionality, the important thing to understand is that when we run adb, we get access to a running instance of the Android Emulator. Here are a couple of examples of using adb. First, let's look to see if we have any available Android Emulator sessions running:

```
adb devices<return>
```

This command will return a list of available Android Emulators; for example, figure 2.8 shows adb locating two running emulator sessions.

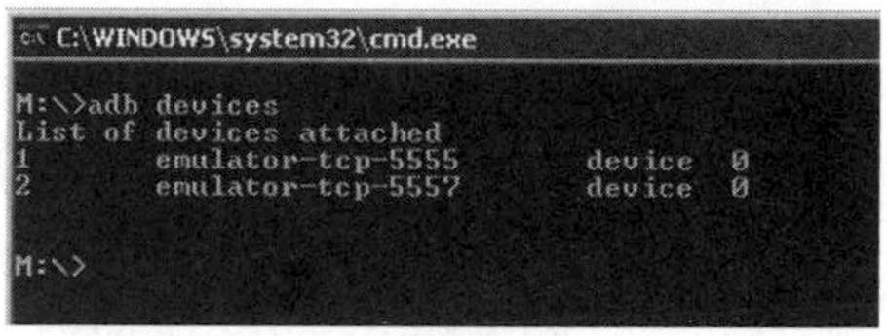

Let's connect to the first Android Emulator session and see if our application is installed. We connect with the syntax adb shell. This is how we would connect if we

Figure 2.8 The adb tool provides interaction at runtime with the Android Emulator.

had a single Android Emulator session active, but because there are two emulators running, we need to specify an identifier to connect to the appropriate session:

```
adb -d 1 shell
```

Figure 2.9 shows off the Android filesystem and demonstrates looking for a specific installed application, namely our Chapter2 sample application, which we'll be building in the next section.

This capability can be very handy when we want to remove a specific file from the emulator's filesystem, kill a process, or generally interact with the operating environment of the Android Emulator. If you download an application from the internet, for example, you can use the adb command to install an application. For example,

```
adb shell install someapplication.apk
```

installs the application named *someapplication* to the Android Emulator. The file is copied to the /data/app directory and is accessible from the Android application

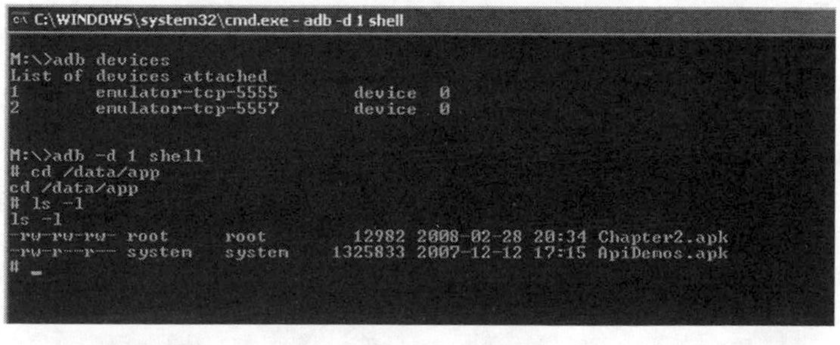

Figure 2.9 Using the shell command, we can browse Android's filesystem.

launcher. Similarly, if you desire to remove an application, you can run adb to remove an application from the Android Emulator. For example, if you desire to remove the Chapter2.apk sample application from a running emulator's filesystem, you can execute the following command from a terminal or Windows command window:

```
adb shell rm /data/app/Chapter2.apk
```

Mastering the command-line tools in the Android SDK is certainly not a requirement of Android application development, but having an understanding of what is available and where to look for capabilities is a good skill to have in your toolbox. If you need assistance with either the aapt or adb command, simply enter the command at the terminal, and a fairly verbose usage/help page is displayed. Additional information on the tools may be found in the Android SDK documentation.

TIP   The Android filesystem is a Linux filesystem. While the adb shell command does not provide a very rich shell programming environment as is found on a desktop Linux or Mac OS X system, basic commands such as ls, ps, kill, and rm are available. If you are new to Linux, you may benefit from learning some very basic shell commands.

One other tool you will want to make sure you are familiar with is telnet. Telnet allows you to connect to a remote system with a character-based UI. In this case, the remote system you connect to is the Android Emulator's console. You can accomplish this with the following command:

```
telnet localhost 5554
```

In this case, localhost represents your local development computer where the Android Emulator has been started because the Android Emulator relies on your computer's loopback IP address of 127.0.0.1. Why port 5554? Recall when we employed adb to find running emulator instances that the output of that command included a name with a number at the end. The first Android Emulator can generally be found at IP port 5555. No matter which port number the Android Emulator is using, the Android Emulator's console may be found at a port number equaling 1 less. For example, if the Android Emulator is running and listed at port 5555, the console is at port 5554.

Using a telnet connection to the emulator provides a command-line means for configuring the emulator while it is running and testing telephony features such as calls and text messages.

It is time to write an Android application to exercise the development environment we have been discussing.

2.3   *Building an Android application in Eclipse*

We are going to build a simple application that gives us the opportunity to modify the UI, provides a little application logic, then executes the application in the Android Emulator. More complex applications are left for later chapters—our focus here is on the development tools. Building an Android application is not too much different from creating other types of Java applications in the Eclipse IDE. It all starts with choosing File > New and selecting an Android application as the build target.

Like many development environments, Eclipse provides for a wizard interface to ease the task of creating a new application. We'll use the Android Project Wizard to get off to a quick start in building an Android application.

2.3.1 Android Project Wizard

The most straightforward manner to create an Android application is to utilize the services of the Android Project Wizard, which is part of the ADT plug-in. The wizard provides a simple means to define the Eclipse project name and location, the `Activity` name corresponding to the main UI class, as well as a name for the application. Of importance also is the Java package name under which the application is created. Once this application is created, it is easy to add new classes to the project.

NOTE   In this example, we are creating a brand-new project in the Eclipse workspace. This same wizard may be used to import source code from another developer, such as the sample code for this book. Note also that the specific screens may vary over time as the Android tools mature.

Figure 2.10 demonstrates the creation of a new project named Chapter2 using the wizard.

TIP   You will want the package name of your applications to be unique from one application to the next.

Clicking Finish creates our sample application. At this point, the application compiles and is capable of running on the emulator—no further development steps are required. Of course, what fun would an empty project be? Let's flesh out this sample application, our Android Tip Calculator.

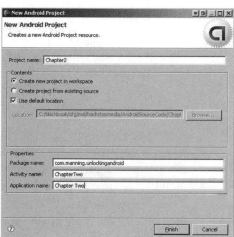

Figure 2.10   Using the Android Project Wizard, it is easy to create an empty Android application, ready for customization.

2.3.2 Android sample application code

The Android Application Wizard takes care of a number of important elements in the Android application structure, including the Java source files, the default resource files, and the AndroidManifest.xml file. Looking at the Package Explorer view in Eclipse we can see all of the elements of this application. Here's a quick description of the elements included in our sample application:

- The src folder contains two Java source files automatically created by the wizard.
- ChapterTwo.java contains the main `Activity` for the application. We will modify this file to add our sample application's tip calculator functionality.
- R.java contains identifiers for each of the UI resource elements in the application. It is important that you never modify this file directly, as it automatically regenerates every time a resource is modified, and any manual changes you make will be lost the next time the application is built.
- Android.jar contains the Android runtime Java classes. This is a reference to the android.jar file found in the Android SDK.
- The res folder contains all of the Android resource files, including:
- Drawables contains image files such as bitmaps and icons. The wizard includes a default Android icon named icon.png.
- Layout contains an xml file called main.xml. This file contains the UI elements for the primary view of our `Activity`. We will modify this file but we will not be making any significant or special changes—just enough to accomplish our meager UI goals for our Tip Calculator. UI elements such as `Views` are covered in detail in chapter 3. It is not uncommon for an Android application to have multiple xml files in the Layout section.
- Values contains the strings.xml file. This file is used for localizing string values such as the application name and other strings used by your application. It contains all of the applications in this book
- AndroidManifest.xml represents the deployment information for this project. While AndroidManifest.xml files can become somewhat complex, this chapter's manifest file can run without modification because no special permissions are required.

Now that we know what is in the project, let's review how we are going to modify the application. Our goal with the Android Tip Calculator is to permit our user to enter the price of a meal, then select a button to calculate the total cost of the meal, tip included. To accomplish this, we need to modify two files, ChapterTwo.java and the UI layout file, main.xml. Let's start with the UI changes by adding a few new elements to the primary `View`, as shown in listing 2.1.

Listing 2.1   Main.xml contains UI elements

```
<?xml version="1.0" encoding="utf-8"?>
<LinearLayout xmlns:android="http://schemas.android.com/apk/res/android"
    android:orientation="vertical"
    android:layout_width="fill_parent"
    android:layout_height="fill_parent"
    >
<TextView
    android:layout_width="fill_parent"
    android:layout_height="wrap_content"                    1  Static TextView
    android:text="Chapter 2 Android Tip Calculator"
```

```
    />
<EditText                        ←──❷  EditText definition
    android:id="@+id/mealprice"        ←
    android:layout_width="fill_parent"   ❸  Assign an id
    android:layout_height="wrap_content"
    android:autoText="true"
/>                               ❹  Button definition,
<Button                              including id
android:id="@+id/calculate"      ←
    android:layout_width="wrap_content"
    android:layout_height="wrap_content"
    android:text="Calculate Tip"
    />
<TextView                        ←──❺  TextView with an id
    android:id="@+id/answer"
    android:layout_width="fill_parent"
    android:layout_height="wrap_content"
    android:text=""
    />
```

```
</LinearLayout>
```

The layout for this application is very straightforward. The overall layout is a vertical, linear layout with only four elements. A static TextView displays the title of the application ❶. An EditText collects the price of the meal for this Tip Calculator application ❷. The EditText element has an attribute of type android:id, with a value of mealprice ❸. When a UI element contains the android:id attribute, it permits us to manipulate this element from our code. We accomplish this by adding this element's id attribute to the R.java file as a unique member of the R class. This identifying value is used in the findViewById method, shown in listing 2.2. If a UI element is static, such as the TextView ❶, and does not need to be set or read from our application code, the android:id attribute is not required.

A button named calculate ❹ is added to the view. Note that this element also has an android:id attribute because we will want to capture click events.

A TextView named answer ❺ is provided for displaying our total cost, including tip. Again, this element has an id because we will need to update it during runtime.

When we save the file main.xml, the file is processed by the ADT plug-in, compiling the resources and generating an updated R.java file. Try it for yourself. Modify one of the id values in the main.xml file, save the file, then open R.java to have a look at the constants generated there. Remember not to modify the R.java file directly, because all of your changes will be lost! If you conduct this experiment, be sure to change the values back as they are listed here to make sure the rest of the project will compile as-is. Provided we have not introduced any syntactical errors into our main.xml file, our UI file is complete.

TIP   Through the maturation of the still very young Android Development Tools, the plug-ins for Eclipse have offered increasingly useful resource editors for manipulating the layout xml files. This means that you do not need to rely on editing the xml files directly.

It is time to turn our attention to the file ChapterTwo.java to implement the desired Tip Calculator functionality. ChapterTwo.java is shown in listing 2.2. Note that we omitted some imports for brevity. You can download the complete source code from the Manning website at http://manning.com/ableson.

Listing 2.2 ChapterTwo.java implements the Tip Calculator logic

```java
package com.manning.unlockingandroid;        ◁———❶ Package name

import com.manning.unlockingandroid.R;

import android.app.Activity;        ◁——❷ Required imports
import java.text.NumberFormat;
import android.util.Log;
// some imports omitted

public class ChapterTwo extends Activity {
  public static final String tag = "Chapter2";
    @Override
    public void onCreate(Bundle icicle) {
      super.onCreate(icicle);
      setContentView(R.layout.main);

      final EditText mealpricefield =                          ❸ Reference EditText
              (EditText) findViewById(R.id.mealprice);    ◁        for mealprice
      final TextView answerfield =
              (TextView) findViewById(R.id.answer);

      final Button button = (Button) findViewById(R.id.calculate);
      button.setOnClickListener(new Button.OnClickListener() {  ◁
        public void onClick(View v) {                              Set up
          Try {                                                    onClick
            //Perform action on click                           ❹ Listener
            Log.i(tag,"onClick invoked.");     ◁——❺ Log entry
            // grab the meal price from the UI
            String mealprice =
            mealpricefield.getText().toString();   ◁——❻ Get meal price
            Log.i(tag,"mealprice is [" + mealprice + "]");
            String answer = "";

            // check to see if the meal price includes a "$"
            if (mealprice.indexOf("$") == -1) {
              mealprice = "$" + mealprice;
            }

            float fmp = 0.0F;
            // get currency formatter
            NumberFormat nf =
            java.text.NumberFormat.getCurrencyInstance();

            // grab the input meal price
            fmp = nf.parse(mealprice).floatValue();

            // let's give a nice tip -> 20%
            fmp *= 1.2;
            Log.i(tag,"Total Meal Price (unformatted) is [" + fmp + "]");
            // format our result
```

```
            answer = "Full Price, Including 20% Tip: " + nf.format(fmp);

            // display the answer
            answerfield.setText(answer);

            Log.i(tag,"onClick complete.");
          } catch (java.text.ParseException pe) {
            Log.i(tag,"Parse exception caught");
            answerfield.setText("Failed to parse amount?");
          } catch (Exception e){
            Log.e(tag,"Failed to Calculate Tip:" + e.getMessage());
            e.printStackTrace();
            answerfield.setText(e.getMessage());
          }
        }
      });
    }
}
```

Display full price, including tip ➐

Catch parse error ➑

Let's examine this sample application, step-by-step. Like all but the most trivial Java applications, this class contains a statement identifying which package it belongs to: com.manning.unlockingandroid ❶. This line containing the package name was generated by the Application Wizard.

We import the com.manning.unlockingandroid.R class to gain access to the definitions used by the UI. Note that this step is not actually required because the R class is part of the same application package; however, it is helpful to include this import because it makes our code easier to follow. Also note that there are some built-in UI elements in the R class. Some are introduced later in the book as part of sample applications.

A number of imports are necessary ❷ to resolve class names in use; most of the import statements have been omitted from this code listing for the sake of brevity. One import that is shown here contains the definition for the java.text.NumberFormat class, which is used to format and parse currency values.

Another import shown is for the android.util.Log class, which is employed to make entries to the log. Calling static methods of the Log class adds entries to the log. Entries in the log may be viewed via the LogCat view of the DDMS Perspective. When making entries to the log, it is helpful to put a consistent identifier on a group of related entries using a common string, commonly referred to as the *tag*. We can filter on this string value so we don't have to sift through the hundreds and thousands of LogCat entries to find our few debugging or informational messages.

We connect the UI element containing mealprice to a class-level variable of type EditText ❸ by calling the findViewById method, passing in the identifier for the mealprice, as defined by our automatically generated R class, found in R.java. With this reference, we can access the user's input and manipulate the meal price data as entered by the user. Similarly, we connect the UI element for displaying the calculated answer back to the user, again by calling the findViewById method.

To know when to calculate the tip amount, we need to obtain a reference to the Button so we can add an event listener. We want to know when the button has been clicked. We accomplish this by adding a new `OnClickListener` method named `onClick` ❹.

When the `onClick` method is invoked, we add the first of a few log entries using the static `i()` method of the `Log` class ❺. This method adds an entry to the log with an Information classification. The `Log` class contains methods for adding entries to the log for different levels, including Verbose, Debug, Information, Warning, and Error.

Now that we have a reference to the `mealprice` UI element, we can obtain the text entered by our user with the `getText()` method of the `EditText` class ❻. In preparation for formatting the full meal price, we obtain a reference to the static currency formatter.

Let's be somewhat generous and offer a 20 percent tip. Then, using the formatter, let's format the full meal cost, including tip. Next, using the `setText()` method of the `TextView` UI element named `answerfield`, we update the UI to tell the user the total meal cost ❼.

Because this code might have a problem with improperly formatted data, it is a good practice to put code logic into `Try/Catch` blocks to keep our application behaving when the unexpected occurs ❽.

There are additional files in this sample project, but in this chapter we are concerned only with modifying the application enough to get custom functionality working. You will notice that as soon as we save our source files, the Eclipse IDE compiles the project source files in the background. If there are any errors, they are listed in the Problems view of the Java Perspective as well as marked in the left-hand margin with a small red x to draw our attention to them.

TIP   Using the command-line tools found in the Android SDK, you can create batch builds of your applications without the use of the IDE. This approach is useful for software shops with a specific configuration-management function and a desire to conduct automated builds. In addition to the Android-specific build tools found under the tools subdirectory of your Android SDK installation, you will also require a Java Developer Kit (JDK) version 5.0 or later in order to complete command-line application builds. Automating builds of Android applications is beyond the scope of this book; however, you can learn more about the topic of build scripts by reading two Manning titles on the topic: *Java Development with Ant* by Erik Hatcher and Steve Loughran found at http://www.manning.com/hatcher/ and *Ant in Action, Second Edition of Java Development with Ant,* by Steve Loughran and Erik Hatcher, found at http://www.manning.com/loughran/.

Assuming there are no errors in the source files, our classes and UI files will compile properly. But what needs to happen before our project can be run and tested in the Android Emulator?

2.3.3   *Building the application*

At this point, our application has compiled and is actually ready to be run on the device. Let's look deeper at what happens after the compilation step. We don't need to perform these steps because the ADTs handle these steps for us, but it is helpful to understand what is happening behind the scenes.

Recall that despite the compile-time reliance upon Java, Android applications do not run in a Java virtual machine. Instead, the Android SDK employs the Dalvik virtual machine. This means that Java bytecodes created by the Eclipse compiler must be converted to the .dex file format for use in the Android runtime. The Android SDK has tools to perform these steps, but the ADT takes care of all of this for us transparently.

The Android SDK contains tools that convert the project files into a file ready to run on the Android Emulator. Figure 2.11 depicts the generalized flow of source files in the Android build process. If you recall from our earlier discussion of Android SDK tools, the tool used at design time is aapt. Application resource xml files are processed by aapt, with the R.java file created as a result—remember that we need to refer to the R class for user-interface identifiers when connecting our code to the UI. Java source files are first compiled to class files by our Java environment, typically Eclipse and the JDT. Once compiled, they are then converted to dex files to be ready for use with Android's Dalvik virtual machine. Surprisingly, the project's xml files are converted to a binary representation, not text as you might expect. However, the files retain their .xml extension on the device.

The converted xml files, a compiled form of the non-layout resources including the Drawables and Values, and the dex file (classes.dex) are packaged by the aapt tool into a file with a naming structure of *projectname*.apk. The resulting file can be read with a pkzip-compatible reader, such as WinRAR or WinZip, or the Java archiver, jar. Figure 2.12 show this chapter's sample application in WinRAR.

We are finally ready to run our application on the Android Emulator! It is important to become comfortable with working in an emulated environment when doing any serious mobile software development. There are many good reasons to have a quality emulator available for development and testing. One simple reason is that having multiple real devices with requisite data plans is a very expensive proposition. A

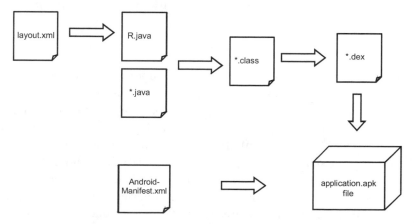

Figure 2.11   The ADT employs tools from the Android SDK to convert source files to a package ready to run on an Android device or emulator.

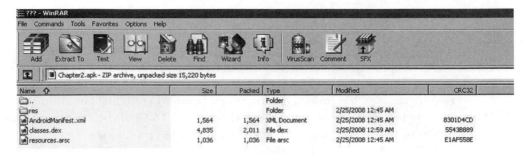

Figure 2.12 The Android application file format is pzip compatible.

single device may be hundreds of dollars alone. If the Open Handset Alliance has its way, Android will find its way onto multiple carriers with numerous devices, often with varying capabilities. Having one of every device is impractical for all but the development shops with the largest of budgets. For the rest of us, a device or two and the Android Emulator will have to suffice. Let's focus on the strengths of emulator-based mobile development.

2.4   *The Android Emulator*

While the best test of an application is running it on the hardware for which it was designed, an emulator often makes the job of the developer much easier. Working in an emulated environment permits a more rapid compile, run, and debug iterative cycle than is typically available when testing on a real hardware device. Taking the time to sync, or copy, an application to a real device typically takes longer than starting an emulator session. Also, it is easier to clean the filesystem of an emulator than performing the same maintenance operation on a real device. When you add in the capability of scripting commands to/from the emulator, it becomes an option worthy of investigation.

Beyond being a faster tool than working with a real device, the emulator tool must consider physical characteristics of a device, primarily the screen dimensions, input devices, and network connectivity.

2.4.1   *Skins*

Not all mobile devices are equally equipped, so it is important to be able to accommodate and test varying device characteristics in an emulated environment. The Android SDK comes with an emulator with distinct skins. The skins represent different hardware layouts as well as portrait and landscape orientations. Figure 2.13 shows two emulator views: one in portrait with a hidden QWERTY keypad, the other in landscape mode with a visible keyboard. The skins found with your SDK may vary from those shown here.

Not only is it important to understand and accommodate how the device looks, it is important to understand what connectivity options a device is able to offer. Have you ever tested a mobile application in an area where there is excellent data coverage only to find out that the location where the application is deployed in the field often has only marginal data service? The ability to test this condition in the confines of our

Figure 2.13 The Android SDK includes multiple emulator skins for testing a variety of device configurations.

development environment gives a real advantage to the application developer. Fortunately, the Android Emulator permits this kind of testing, as shown in the next section.

2.4.2 *Network speed*

Network speed simulation is a key element of mobile software development. This feature is helpful because the actual user experience will vary during real-world use, and it is important that mobile applications degrade gracefully in the absence of a reliable network connection. The Android Emulator provides for a rich set of emulation tools for testing various network conditions and speeds. Table 2.1 lists the available network speed and latency conditions available in the Android Emulator.

Table 2.1 The Android Emulator supports a variety of network speed options.

Network Speed	Network Latency
Full speed (Use the development environment's full internet connection)	None—no latency introduced
GSM	GPRS
HSCSD	EDGE
GPRS	UMTS
EDGE	
UMTS	
HSPDA	

The higher-speed network environment found in the Android Emulator is welcome when testing core features of our applications. This is because functional test cases are often run hundreds or even thousands of times before releasing a product. If we had to compile the application, sync the application to the device, and run our application over a wireless data network, the testing time would add up quickly, reducing the number of tests performed in a given amount of time and elevating the associated costs. Worse yet, the challenges of mobile data connectivity testing may entice us to minimize application testing in the first place! Considering that most software development timeframes are aggressive, every moment counts, so a quality emulator environment is valuable for rapid and cost-effective mobile application development activities. Also, it is important to consider that there may be usage charges for voice and data consumption on a mobile communications plan. Imagine paying by the kilobyte for every downloaded data packet when testing a new streaming audio player!

The Android SDK contains a command-line program named, appropriately, emulator, which runs the Android Emulator. There are many command-line switches available in the Android Emulator, permitting us to customize the emulator's environment: how it looks and behaves. Some of these options are exposed in the Eclipse IDE via the ADT plug-in. The majority of our focus is on employing the

Emulator vs. simulator

You may hear the words *emulator* and *simulator* thrown about interchangeably. While they have a similar purpose—testing applications without the requirement of real hardware—those words should be used with care. A simulator tool works by creating a testing environment that behaves as close to 100 percent of the same manner as the real environment; however, it is just an approximation of the real platform. But this does not mean that the code targeted for a simulator will run on a real device, because it is compatible only at the source-code level. Simulator code is often written to be run as a software program running on a desktop computer with Windows DLLs or Linux libraries that mimic the application programming interfaces (APIs) available on the real device. In the build environment, you typically select the CPU type for a target, and that is often x86/Simulator. In an emulated environment, the target of our projects is compatible at the binary level. The code we write works on an emulator as well as the real device. Of course, some aspects of the environment differ in terms of how certain functions are implemented on an emulator. For example, a network connection on an emulator will run through your development machine's network interface card, whereas the network connection on a real phone runs over the wireless connection such as a GPRS, EDGE or EVDO network. Emulators are preferred because they more reliably prepare us for running our code on real devices. Fortunately, the environment available to Android developers is an emulator, not a simulator.

Android Emulator from Eclipse, but you are encouraged to examine the command-line options available in the emulator because they will undoubtedly be of value as you progress to building more complex Android applications and your application testing requirements grow.

2.4.3 Emulator profiles

At this point, our sample application, the Android Tip Calculator, has compiled successfully. We now want to run our application in the Android Emulator.

TIP   If you have had any trouble building the sample application, now would be a good time to go back and clear up any syntax errors preventing the application from building. In Eclipse you can easily see errors because they are marked with a red *x* next to the project source file and on the offending line(s). If you continue to have errors, make sure that your build environment is set up correctly. Refer to appendix A of this book for details on configuring the build environment.

Figure 2.14 Creating a new launch configuration for testing our Android application

Our approach is to create a new Android Emulator profile so we can easily reuse our test environment settings. Our starting place is the Open Run Dialog menu in the Eclipse IDE, as shown in figure 2.14. As new releases of Eclipse become available, these screen shots may vary slightly from your personal development environment.

We want to create a new launch configuration, as shown in figure 2.15. To begin this process, highlight the Android Application entry in the list to the left, and click the New Launch Configuration button, shown circled in red in figure 2.15.

We now want to give our launch configuration a name that we can readily recognize. We are going to have quite a few of these launch configurations on the menu, so give the name something unique and easy to identify. The sample is titled Android Tip Calculator, as shown in figure 2.16. There are three tabs with options to configure, the first allowing the selection of the project and the first `Activity` in the project to launch.

Figure 2.15 Select the Android Application run template.

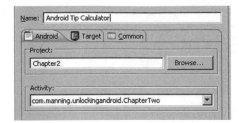

Figure 2.16   Setting up the Android Emulator launch configuration

The next tab permits the selection of the desired skin, which includes the screen layout, the network speed, and the network latency. In addition, any command-line parameters desired can be passed through to the emulator, as shown in figure 2.17. When writing Android applications, keep in mind that the application may be run on different size screens, because not all devices have the same physical characteristics. This setting in the Android Emulator launch configuration is a great way to test an application's handling of different screen sizes and layouts.

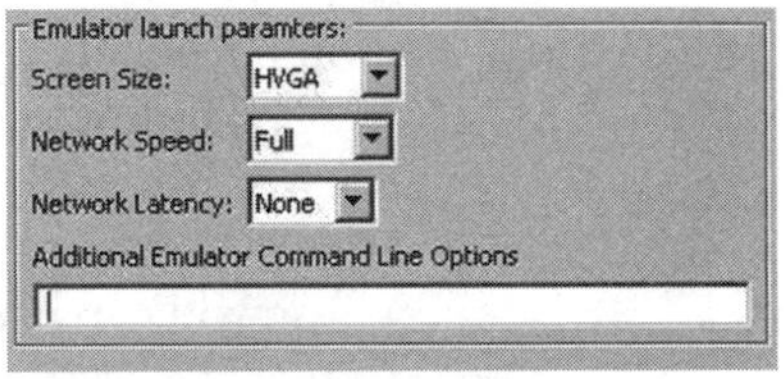

The third tab permits us to put this configuration on the favorites menu in the Eclipse IDE for easy access, as shown in figure 2.18. We can select Run and/or Debug. Let's make both selections, since it makes for easier launching when we want to test or debug the application.

We're now ready to start the Android Emulator to test our Tip Calculator application, so we select our new launch configuration from the favorites menu, as shown in figure 2.19.

The Android Tip Calculator should now be running in the Android Emulator! Go ahead; test it out. But wait, what if there is a problem with the code but we're not sure where? It's time to have a brief look at debugging an Android application.

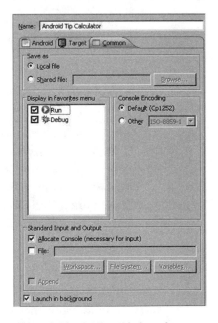

Figure 2.17   Selecting the operating characteristics of the Android Emulator

Figure 2.18   Adding this launch configuration to the toolbar menu

Figure 2.19   Starting this chapter's sample application, Android Tip Calculator

2.5 *Debugging*

Debugging an application is a skill no programmer can survive without, and fortunately it is a straightforward task to debug an Android application under Eclipse. The first step to take is to switch to the Debug Perspective in the Eclipse IDE. Remember, switching from one perspective to another takes place by using the Open Perspective submenu found under the Window menu. Starting an Android application for debugging is just as simple as running the application. Instead of selecting the application from the favorites run menu, use the favorites debug menu instead. This is the menu item with a picture of an insect (that is, a "bug"). Remember, when we set up the launch configuration, we added this configuration to both the run and the favorites debug menus.

The Debug Perspective gives us debugging capabilities similar to other development environments, including the ability to single step into, or over, method calls and peer into variables to examine their value. Breakpoints can be set by double-clicking in the left margin on the line of interest. Figure 2.20 demonstrates stepping through the Android Tip Calculator project and the resulting values showing up in the LogCat view. Note that full meal price, including tip, has not yet been displayed on the Android Emulator, because that line has not yet been reached.

Now that we've gone through a complete cycle of building an Android application and we have a good foundational understanding of using the Android development tools, we're ready to move on to digging in and *Unlocking Android* application development by learning about each of the fundamental aspects of building Android applications.

Figure 2.20   The Debug Perspective permits line-by-line stepping through of an Android application.

2.6   *Summary*

This chapter introduced the Android SDK and offered a glance at the Android SDK's Java packages in order to get you familiar with the contents of the SDK from a class library perspective. We introduced the key development tools for Android application development including the Eclipse IDE and the ADT plug-in as well as some of the behind-the-scenes tools available in the SDK.

While building out the Android Tip Calculator, this chapter's sample application, we had the opportunity to navigate between the relevant perspectives in the Eclipse IDE. We used the Java Perspective to develop our application and both the DDMS Perspective and the Debug Perspective to interact with the Android Emulator while our application was running. A working knowledge of the Eclipse IDE's perspectives will be very helpful as you progress to build out the sample applications and study the development topics in the remainder of this book.

We discussed the Android Emulator and some of its fundamental permutations and characteristics. Employing the Android Emulator is a good practice because of the benefits of using emulation for testing and validating mobile software applications in a consistent and cost-effective manner.

From here, the book moves on to dive deeper into the core elements of the Android SDK and Android application development. The next chapter continues this journey with a discussion of the fundamentals of the Android UI.

Part 2

Exercising
the Android SDK

The Android SDK provides a rich set of functionality enabling developers to create a wide range of applications. In part 2 we systematically examine the major portions of the Android SDK, including practical examples in each chapter.

We start off with a look at the application lifecycle and user interfaces (chapter 3), graduating to Intents and Services (chapter 4). No platform discussion is complete without a thorough examination of the available persistence and storage methods (chapter 5) and in today's connected world, we cannot overlook core networking and web services skills (chapter 6).

Because the Android platform is a telephone, among other things, we take a look at the telephony capabilities of the platform (chapter 7). Next we move on to notifications and alarms (chapter 8). Android graphics and animation are covered (chapter 9) as well as multimedia (chapter 10).

Part 2 concludes with a look at the location-based services available to the Android developer (chapter 11).

User interfaces 3

With our introductory tour of the main components of the Android platform and development environment complete, it is time to look more closely at the fundamental Android concepts surrounding activities, views, and resources. Activities are essential because, as you learned in chapter 1, they make up the screens of your application and play a key role in the all-important Android application lifecycle. Rather than allowing any one application to wrest control of the device away from the user and from other applications, Android introduces a well-defined lifecycle to manage processes as needed. This means it is essential to understand not only how to start and stop an Android `Activity` but also how to suspend and resume one. Activities themselves are made up of subcomponents called *views*.

Views are what your users will see and interact with. Views handle layout, provide text elements for labels and feedback, provide buttons and forms for user input, and draw graphics to the screen. Views are also used to register interface event listeners, such as those for touch-screen controls. A hierarchical collection of views is used to "compose" an `Activity`. You are the conductor, an `Activity` is your symphony, and `View` objects are your musicians.

Musicians need instruments, so we will stretch this analogy a bit further to bring Android resources into the mix. Views and other Android components make use of strings, colors, styles, and graphics, which are compiled into a binary form and made available to applications as resources. The automatically generated `R.java` class, which was introduced in chapter 1, provides a reference to individual resources and is the bridge between binary references and source. The `R` class is used, for example, to grab a string or a color and add it to a `View`. The relationship among activities, views, and resources is depicted in figure 3.1.

Along with the components you use to build an application—views, resources, and activities—Android includes the manifest file you were introduced to in chapter 1, AndroidManifest. xml. This XML file describes where your application begins, what its permissions are, and what activities (and services and receivers, which you will see in the next two chapters) it includes. Because this file is central to every Android application, we are going to address it further in this chapter, and we will come back to it frequently in later parts of the book. The manifest is the one-stop shop for the platform to boot and manage your application.

Overall, if you have done any development involving UIs of any kind on any platform, the concepts activities, views, and resources represent may be somewhat familiar or intuitive, at least on a fundamental level. The way these concepts are implemented in Android is, nevertheless, somewhat unique—and this is where we hope to shed some light. Here we will be introducing a sample application that we will use to walk through these concepts, beginning with getting past the theory and into the code to build an `Activity`.

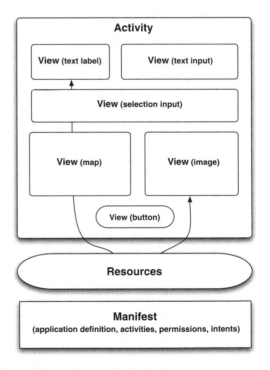

Figure 3.1   High-level diagram of `Activity`, `View`, resources, and manifest relationship showing that activities are made up of views, and views use resources.

3.1   *Creating the Activity*

Over the course of this chapter and the next, we will be building a sample application that allows the user to search for restaurant reviews based on location and cuisine. This application, RestaurantFinder, will also allow the user to call, visit the website of, or map directions to a selected restaurant. We chose this application as a starting point because it has a very clear and simple use case and because it involves many different parts of the Android platform. This will allow us to cover a lot of ground fast—as well as, we hope, having the side benefit of being actually useful on your phone!

To create this application we will need three basic screens to begin with:

- A criteria screen where a user enters parameters to search for restaurant reviews
- A list-of-reviews screen that shows paged results that match the specified criteria
- A detail page that shows the review details for a selected review item

Recall from chapter 1 that a screen is roughly analogous to an `Activity`, so that means we will need three `Activity` classes. When complete, the three screens for our RestaurantFinder application will look like what is shown in figure 3.2.

Our first step in exploring activities and views will be to build the RestaurantFinder `ReviewCritiera` screen. From there, we will move on to the others. Along the way we will highlight many aspects of designing and implementing your Android UI.

Figure 3.2 RestaurantFinder application screen shots, showing three `Activitys`: `ReviewCriteria`, `ReviewList`, and `ReviewDetail`

3.1.1 Creating an Activity class

To create a screen we will be extending the android.app.Activity base class, as we did in chapter 1, and overriding the key methods it defines. Listing 3.1 shows the first portion of the RestaurantFinder ReviewCriteria class.

Listing 3.1 The first half of the `ReviewCriteria Activity` class

```
public class ReviewCriteria extends Activity {          ◀──❶ Extend android.app.Activity

    private static final int MENU_GET_REVIEWS = Menu.FIRST;
    private Spinner cuisine;
    private Button grabReviews;                            ❷  Define Views
    private EditText location;

    @Override
    public void onCreate(Bundle savedInstanceState) {    ◀──❸ Override onCreate()
        super.onCreate(savedInstanceState);

        this.setContentView(R.layout.review_criteria);       Define layout with
                                                         ❹  setContentView
        this.location = (EditText)
          findViewById(R.id.location);
        this.cuisine = (Spinner)
          findViewById(R.id.cuisine);                  ◀──❺ Inflate views
        this.grabReviews = (Button)                          from XML
          findViewById(R.id.get_reviews_button);      ◀──

        ArrayAdapter<String> cuisines =
            new ArrayAdapter<String>(this, R.layout.spinner_view,   ❻ Define
              getResources().                                          ArrayAdapter
                getStringArray(R.array.cuisines));                     instance
        cuisines.setDropDownViewResource(
          R.layout.spinner_view_dropdown);                        Set View for
        this.cuisine.setAdapter(cuisines);   ◀──❽ Use Adapter  ❼ dropdown

        this.grabReviews.setOnClickListener(
          new OnClickListener() {                    Add Button
                                                 ❾  OnClickListener
            public void onClick(View v) {
                handleGetReviews();
            }
        });
    }
```

The ReviewCriteria class extends android.app.Activity ❶, which does a number of very important things: it gives our application a context, because Activity itself extends android.app.ApplicationContext; it brings the Android lifecycle methods into play; it gives the framework a hook to start and run your application; and it provides a container into which View elements can be placed.

Because an Activity represents an interaction with the user, it needs to provide components on the screen. This is where views come into play. In our ReviewCriteria class we have referenced three views in the code: location, cuisine, and grabReviews ❷. Location is a type of View known as an EditText, a basic text-entry component. Next, cuisine is a fancy select list component, known in Android terms as a Spinner, and grabReviews is a Button.

View elements such as these are placed within an `Activity` using a particular layout to create a screen. Layout and views can be defined directly in code or in a layout XML resource file. You will learn more about views as we progress through this section, and we will focus specifically on layout in section 3.2.5.

Location as an EditText View

Why are we using an `EditText View` for the location field in the `ReviewCriteria Activity` when Android includes technology that could be used to derive this value from the current physical location of the device (or allow the user to select it using a `Map`, rather than type it in)? Good eye, but we are doing this intentionally here. We want this early example to be complete and nontrivial but not too complicated. You will learn more about using the location support Android provides and `MapViews` in later chapters.

After an `Activity`, complete with necessary views, is started, the lifecycle takes over and the `onCreate()` method is invoked ❸. This is one of a series of important lifecycle methods the `Activity` class provides. Every `Activity` will override `onCreate()`, where component initialization steps are invoked, though not every `Activity` will need to override other lifecycle methods. The `Activity` lifecycle is worthy of an in-depth discussion of its own, and for that reason we will explore these methods further, in section 3.1.2.

Once inside the `onCreate()` method, the `setContentView()` method is where you will normally associate an XML layout file ❹. We say *normally,* because you do not have to use an XML file at all; you can instead define all of your layout and `View` configuration in code, as Java objects. Nevertheless, it is often easier, and better practice by decoupling, to use an XML layout resource for each `Activity`. An XML layout file defines `View` objects, which are laid out in a tree, and can then be set into the `Activity` for use.

Layout and view details, defined in XML or in code, are also topics we will address in later sections of this chapter. Here we simply need to stress that views are typically defined in XML and then are set into the `Activity` and "inflated." Views that need some runtime manipulation, such as binding to data, can then be referenced in code and cast to their respective subtypes ❺. Views that are static, those you don't need to interact with or update at runtime, like labels, do not need to be referenced in code (they show up on the screen, because they are part of the `View` tree as defined in the XML, but need no explicit setup in code). Going back to the screen shots in figure 3.1, you will notice that the `ReviewCriteria` screen has two labels as well as the three inputs we have already discussed. These labels are not present in the code; they are defined in the review_criteria.xml file that you will see when we discuss XML-defined resources.

The next area of our `ReviewCriteria Activity` is where we bind data to our select list views, the `Spinner` objects. Android employs a handy "adapter" concept to link views that contain collections with data. Basically an `Adapter` is a collection handler

that returns each item in the collection as a View. Android provides many basic adapt-
ers: ListAdapter, ArrayAdapter, GalleryAdapter, CursorAdapter, and more. You can
also easily create your own Adapter, a technique we will use when we discuss creating
custom views in section 3.2. Here we are using an ArrayAdapter that is populated with
our Context (this), a View element defined in an XML resource file, and an array
representing the data (also defined as a resource in XML—which you will learn more
about in section 3.3) ❻. When we create the ArrayAdapter we define the View to be
used for the element shown in the Spinner before it is selected; after it is selected it
uses the View defined in the drop-down ❼. Once our Adapter and its View elements
are defined, we set it into the Spinner object ❽.

   The last thing this initial Activity demonstrates is our first explicit use of event
handling. UI elements in general support many types of events, which you will learn
more about in section 3.2.7. In this case we are using an OnClickListener with our
Button, in order to respond when the button is clicked ❾.

   After the onCreate() method is complete, with the binding of data to our Spinner
views, we have menu buttons (which are different than on-screen Button views, as you
shall see) and associated actions. We show how these are implemented in the last part
of ReviewCriteria in listing 3.2.

Listing 3.2   The second half of the ReviewCriteria Activity class

```
. . .

@Override
public boolean onCreateOptionsMenu(Menu menu) {          ◁─────┐   Create options
    super.onCreateOptionsMenu(menu);                           ❶  menu
    menu.add(0, ReviewCriteria.MENU_GET_REVIEWS, 0,
        R.string.menu_get_reviews).setIcon(
        android.R.drawable.ic_menu_more);
    return true;
}

@Override
public boolean onMenuItemSelected(int featureId, MenuItem item) {
    switch (item.getItemId()) {
        case MENU_GET_REVIEWS:          ◁─────┐   Respond when
            handleGetReviews();                ❷  menu item selected
            return true;
    }
    return super.onMenuItemSelected(featureId, item);
}

private void handleGetReviews() {          ◁─────┐   Define method to
    if (!validate()) {                            ❸  process reviews
        return;
    }

    RestaurantFinderApplication application =
        (RestaurantFinderApplication)                ❹  Use Application
            getApplication();          ◁─────┘          object for state
    application.setReviewCriteriaCuisine(
        this.cuisine.getSelectedItem().toString());
    application.setReviewCriteriaLocation(
        this.location.getText().toString());

    Intent intent =
```

```
        new Intent(Constants.INTENT_ACTION_VIEW_LIST);        ←⑤ Create Intent
        startActivity(intent);        ←
    }                                        ⑥ Start Activity

private boolean validate() {
    boolean valid = true;
    StringBuilder validationText = new StringBuilder();
    if ((this.location.getText() == null) ||
            this.location.getText().toString().equals("")) {
        validationText.append(getResources().getString(
            R.string.location_not_supplied_message));
        valid = false;
    }
    if (!valid) {                                        Use AlertDialog  ⑦
        newAlertDialog.Builder(this).
        setTitle(getResources().getString(R.string.alert_label)).        ←
        setMessage(validationText.toString()).
        SetPositiveButton("Continue",
          new android.content.DialogInterface.
            OnClickListener() {                        ←        Respond to
                public void onClick(                       ⑧ button click
                    DialogInterface dialog, int arg1) {
                    // do nothing, show alert is enough
                }
            }).show();
        validationText = null;
    }
    return valid;
}
}
```

The menu items at the bottom of the Activity screens in figure 3.2 are all created using the onCreateOptionsMenu() method ❶. Here we are using the Menu class add() method to create a single MenuItem element ❶. We are passing a group ID, an ID, an order, and a text resource reference to create the menu item. We are also assigning to the menu item an icon with the setIcon method. The text and the image are externalized from the code, again using Android's concept of resources. The MenuItem we have added duplicates the on-screen Button with the same label for the "Get reviews" purpose.

Using the Menu vs. on-screen buttons

We have chosen to use the Menu here, in addition to the on-screen buttons. Though either (or both) can work in many scenarios, you need to consider whether the menu, which is invoked by pressing the Menu button on the device and tapping a selection (button and a tap) is appropriate for what you are doing, or whether an on-screen button (single tap) is more appropriate. Generally on-screen buttons should be tied to UI elements (a search button for a search form input, for example), and menu items should be used for screen-wide actions (submitting a form, performing an action like create, save, edit, or delete). Because all rules need an exception, if you have the screen real estate, it may be more convenient for users to have on-screen buttons for actions as well (as we have done here). The most important thing to keep in mind with these types of UI decisions is to be consistent. If you do it one way on one screen, use that same approach on other screens.

In addition to creating the menu item, we add support to react and perform an action when the item is selected. This is done in the onMenuItemSelected() event method ❷, where we parse the ID of the multiple possible menu items with a case/switch statement. When the MENU_GET_REVIEWS item is determined to have been selected, we then call the handleGetReviews method ❸. This method puts the user's selection state in the Application object ❹ and sets up to call the next screen. We have moved this logic into its own method because we are using it from multiple places, from our on-screen Button and again from our MenuItem.

The Application object is used internally by Android for many purposes, and it can be extended, as we have done with RestaurantFinderApplication (which includes a few member variables in JavaBean style), to store global state information. We will reference this object again in other activities to retrieve the information we are storing here. There are several ways to pass objects back and forth between activities; using Application is one of them. You can also use public static members and Intent extras with Bundle objects. In addition, you can use the provided SQLite database, or you can implement your own ContentProvider and store data there. We will cover more about state, and data persistence in general, including all these concepts, in chapter 5. The important thing to take away here is that at this point we are using the Application object to pass state between activities.

After we store the criteria state we fire off an action in the form of an Android Intent ❺. We touched on intents in chapter 1, and we will delve into them further in the next chapter, but basically we are asking another Activity to respond to the user's selection of a menu item by calling startActivity(Intent intent) ❻.

Using startActivity vs. startActivityForResult

The most common way to invoke an Activity is by using the startActivity() method, but there is also another method you will see used in specific instances—startActivityForResult(). Both pass control to a different Activity. The difference with regard to startActivityforResult is that it returns a value to the current Activity when the Activity being invoked is complete. It in effect allows you to chain activities and expect callback-style responses (you get the response by implementing the onActivityResult() method).

Also notable within the ReviewCriteria example is that we are using an Alert-Dialog ❼. Before we allow the next Activity to be invoked, we call a simple validate() method that we have created, where we display a pop-up-style alert dialog to the user if the location has not been specified. Along with generally demonstrating the use of AlertDialog, this demonstrates how a button can be made to respond to a click event with an OnClickListener() ❽.

With that we have covered a good deal of material and have completed Review-Criteria, our first Activity. Now that this class is fully implemented, we next need to

The Builder pattern

You may have noticed the usage of the Builder pattern when we added parameters to the `AlertDialog` we created in the `ReviewCriteria` class. If you are not familiar with this approach, basically each of the methods invoked, such as `AlertDialog.setMessage()` and `AlertDialog.setTitle()`, returns a reference to itself (`this`), which means we can continue chaining method calls. This avoids either an extra-long constructor with many parameters or the repetition of the class reference throughout the code. Intents make use of this handy pattern too; it is something you will see time and time again in Android.

take a closer look at the all-important Android `Activity` lifecycle and how it relates to processes on the platform.

3.1.2 *Exploring Activity lifecycle*

Every process running on the Android platform is placed on a stack. When you use an `Activity` in the foreground, the system process that hosts that `Activity` is placed at the top of the stack, and the previous process (the one hosting whatever `Activity` was previously in the foreground) is moved down one notch. This is a key point to understand. Android tries to keep processes running as long as it can, but it can't keep every process running forever because, after all, system resources are finite. So what happens when memory starts to run low or the CPU gets too busy?

UNDERSTANDING HOW PROCESSES AND ACTIVITIES RELATE

When the Android platform decides it needs to reclaim resources, it goes through a series of steps to prune processes (and the activities they host). It decides which ones to get rid of based on a simple set of priorities:

1 The process hosting the foreground `Activity` is the most important.
2 Any process hosting a visible but not foreground `Activity` is next in line.
3 Any process hosting a background `Activity` is next in line.
4 Any process not hosting any `Activity` (or `Service` or `BroadcastReceiver`), known as an *empty* process, is last in line.

A very useful tool for development and debugging, especially in the context of process priority, is the Android Debug Bridge (adb), which you first met in chapter 1. You can see the state of all the running processes in the emulator by issuing the following command:

```
adb shell dumpsys activity
```

This command will output a lot of information about all the running processes, including the package name, PID, foreground or background status, the current priority, and more.

Because a user can elect to change directions at just about any time—make a phone call, change the screen orientation, respond to an SMS message, decide to stop using your wonderful stock market analysis application and start playing Android Poker—which in turn can affect overall system resources, all `Activity` classes have to be able to handle being stopped and shut down at any time. If the process your `Activity` is in falls out of the foreground, it is eligible to be killed (it's not up to you; it's up to the platform, based on resources and priorities).

To manage this environment, Android applications, and the `Activity` classes they host, have to be designed a bit differently than what you may be used to. Using a series of event-related callback type methods the `Activity` class defines, you can set up and tear down state gracefully. The `Activity` subclasses that you implement (as you saw a bit of with `ReviewCriteria` in the previous section) override a set of lifecycle methods to make this happen. As we discussed in section 3.1.1, every `Activity` has to implement the `onCreate()` method. This is the starting point of the lifecycle. In addition to `onCreate()`, most activities will also want to implement the `onPause()` method, where data and state can be persisted before the hosting process potentially falls out of scope.

The lifecycle methods that the `Activity` class provides are called in a specific order by the platform as it decides to create and kill processes. Because you, as an application developer, cannot control the processes, you have to rely on your use of the callback lifecycle methods to control state in your `Activity` classes as they come into the foreground, move into the background, and fall away altogether. This is a very significant, and clever, part of the overall Android platform. As the user makes choices, activities are created and paused in a defined order by the system as it starts and stops processes.

ACTIVITY LIFECYCLE

Beyond `onCreate()` and `on-Pause()`, Android provides other distinct stages, each of which is a part of a particular phase of the life of an `Activity` class. The most commonly encountered methods and the phases for each part of the lifecycle are shown in figure 3.3.

Each of the lifecycle methods Android provides has a distinct purpose, and each happens during part of the foreground, visible, or entire lifecycle phase.

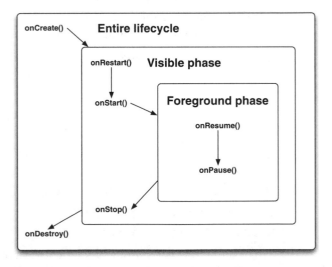

Figure 3.3 Android `Activity` lifecycle diagram, showing the methods involved in the foreground and background phases

- In the foreground phase, the Activity is viewable on the screen and on top of everything else (when the user is interacting with the Activity to perform a task).
- In the visible phase, the Activity is on the screen, but it may not be on top and interacting with the user (when a dialog or floating window is on top of the Activity, for example).
- The entire lifecycle phase refers to the methods that may be called when the application is not on the screen, before it is created, and after it is gone prior to being shut down.

Table 3.1 provides further information about the lifecycle phases and outlines the main high-level related methods on the Activity class.

Table 3.1 Android Activity main lifecycle methods and purpose

Method	Purpose
onCreate()	Called when the Activity is created. Setup is done here, Also provided is access to any previously stored state in the form of a Bundle.
onRestart()	Called if the Activity is being restarted, if it is still in the stack, rather than starting new.
onStart()	Called when the Activity is becoming visible on the screen to the user.
onResume()	Called when the Activity starts interacting with the user. (This is always called, whether starting or restarting.)
onPause()	Called when the Activity is pausing or reclaiming CPU and other resources. This method is where state should be saved so that when an Activity is restarted it can start from the same state it had when it quit.
onStop()	Called to stop the Activity and transition it to a nonvisible phase and subsequent lifecycle events.
onDestroy()	Called when an Activity is being completely removed from system memory. Happens either because onFinish() is directly invoked or the system decides to stop the Activity to free up resources.

Beyond the main high-level lifecycle methods outlined in table 3.1, there are further finer-grained methods that are available as well. Methods such as onPostCreate and onPostResume aren't normally needed, so we won't go into detail on them, but be aware that they exist if you need that level of control (see the Activity Javadoc for full method details).

As for the main lifecycle methods that you will use the majority of the time, it is very important to be aware that onPause() is the last opportunity you have to clean up and save state information. The processes that host your Activity classes will not be killed by the platform until after the onPause() method has completed, but they may be killed thereafter. This means the system will attempt to run through all of the lifecycle methods every time, but if resources are spiraling out of control (as determined by the platform), a fire alarm may be sounded and the processes that are hosting activities that are beyond the onPause() method may be killed *at any point*. Any time your Activity is moved to the background, onPause() is called. Before your Activity is completely removed, onDestroy() is not guaranteed to have been called (it probably will be called, under normal circumstances, but not always).

The onPause() method is definitely where you need to save persistent state. Whether that persistent state is specific to your application (such as user preferences) or global shared information (such as the contacts database), onPause() is where you need to make sure all the loose ends are tied up—every time. We will discuss how to save data in chapter 5, but here the important thing is to know when and where that needs to happen.

NOTE   In addition to persistent state there is one more aspect you should be familiar with, and that is *instance state.* Instance state refers to the state of the UI itself. The onSave-InstanceState() Activity method is called when an Activity may be destroyed, so that at a future time the interface state can be restored. This method is used by the platform to handle the view state processing in the vast majority of cases. This means you normally don't have to mess with it. Nevertheless, it is important to know that it is there and that the Bundle it saves is handed back to the onCreate() method when an Activity is restored. If you need to customize the view state, you can, by overriding this method, but don't confuse this with the more common general lifecycle methods.

Managing activities with lifecycle events in this way, through parent processes the platform controls, allows Android to do the heavy lifting, deciding when things come into and out of scope, relieving applications of the burden themselves, and ensuring a level playing field. This is a key aspect of the platform that varies somewhat from many other application development environments. In order to build robust and responsive Android applications you have to pay careful attention to the lifecycle.

Now that we have some background in place concerning the Activity lifecycle and have created our first screen, we will next further investigate views and fill in some more detail.

3.2   *Working with views*

Though it is a bit cliché, it is true that views are the building blocks of the UI of an Android application. Activities, as we have seen, contain views, and View objects represent elements on the screen and are responsible for interacting with users through events.

Every Android screen contains a hierarchical tree of View elements. These views come in a variety of shapes and sizes. Many of the views you will need on a day-to-day basis are provided for you as part of the platform—basic text elements, input elements, images, buttons, and the like. In addition, you can create your own composite and/or custom views when the need arises. Views can be placed into an Activity (and thus on the screen) either directly in code or through the use of an XML resource that is later "inflated" at runtime.

In this section we will discuss fundamental aspects of views: the common views that Android provides, custom views that can be created as needed, layout in relation to views, and event handling. We won't address views defined in XML here, because that will be covered in section 3.3 as part of a larger resources discussion. Here we begin with the common View elements Android provides by taking a short tour of the API.

3.2.1 *Exploring common views*

Android provides a healthy set of View objects in the android.view package. These objects range from familiar constructs like the EditText, Spinner, and TextView that we have already seen in action to more specialized widgets such as AnalogClock, Gallery, DatePicker, TimePicker, and VideoView. For a quick glance at some of the more eye-catching views, check out the sample page in the Android documentation: http://code.google.com/android/reference/view-gallery.html.

The class diagram in figure 3.4 provides a high-level snapshot of what the overall View API looks like. This diagram shows how the specializations fan out and includes many, but not all, of the View-derived classes.

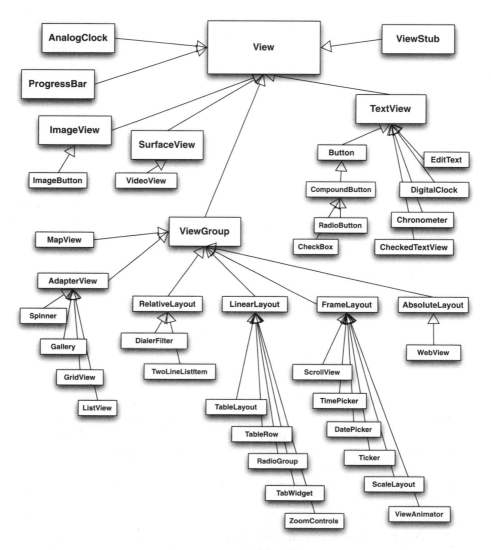

Figure 3.4 A class diagram of the Android View API, showing the root View class and specializations from there; notice that ViewGroup classes, such as layouts, are also a type of View.

As is evident from the diagram in figure 3.4 (which is not comprehensive), the View API has quite a few classes. ViewGroup, a special subclass of View related to layout, is a subclass of View, as are other elements such as TextView. Everything is ultimately a View, even the layout classes (which extend ViewGroup).

Of course, everything that extends View has access to the base class methods. These methods allow you to perform important UI-related operations, such as setting the background, setting the minimum height and width, setting padding, setting and enabling events (like clickable and focusable), setting layout parameters, and more. Table 3.2 includes an example of some of the methods available on the root View class.

Table 3.2 A subset of methods in the base Android View API

Method	Purpose
setBackgroundColor(int color)	Set the background color.
setBackgroundDrawable(Drawable d)	Set the background drawable (image).
setMinimumHeight(int minHeight)	Set the minimum height (parent may override).
setMinimumWidth(int minWidth)	Set the minimum width (parent may override).
setPadding(int left, int right, int top, int bottom)	Set the padding.
setClickable(boolean c)	Set whether or not element is clickable.
setFocusable(boolean f)	Set whether or not element is focusable.
setOnClickListener(OnClickListener l)	Set listener to fire when click event occurs.
setOnFocusChangeListener(OnFocusChangeListener l)	Set listener to fire when focus event occurs.
setLayoutParams(ViewGroup.LayoutParams l)	Set the LayoutParams (position, size, and more).

Beyond the base class, each View subclass typically adds a host of refined methods to further manipulate its respective state, such as what is shown for TextView in table 3.3.

Using the combination of the base class methods with the subtype methods, you can see that you can set layout, padding, focus, events, gravity, height, width, colors, and basically everything you might need. Using these methods in code, or their counterpart attributes in the android: namespace in XML when defining views in XML (something you will see done in section 3.3), is how you manipulate a View element. Each View element you use has its own path through the API and therefore a particular set of methods available; for details on all the methods see the Android Javadocs: http://code.google.com/android/reference/android/view/View.html.

Table 3.3   Further `View` methods for the `TextView` subclass

Method	Purpose
`setGravity(int gravity)`	Set alignment gravity: top, bottom, left, right, and more.
`setHeight(int height)`	Set height dimension.
`setWidth(int width)`	Set width dimension.
`setTypeFace(TypeFace face)`	Set typeface.
`setText(CharSequence text)`	Set text.

When you couple the wide array of classes with the rich set of methods available from the base `View` class on down, the Android `View` API can quickly seem intimidating. Thankfully, despite the initial impression, many of the concepts involved quickly become evident, and usage becomes more intuitive as you move from `View` to `View` (because they all are specializations on the same object at the core). So even though the "747 cockpit" analogy could be applied, once you start working with Android you should be able to earn your wings fairly quickly.

Though our RestaurantFinder application will not use many of the views listed in our whirlwind tour here, these are still useful to know about, and many of them will be used in later examples throughout the book. The next thing we will focus on is a bit more detail concerning one of the most common nontrivial `View` elements, specifically the `ListView` component.

3.2.2   Using a ListView

On the `ReviewList Activity` of the RestaurantFinder application, shown in figure 3.2, you can see a different type of `View` than the simple user inputs and labels we have used up to this point—this screen presents a scrollable list of choices for the user to choose from.

This `Activity` is using a `ListView` component to display a list of review data that is obtained from calling the Google Base Atom API using HTTP (we will refer to this as a "web service," even though it is not technically SOAP or any other formal standard). After we make the HTTP call, by appending the user's criteria to the required Google Base URL, we will then parse the results with the Simple API for XML (SAX) and create a `List` of reviews. The details of XML parsing won't be our focus here—that will come in chapter 11—and neither will the use of the network itself, which is covered in chapter 6, but the views we will build based on the data we get back will be. The resulting `List` will be used to populate our screen's list of items to choose from.

The code in listing 3.3 shows how we create and use a `ListView` to represent this list of items to choose from on an `Activity` screen.

Listing 3.3   First half of the `ReviewList Activity` class, showing a `ListView`

```
public class ReviewList extends ListActivity {          ◄──❶ Extend ListActivity

    private static final int MENU_CHANGE_CRITERIA = Menu.FIRST + 1;
    private static final int MENU_GET_NEXT_PAGE = Menu.FIRST;
    private static final int NUM_RESULTS_PER_PAGE = 8;

    private TextView empty;
    private ProgressDialog progressDialog;             ❷ Use ReviewAdapter
    private ReviewAdapter reviewAdapter;          ◄──
    private List<Review> reviews;                 ◄──❸ Back Adapter with List

    private final Handler handler = new Handler() {    ◄──
        public void handleMessage(final Message msg) {     ❹ Use Handler
            progressDialog.dismiss();                         for messages
            if ((reviews == null) || (reviews.size() == 0)) {
                empty.setText("No Data");
            } else {
                reviewAdapter = new ReviewAdapter(ReviewList.this, reviews);
                setListAdapter(reviewAdapter);
            }
        }
    };

    @Override
    public void onCreate(Bundle savedInstanceState) {
        super.onCreate(savedInstanceState);            ❺ Use resourced-
        this.setContentView(R.layout.review_list);  ◄──  defined layout
        this.empty = (TextView)
          findViewById(R.id.empty);                  ◄──
                                                         ❻ Define TextView
        ListView listView = getListView();               for empty
        listView.setItemsCanFocus(false);
        listView.setChoiceMode(ListView.CHOICE_MODE_SINGLE);   ❼ Set properties
        listView.setEmptyView(this.empty);                        for ListView
    }

    @Override
    protected void onResume() {
        super.onResume();                              ❽ Use Application
        RestaurantFinderApplication application =         for global state
            (RestaurantFinderApplication) getApplication();  ◄──
        String criteriaCuisine = application.getReviewCriteriaCuisine();
        String criteriaLocation = application.getReviewCriteriaLocation();

        int startFrom = getIntent().getIntExtra(
            Constants.STARTFROM_EXTRA, 1);         ◄──❾ Use Intent extra
        loadReviews(criteriaLocation,
            criteriaCuisine, startFrom);           ◄──❿ Load review data
    }

    // onCreateOptionsMenu omitted for brevity
```

. . .

The ReviewList Activity extends ListActivity ❶, which is used to host a List-
View. The default layout of a ListActivity is a full screen, centered list of choices for
the user to select from. A ListView is similar in concept to a Spinner; in fact, they are
both subclasses of AdapterView, as you saw in the class diagram in figure 3.4. This
means that ListView, like Spinner, also uses an Adapter to bind to data. In this case

we are using a custom `ReviewAdapter` class ❷. You will learn more about `Review-Adapter` in the next section, when we discuss custom views. The important part here is that we are using an `Adapter` for our `ListView` (even though it's a custom adapter), and we use a `List` of `Review` objects to populate the `Adapter` ❸.

Because we don't yet have the data to populate the list, which we will get from a web service call in another `Thread`, we need to include a `Handler` to allow for fetching data and updating the UI to occur in separate steps ❹. Don't worry too much about these concepts here, as they will make more sense shortly when we discuss them while looking at the second half of `ReviewList` in listing 3.4.

After our `ListView` and its data are declared, we move on to the typical `onCreate()` tasks we have already seen, including using a layout defined in a resources XML file ❺. This is significant with respect to `ListActivity` because a `ListView` with the ID name "list" is required if you want to customize the layout, as we have done (the ID name is in the layout XML file, which you will see in section 3.3.3). If you don't provide a layout, you can still use `ListActivity` and `ListView`; you just get the system default. We are also defining an element that will be used to display the message "No Data" if our `List` backing our `View` has no elements ❻. We also set several specific properties on the `ListView`, using its customization methods, such as whether or not the list items themselves are focusable, how many elements can be selected at a time, and what `View` to use when the list is empty ❼.

After we set up the `View` elements needed on the `Activity`, we get the criteria to make our web service call from the `Review` object we placed in the `Application` from the `ReviewCriteria Activity` ❽. Here we also use an `Intent` extra to store a primitive `int` for page number ❾. We pass all the criteria data (`criteriaLocation`, `criteria-Cuisine`, and `startFrom`) into the `loadReviews()` method ❿, which eventually makes our web service call to populate our data list. This method, and several others that show how we deal with items in the list being clicked on, are shown in the second half of the `ReviewList` class, in listing 3.4.

Listing 3.4   The second half of the `ReviewList Activity` class

```
. . .
                                                Override onMenuItemSelected  ❶
    @Override
    public boolean onMenuItemSelected(int featureId, MenuItem item) {
        Intent intent = null;
        switch (item.getItemId()) {
            case MENU_GET_NEXT_PAGE:
                intent = new Intent(Constants.INTENT_ACTION_VIEW_LIST);
                intent.putExtra(Constants.STARTFROM_EXTRA,
                    getIntent().getIntExtra(Constants.STARTFROM_EXTRA, 1)
                    + ReviewList.NUM_RESULTS_PER_PAGE);
                startActivity(intent);                Increment startFrom
                return true;                             Intent extra  ❷
            case MENU_CHANGE_CRITERIA:
                intent = new Intent(this, ReviewCriteria.class);
                startActivity(intent);
                return true;
        }
```

```
        return super.onMenuItemSelected(featureId, item);
    }

    @Override
    protected void onListItemClick(ListView l, View v,
        int position, long id) {
        RestaurantFinderApplication application =
            (RestaurantFinderApplication) getApplication();
        application.setCurrentReview(this.reviews.get(position));

        Intent intent = new Intent(Constants.INTENT_ACTION_VIEW_DETAIL);
        intent.putExtra(Constants.STARTFROM_EXTRA, getIntent().getIntExtra(
            Constants.STARTFROM_EXTRA, 1));
        startActivity(intent);
    }
    private void loadReviews(String location, String cuisine,
        int startFrom) {

        final ReviewFetcher rf = new ReviewFetcher(location,
        cuisine, "ALL", startFrom,
            ReviewList.NUM_RESULTS_PER_PAGE);

        this.progressDialog =
            ProgressDialog.show(this, " Working...",
                " Retrieving reviews", true, false);

        new Thread() {
            public void run() {
                reviews = rf.getReviews();
                handler.sendEmptyMessage(0);
            }
        }.start();
    }
}
```

3 Override onListItemClick

4 Get Application object and set state

5 Pass startFrom extra value

6 Create loadReviews method

7 Instantiate ReviewFetcher instance

8 Show ProgressDialog

9 Make web service call

10 Update handler

This Activity has a menu item that allows the user to get the next page of results or change the list criteria. To support this we have to implement the onMenuItemSelected method **1**. If the MENU_GET_NEXT_PAGE menu item is selected, we then define a new intent to reload the screen with an incremented startFrom value (and we use the getExtras() and putExtras() intent methods to do this) **2**.

After the menu-related methods, we see a special onListItemClick() method **3**. This method is used to respond when one of the list items in a ListView is clicked. Here we use the position of the clicked item to reference the particular Review item the user chose, and we set this into the Application for later usage in the Review-Detail Activity (which we will begin to implement in section 3.3) **4**. After we have the data set, we then call the next Activity (including the startFrom extra) **5**.

Lastly in the ReviewList class we have the loadReviews() method, which, strangely enough, loads reviews **6**. This method is significant for several reasons. First it sets up the ReviewFetcher class instance, which will be used to call out to the Google Base API over the network and return a List of Review objects **7** (again, networking details are in chapter 6). Then it invokes the ProgressDialog.show() method to show the user we are retrieving data **8**. Finally it sets up a new Thread **9**, within which the ReviewFetcher is used, and the earlier Handler we saw in the first half of ReviewList is sent an empty message **10**. If you refer back to when the Handler was established, in listing 3.3, you can see that is where, when the message is received, we dismiss the `ProgressDialog`, populate the `Adapter` our `ListView` is using, and call `setListAdapter()` to update the UI. The `setListAdapter()` method will iterate the `Adapter` it is handed and display a returned `View` for every item.

With the `Activity` created and set up and the `Handler` being used to update the `Adapter` with data, we now have a second screen in our application. The next thing we need to do is fill in some of the gaps surrounding working with handlers and different threads. These concepts are not view-specific but are worth a small detour at this point because you will want to use these classes when trying to perform tasks related to retrieving and manipulating data needed for the UI.

3.2.3 *Multitasking with Handler and Message*

The `Handler` is the Swiss army knife of messaging and scheduling operations for Android. This class allows you to queue tasks to be run on different threads and allows you schedule tasks using `Message` and `Runnable` objects.

The Android platform monitors the responsiveness of applications and kills those that are considered nonresponsive. An Application Not Responding (ANR) event is defined as no response to a user input for five seconds. (A user touches the screen, or presses a key, or the like, and your application must respond). So does this mean your code always has to complete within five seconds? No, of course not, but the main UI thread does have to *respond* within that time frame. To keep the main UI thread snappy, any long-running tasks, such as retrieving data over the network or getting a large amount of data from a database or complicated calculations, should be performed in a separate thread.

Getting tasks into a separate thread, then getting results back to the main UI thread is where the `Handler`, and related classes, come into play. When a `Handler` is created, it is associated with a `Looper`. A `Looper` is a class that contains a `MessageQueue` and processes `Message` or `Runnable` objects that are sent via the `Handler`.

In the `Handler` usage, shown in listings 3.3 and 3.4, we created a `Handler` with a no-argument constructor. With this approach, the `Handler` is automatically associated with the `Looper` of the current running thread, typically the main UI thread. The main UI thread, which is created by the process of the running application, is an instance of a `HandlerThread`, which is basically an Android `Thread` specialization that provides a `Looper`. The key parts involved in this arrangement are depicted in the diagram in figure 3.5.

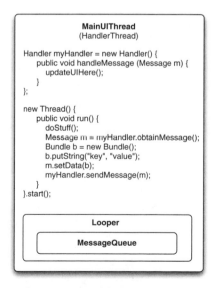

Figure 3.5 Usage of the `Handler` class with separate threads, and the relationship of `HandlerThread`, `Looper`, and `MessageQueue`

When implementing a `Handler` you will have to provide a `handleMessage(Message m)` method. This method is the hook that lets you pass messages. When you create a new `Thread`, you can then call one of several `sendMessage` methods on `Handler` from within that thread's run method, as our examples and diagram demonstrate. Calling `sendMessage` puts your message on the `MessageQueue`, which the `Looper` maintains.

Along with sending messages into handlers, you can also send `Runnable` objects directly, and you can schedule things to be run at different times in the future. You send messages and `post` runnables. Each of these concepts supports methods such as `sendEmptyMessage(int what)`, which we have already used, and the counterparts `sendEmptyMessageAtTime(int what, long time)` and `sendEmptyMessageDelayed(int what, long delay)`. Once it is in the queue, your message is processed as soon as possible (unless you schedule or delay it using the respective `send` or `post` method).

You will see more of `Handler` and `Message` in other examples throughout the book, and we will cover more detail in some instances, but the main point to remember when you see these classes is that they are used to communicate between threads and for scheduling.

Getting back to our RestaurantFinder application and more directly view-oriented topics, we next need to elaborate on the `ReviewAdapter` our RestaurantFinder `ReviewList` screen now uses, after it is populated with data from a `Message`. This adapter returns a custom `View` object for each data element it processes.

3.2.4   *Creating custom views*

Though you can often get away with simply using the views that are provided with Android, there may also be situations, like the one we are now facing, where you need a custom view to display your own object in a unique way.

In the `ReviewList` screen we used an `Adapter` of type `ReviewAdapter` to back our `ListView`. This is a custom `Adapter` that contains a custom `View` object, `ReviewListView`. A `ReviewListView` is what our `ReviewList` `Activity` displays for every row of data it contains. The `Adapter` and `View` are shown in listing 3.5.

Listing 3.5   The `ReviewAdapter` and inner `ReviewListView` classes

```
public class ReviewAdapter extends BaseAdapter {        ◁━━❶ Extend BaseAdapter

   private final Context context;                    ❷ Include Context and
   private final List<Review> reviews;                  List<Review>

   public ReviewAdapter(Context context, List<Review> reviews) {
      this.context = context;
      this.reviews = reviews;
   }
                                          ❸ Override basic
   @Override                                Adapter methods
   public int getCount() {              ◁━┙
      return this.reviews.size();
   }
                                          ❹ Override Adapter
   @Override                                getView
   public Object getItem(int position) {   ◁━┙
      return this.reviews.get(position);
   }
```

```
@Override
public long getItemId(int position) {        ◁──┐   Override basic          Override  4
    return position;                              3  Adapter methods          Adapter
}                                                                             getView

@Override                                                                          ◁──┐
public View getView(int position, View convertView, ViewGroup parent) {
    Review review = this.reviews.get(position);
    return new ReviewListView(this.context, review.name, review.rating);
}

private final class ReviewListView extends LinearLayout {      ◁──    Define
                                                                      custom inner
    private TextView name;                                         5  View class
    private TextView rating;

    public ReviewListView(Context context, String name, String rating) {

        super(context);
        setOrientation(LinearLayout.VERTICAL);

        LinearLayout.LayoutParams params = new LinearLayout.LayoutParams(
            ViewGroup.LayoutParams.WRAP_CONTENT,
            ViewGroup.LayoutParams.WRAP_CONTENT);      ◁──6  Set layout in code
        params.setMargins(5, 3, 5, 0);

        this.name = new TextView(context);            ◁──┐
        this.name.setText(name);
        this.name.setTextSize(16f);
        this.name.setTextColor(Color.WHITE);             7  Instantiate
        this.addView(this.name, params);                    TextView
                                                            members
        this.rating = new TextView(context);          ◁──┘
        this.rating.setText(rating);
        this.rating.setTextSize(16f);
        this.rating.setTextColor(Color.GRAY);
        this.addView(this.rating, params);      ◁──8  Add TextView to tree
    }
  }
}
```

The first thing to note in ReviewAdapter is that it extends BaseAdapter ❶. Base-
Adapter is an Adapter implementation that provides basic event-handling support.
Adapter itself is an interface in the android.Widget package that provides a way to
bind data to a View with some common methods. This is often used with collections of
data, such as we saw with Spinner and ArrayAdapter in listing 3.1. Another common
usage is with a CursorAdapter, which returns results from a database (something we
will see in chapter 5). Here we are creating our own Adapter, because we want it to
return a custom View.

Our ReviewAdapter class accepts two parameters in the constructor and sets those
values to two simple member objects: Context and List<Review> ❷. Then this class
goes on to implement the straightforward required Adapter interface methods that return a count, an item, and an ID (we just use the position in the collection as the ID) ❸.
The next Adapter method we have to implement is the important one, getView(). This
is where the Adapter will return any View we create for a particular item in the collection
of data it is supporting. Within this method we get a particular Review object based on
the position/ID, and then we create an instance of a custom ReviewListView object to
return as the View ❹.

ReviewListView itself, which extends LinearLayout (something you will learn more about in section 3.2.4), is an inner class inside ReviewAdapter (since we will never use it outside of returning a view from ReviewAdapter) ❺. Within it we see an example of setting layout and View details in code, rather than in XML. Here we set the orientation, parameters, and margin for our layout ❻. Then we populate the simple TextView objects that will be children of our new View and represent data ❼. Once these are set up via code, we add them to the parent container (in this case the parent is our custom class ReviewListView) ❽. This is where the data binding happens—the bridge to the View from data. Another important thing to note about this is that we have created not only a custom View but a composite one as well. That is, we are using simple existing View objects in a particular layout to construct a new type of reusable View, which shows the detail of a selected Review object on screen, as shown in figure 3.2.

Our ReviewListView object, while custom, is admittedly (and intentionally) fairly simple. In many cases you will be able to create custom views by combining existing views in this manner. Nevertheless, you should also be aware that you can go deeper and extend the View class itself. Then you can implement core methods as needed. Using this approach you have access to the lifecycle methods of a View (not an Activity as we have already covered, but an individual View). These include onMeasure(), onLayout(), onDraw(), onVisibilityChanged(), and others. Though we don't need that level of control here, you should be aware that extending View gives you a great deal of power to create custom components.

Now that you have seen how we get the data for our reviews and what the Adapter and custom View we are using look like, the next thing we need to do is take a closer look at a few more aspects of views, including layout.

3.2.5   *Understanding layout*

One of the most significant aspects of creating your UI and designing your screens is understanding layout. In Android, screen layout is defined in terms of ViewGroup and LayoutParams objects. ViewGroup is a View that contains other views (has children) and also defines and provides access to the layout.

On every screen all the views are placed in a hierarchical tree, so every element has children, and somewhere at the root is a ViewGroup. All the views on the screen support a host of attributes that pertain to background color, color, and so on. We touched on many of these attributes in section 3.2.2 when we discussed the methods on the View class. Dimensions—width and height—and other properties such as relative or absolute placement and margins are based on the LayoutParams a view requests and what the parent—based on its type, its own dimensions, and the dimensions of all of its children—can accommodate.

The main ViewGroup classes are shown in the class diagram you saw in figure 3.4. The diagram in figure 3.6 expands on this class structure to show the specific Layout-Params inner classes of the view groups and layout properties each type provides.

As figure 3.6 shows, the base `ViewGroup.LayoutParams` class are `height` and `width`. From there an `AbsoluteLayout` type with `AbsoluteLayout.LayoutParams` allows you to specify the exact *X* and *Y* coordinates of the child `View` objects placed within.

As an alternative to absolute layout, you can use the `FrameLayout`, `LinearLayout`, and `RelativeLayout` subtypes, which all support variations of `LayoutParams` that are derived from `ViewGroup.MarginLayoutParams`. A `FrameLayout` is intended to simply frame one child element, such as an image. A `FrameLayout` does support multiple children, but all the items are pinned to the top left—meaning they will overlap each other in a stack. A `LinearLayout` aligns child elements in either a horizontal or a vertical line. Recall that we used a `LinearLayout` in code in our `ReviewListView` in listing 3.5. There we created our `View` and its `LayoutParams` directly in code. And, in our previous `Activity` examples, we used a `RelativeLayout` in our XML layout files that was inflated into our code (again, we will cover XML resources in detail in section 3.3). A `RelativeLayout` specifies child elements relative to each other (`above`, `below`, `toLeftOf`, and so on).

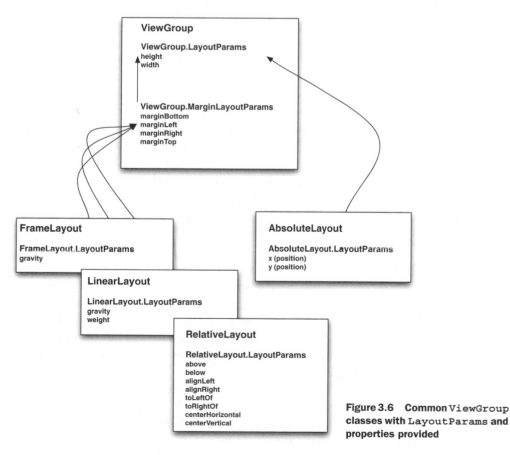

Figure 3.6 Common `ViewGroup` **classes with** `LayoutParams` **and properties provided**

So the container is a ViewGroup, and a ViewGroup supports a particular type of LayoutParams. Child View elements are then added to the container and must fit into the layout specified by their parents. A key concept to grasp is that even though a child View has to lay itself out based on its parents' LayoutParams, it can also specify a different layout for its own children. This design creates a very flexible palette upon which you can construct just about any type of screen you desire.

For each dimension of the layout a view needs to provide, based on the LayoutParams of its parents, it specifies one of three values:

- An exact number
- FILL_PARENT
- WRAP_CONTENT

The FILL_PARENT constant means take up as much space in that dimension as the parent does (subtracting padding). WRAP_CONTENT means take up only as much space as is needed for the content within (adding padding). A child View therefore requests a size, and the parent makes a decision. In this case, unlike what happens sometimes with actual kids, the children have to listen—they have no choice, and they can't talk back.

Child elements do keep track of what size they initially asked to be, in case layout is recalculated when things are added or removed, but they cannot force a particular size. Because of this View elements have two sets of dimensions, the size and width they want to take up (getMeasuredWidth() and getMeasuredHeight()) and the actual size they end up after a parent's decision (getWidth() and getHeight()).

Layout takes place in a two-step process: first measurements are taken, using the LayoutParams, then items are placed on the screen. Components are drawn to the screen in the order they are found in the layout tree: parents first, then children (parents end up behind children, if they overlap in positioning).

Layout is a big part of understanding screen design with Android. Along with placing your View elements on the screen, you need to have a good grasp of focus and event handling in order to build effective applications.

3.2.6 *Handling focus*

Focus is like a game of tag; one and only one component on the screen is always "it." All devices with UIs support this concept. When you are turning the pages of a book, your focus is on one particular page (or even word or letter) at a time. Computer interfaces are no different. Though there may be many different windows and widgets on a particular screen, only one has the current focus and can respond to user input. An event, such as movement of the mouse, a mouse click, or keyboard press, may trigger the focus to shift to another component.

In Android focus is handled for you by the platform a majority of the time. When a user selects an Activity, it is invoked and the focus is set to the foreground View. Internal Android algorithms then determine where the focus should go next (who should be tagged) based on events (buttons being clicked, menus selected, services returning callbacks, and so on). You can override the default behavior and provide hints about where specifically you want the focus to go using the following View class methods (or their counterparts in XML):

- nextFocusDown
- nextFocusLeft
- nextFocusRight
- nextFocusUp

Views can also indicate a particular focus type, DEFAULT_FOCUS or WEAK_FOCUS, to set the priority of focus they desire, themselves (default) versus their descendants (weak). In addition to hints, such as UP, DOWN, and WEAK, you can use the View.requestFocus() method directly, if need be, to indicate that focus should be set to a particular View at a given time. Manipulating the focus manually should be the exception rather than the rule (the platform logic generally does what you would expect).

Focus gets changed based on event-handling logic using the OnFocusChange-Listener object and related setOnFocusChangedListener() method. This takes us into the world of event handling in general.

3.2.7 *Grasping events*

Events are used for changing the focus and for many other actions as well. We have already implemented several onClickListener() methods for buttons in listing 3.2. Those OnClickListener instances were connected to button presses. The events they were indicating were "Hey, somebody pressed me." This is exactly the same process that focus events go through when announcing or responding to OnFocus-Change events.

Events have two halves: the component raising the event and the component (or components) that responds to the event. These two halves are variously known as Observable and Observer in design pattern terms (or sometimes subject and observer). Figure 3.7 is a class diagram of the relationships in this pattern.

An Observable component provides a way for Observer instances to register. When an event occurs, the Observable notifies all the observers that something has taken place. The observers can then respond to that notification however they see fit. Interfaces are typically used for the various types of events in a particular API.

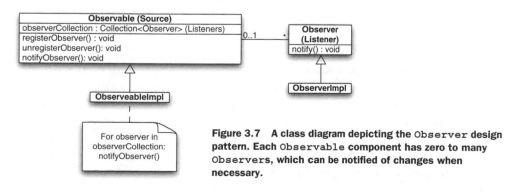

Figure 3.7 A class diagram depicting the Observer design pattern. Each Observable component has zero to many Observers, which can be notified of changes when necessary.

With regard to an Android `Button` the two halves are represented as follows:

- Observable—`Button.setOnClickListener(OnClickListener listener)`
- Observer—`listener.onClick(View v)`

This pattern comes into play in terms of Android `View` items in that many things are `Observable` and allow other components to attach and listen for events. For example, most of the `View` class methods that begin with `on` are related to events: `onFocusChanged()`, `onSizeChanged()`, `onLayout()`, `onTouchEvent()`, and the like. Similarly, the `Activity` lifecycle methods we have already discussed—`onCreate()`, `onFreeze()`, and such—are also event-related (on a different level).

Events happen in the UI and all over the platform. For example, when an incoming phone call occurs or a GPS-based location changes based on physical movement, many different reactions may occur down the line; many components may want to be notified when the phone rings or when the location changes (not just one and not just the UI). Views support events on many levels. When an interface event comes in (a user pressed a button, or scrolled, or selected a portion of a window), it is dispatched to the appropriate view. In general, click events, keyboard events, touch events, and focus events are the main types of events you will deal with in the UI.

One very important aspect of the `View` in Android is that the interface is single-threaded. If you are calling a method on a `View`, you have to be on the UI thread. This is, again, why we used a `Handler` in listing 3.3—to get data outside of the UI thread and notify the UI thread to update the `View` via the `setMessage()` event.

We are admittedly discussing events here on a fairly broad level, to make sure that the overarching concepts are clear. We do this because we cannot cover all of the event methods in the Android APIs in one chapter. Yet you will see events in examples throughout the book and in your day-to-day experiences with the platform. We will call out event examples when necessary, and we will cover them in more detail as we come to specific examples.

Our coverage of events in general, and how they relate to layout, rounds out the majority of our discussion of views, but we still have one notable related concept to tackle, resources. Views are closely related to resources, but they also go beyond the UI. In the next section we will address all the aspects of resources, including XML-defined views.

3.3   *Using resources*

We have mentioned Android resources in several areas up to now, and they were initially introduced in chapter 1. Here we will revisit resources with more depth in order to expand on this important topic and to begin completing the third and final `Activity` in RestaurantFinder—the `ReviewDetail` screen.

When you begin working with Android you will quickly notice many references to a class named `R`. This class was introduced in chapter 1, and we have used it in our previous `Activity` examples in this chapter. This is the Android resources reference class. Resources are non-code items that are included with your project automatically by the platform.

To begin looking at resources we will first discuss how they are classified into types in Android, and then we will work on examples of each type.

3.3.1 Supported resource types

In source, resources are kept in the res directory and can be one of several types:

- *res/anim*—XML representations of frame-by-frame animations
- *res/drawable*—.png, .9.png, and .jpg images
- *res/layout*—XML representations of View objects
- *res/values*—XML representations of strings, colors, styles, dimensions, and arrays
- *res/xml*—User-defined XML files (that are also compiled into a binary form)
- *res/raw*—Arbitrary and uncompiled files that can be added

Resources are treated specially in Android because they are typically compiled into an efficient binary type (with the noted exception of items that are already binary and the raw type, which is not compiled). Animations, layouts and views, string and color values, and arrays can all be defined in an XML format on the platform. These XML resources are then processed by the aapt tool, which we met in chapter 2, and compiled. Once resources are in compiled form they are accessible in Java through the automatically generated R class.

3.3.2 Referencing resources in Java

The first portion of the ReviewDetail Activity, shown in listing 3.6, reuses many of the Activity tenets we have already learned and uses several subcomponents that come from R.java, the Android resources class.

> **Listing 3.6 First portion of ReviewDetail showing multiple uses of the R class**

```
public class ReviewDetail extends Activity {
    private static final int MENU_CALL_REVIEW = Menu.FIRST + 2;
    private static final int MENU_MAP_REVIEW = Menu.FIRST + 1;
    private static final int MENU_WEB_REVIEW = Menu.FIRST;

    private String imageLink;
    private String link;
    private TextView location;
    private TextView name;                          ❶ Define inflatable
    private TextView phone;                           View items
    private TextView rating;
    private TextView review;
    private ImageView reviewImage;
                                                    ❷ Use Handler
    private Handler handler = new Handler() {  ◁──┘   to get image
        public void handleMessage(Message msg) {
            if ((imageLink != null) && !imageLink.equals("")) {
                try {
                    URL url = new URL(imageLink);
                    URLConnection conn = url.openConnection();
                    conn.connect();
                    BufferedInputStream bis = new
    BufferedInputStream(conn.getInputStream());
```

```
                    Bitmap bm = BitmapFactory.decodeStream(bis);
                    bis.close();
                    reviewImage.setImageBitmap(bm);
                } catch (IOException e) {
                    // log and or handle here
                }
            } else {
                reviewImage.setImageResource(R.drawable.no_review_image);
            }
        }
    };

    @Override
    public void onCreate(Bundle savedInstanceState) {
        super.onCreate(savedInstanceState);

        this.setContentView(R.layout.review_detail);          ◀──┐   ❸ Set layout using
                                                                         setContentView()
        this.name =
            (TextView) findViewById(R.id.name_detail);
        this.rating =
            (TextView) findViewById(R.id.rating_detail);
        this.location =
            (TextView) findViewById(R.id.location_detail);     ┤   ❹ Inflate
        this.phone =                                                   views using
            (TextView) findViewById(R.id.phone_detail);                findViewById()
        this.review =
            (TextView) findViewById(R.id.review_detail);
        this.reviewImage =
            (ImageView) findViewById(R.id.review_image);

        RestaurantFinderApplication application =
            (RestaurantFinderApplication) getApplication();
        Review currentReview = application.getCurrentReview();

        this.link = currentReview.link;
        this.imageLink = currentReview.imageLink;
        this.name.setText(currentReview.name);
        this.rating.setText(currentReview.rating);
        this.location.setText(currentReview.location);
        this.review.setText(currentReview.content);

        if ((currentReview.phone != null) && !currentReview.phone.equals("")) {
            this.phone.setText(currentReview.phone);
        } else {
            this.phone.setText("NA");
        }
    }

    @Override
    public boolean onCreateOptionsMenu(Menu menu) {
        super.onCreateOptionsMenu(menu);
        menu.add(0, ReviewDetail.MENU_WEB_REVIEW, 0,
        R.string.menu_web_review).setIcon(
            android.R.drawable.ic_menu_info_details);      ◀──┐
        menu.add(0, ReviewDetail.MENU_MAP_REVIEW, 1,
        R.string.menu_map_review).setIcon(
            android.R.drawable.ic_menu_mapmode);            ┤   ❺ Use String
        menu.add(0, ReviewDetail.MENU_CALL_REVIEW, 2,              and Drawable
        R.string.menu_call_review).setIcon(                       resources
            android.R.drawable.ic_menu_call);              ◀──┘
        return true;
    }
```

. . . remainder of this class is in Chapter 4, when we discuss Intents

In the `ReviewDetail` class we are first defining `View` components that we will later reference from resources ❶. From there we see a `Handler` that is used to perform a network call to populate an `ImageView` based on a URL. This doesn't relate to resources but is included here for completeness. Don't worry too much about the details of this here, as it will be covered more when we specifically discuss networking in chapter 5 ❷. After the `Handler`, we set the layout and `View` tree using `setContentView(R.layout.review_detail)` ❸. This maps to an XML layout file at src/res/layout/review_detail.xml. Next we also reference some of the `View` objects in the layout file directly through resources and corresponding IDs ❹.

Views that are defined in XML are inflated by parsing the XML and injecting the corresponding code to create the objects for you. This is handled automatically by the platform. All of the `View` and `LayoutParams` methods we have discussed previously have counterpart attributes in the XML format. This inflation approach is one of the most important aspects of `View`-related resources, and it makes them very convenient to use and reuse. We will examine the layout file we are referring to here and the specific views it contains more closely in the next section.

You reference resources in code, such as we are here, through the automatically generated `R` class. The `R` class is made up of static inner classes (one for each resource type) that hold references to all of your resources in the form of an `int` value. This value is a constant pointer to an object file through a resource table (which is contained in a special file the aapt tool creates and the `R` file utilizes).

The last reference to resources in listing 3.6 is for the creation of our menu items ❺. For each of these we are referencing a `String` for text from our own local resources, and we are also assigning an icon from the `android.R.drawable` resources namespace. You can qualify resources in this way and reuse the platform drawables: icons, images, borders, backgrounds, and so on. You will likely want to customize much of your own applications and provide your own drawable resources, which you can do, but the platform resources are also available if you need them (and they are arguably the better choice in terms of consistency for the user, if you are calling out to well-defined actions as we are here: map, phone call, and web page).

We will cover how all the different resource types are handled and where they are placed in source in the next several sections. The first types of resources we will look at more closely are those of layouts and views.

3.3.3 *Defining views and layouts through XML resources*

As we have noted in several earlier sections, views and layout can be, and often are, defined in XML rather than in Java code. Defining views and layout as resources in this way makes them easier to work with, decoupled from the code, and in some cases reusable in different contexts.

View resource files are placed in the res/layout source directory. The root of these XML files is usually one of the `ViewGroup` layout subclasses we have already discussed: `RelativeLayout`, `LinearLayout`, `FrameLayout`, and so on. Within these root elements are child XML elements that represent the view/layout tree.

An important thing to understand here is that resources in the res/layout directory *don't* have to be layouts. You can define a single TextView in a layout file the same
way you might define an entire tree starting from an AbsoluteLayout. Yes, this makes
the layout name and path potentially confusing, but that is how it is set up. (It might
make more sense to have separate res/layout and res/view directories, but that might
be confusing too, so just keep in mind that res/layout is useful for more than layout.)

You can have as many XML layout/view files as needed, all defined in the res/lay-
out directory. Each View is then referenced in code based on the *type and ID*. Our layout file for the ReviewDetail screen, review_detail.xml, which is shown in listing 3.7,
is referenced in the Activity code as R.layout.review_detail—which is a pointer
to the RelativeLayout parent View object in the file.

Listing 3.7 XML layout resource file for review_detail.xml

```
<?xml version="1.0" encoding="utf-8"?>        ❶  Define root View element
<RelativeLayout
    xmlns:android="http://schemas.android.com/apk/res/android"
    android:layout_width="fill_parent"                    ❷ Define
      android:layout_height="fill_parent"                    LayoutParams
    android:gravity="center_horizontal"
      android:padding="10px"                          Define View
    android.setVerticalScrollBarEnabled="true"    ❸ parameters in XML
    >

        <ImageView android:id="@+id/review_image"      Include child
            android:layout_width="100px"              ❹ element with ID
            android:layout_height="100px"
            android:layout_marginLeft="10px"
            android:layout_marginBottom="5px" />

    <TextView android:id="@+id/name_detail"
        android:layout_width="fill_parent"
        android:layout_height="wrap_content"          ❺ Reference another
        android:layout_below="@id/review_image"          resource
        android:layout_marginLeft="10px"
        android:layout_marginBottom="5px"
            style="@style/intro_blurb" />                  Reference a
    <TextView android:id="@+id/rating_label_detail"    ❻ style for a View
        android:layout_width="wrap_content"
        android:layout_height="wrap_content"
        android:layout_below="@id/name_detail"
        android:layout_marginLeft="10px"
            android:layout_marginBottom="5px"
        style="@style/label"
            android:text="@string/rating_label" />

. . .  remainder of file omitted for brevity

</RelativeLayout>
```

In this file we are using a RelativeLayout ❶. This is the ViewGroup at the root of the
View tree. LayoutParams are then also defined in XML using the android:
layout_[attribute] convention (where [attribute] refers to a layout attribute) ❷.
Along with layout, other View-related attributes can also be defined in XML with

counterpart XML attributes to the methods available in code, such as `android:padding`, which is analogous to `setPadding()` ❸.

After the `RelativeLayout` parent itself is defined, the child `View` elements are added. Here we are using an `ImageView` and multiple `TextView` components. Each of the components is given an ID using the form `android:id="@+id/[name]"` ❹. When an ID is established in this manner, an int reference is defined in the resource table and named with the specified name. This allows other components to reference the ID by the friendly textual name.

Once views are defined as resources, the `Activity` method `findViewById()` can be used to obtain a reference to a particular `View` using the name. That `View` can then be manipulated in code. For example, in listing 3.6 we grabbed the `rating TextView` as follows:

```
rating = (TextView) findViewById(R.id.rating_detail).
```

This inflates and hands off the `rating_detail` element we saw in listing 3.7. Note that child views of layout files end up as `id` type in `R.java` (they are not `R.layout.name`; rather they are `R.id.name`, even though they are required to be placed in the res/layout directory).

The properties for the `View` object are all defined in XML, and this includes the layout. Because we are using a `RelativeLayout` we use attributes that place one `View` relative to another, such as `below` or `toRightOf`. This is done with the `android:layout_below="@id/[name]` syntax ❺. The `@id` syntax is a way to reference other resource items from within a current resource file. Using this approach you can reference other elements defined in the file you are currently working on or other elements defined in other resource files.

Some of our views represent labels, which are shown on the screen as is and are not manipulated in code, such as `rating_label_detail`. Others we will populate at runtime; these don't have a text value set, such as `name_detail`. The elements that we do know the values of, the labels, are defined with references to externalized strings.

The same approach is applied with regard to styles, using the syntax `style="@style/[stylename]"` ❻. Strings, styles, and colors are themselves defined as resources in another type of resource file.

3.3.4 *Externalizing values*

It is fairly common practice in the programming world to externalize string literals from code. In Java this is done with a `ResourceBundle` or a properties file. Externalizing references to strings in this way allows the value of a component to be stored and updated separately from the component itself, away from code.

Android includes support for values resources that are subdivided into several groups: animations, arrays, styles, strings, dimensions, and colors. Each of these items is defined in a specific XML format and made available in code as references from the

R class, just like layouts, views, and drawables. For the RestaurantFinder application we are using externalized strings, as shown in listing 3.8, strings.xml.

Listing 3.8 Externalized strings for the RestaurantFinder application, strings.xml

```xml
<?xml version="1.0" encoding="utf-8"?>
<resources>
    <string name="app_name_criteria">RestaurantFinder - Criteria</string>
    <string name="app_name_reviews">RestaurantFinder - Reviews</string>
    <string name="app_name_review">RestaurantFinder - Review</string>
    <string name="app_short_name">Restaurants</string>

    <string name="menu_get_reviews">Get reviews</string>
    <string name="menu_web_review">Get full review</string>
    <string name="menu_map_review">Map location</string>
    <string name="menu_call_review">Call restaurant</string>
    <string name="menu_change_criteria">Change review criteria</string>
    <string name="menu_get_next_page">Get next page of results</string>

    <string name="intro_blurb_criteria">Enter review criteria</string>
    <string name="intro_blurb_detail">Review details</string>

. . . remainder omitted for brevity

</resources>
```

Using a string element with a name attribute ❶

As is evident from the strings.xml example, this is very straightforward. This file uses a `<string>` element with a `name` attribute ❶ for each string value you need. We have used this file for the application name, menu buttons, labels, and alert validation messages. This format is known as *simple value* in Android terms. This file is placed in source at the res/values/strings.xml location. In addition to strings, colors and dimensions can be defined in the same way.

Dimensions are placed in dimens.xml and defined with the `<dimen>` element: `<dimen name=dimen_name>dimen_value</dimen>`. Dimensions can be expressed in any of the following units:

- pixels (px)
- inches (in)
- millimeters (mm)
- points (pt)
- density-independent pixels (dp)
- scale-independent pixels (sp)

Colors can be defined in colors.xml and are defined with the `<color>` element: `<color name=color_name>#color_value</color>`. Colors values are expressed in RGB codes. Color and dimension files are also placed in the res/values source location.

Although we haven't defined separate colors and dimensions for the Restaurant-Finder application, we are using several styles, which we referenced in listing 3.7. The style definitions are shown in listing 3.9. This is where we move beyond a simple value layout to a specific style XML structure (although styles are still placed in source in the res/values directory, which can be confusing).

Listing 3.9 Values resource defining reusable styles, styles.xml

```xml
<?xml version="1.0" encoding="utf-8"?>
<resources>
   <style name="intro_blurb">
      <item name="android:textSize">22sp</item>
      <item name="android:textColor">#ee7620</item>
      <item name="android:textStyle">bold</item>
   </style>

   <style name="label">
      <item name="android:textSize">18sp</item>
      <item name="android:textColor">#ffffff</item>
   </style>

   <style name="edit_text">
      <item name="android:textSize">16sp</item>
      <item name="android:textColor">#000000</item>
   </style>

   . . . remainder of file omitted for brevity
</resources>
```

❶ Use a <style> element

❷ Use an <item> element

The Android styles approach is a similar concept to using Cascading Style Sheets (CSS) with HTML. Styles are defined in styles.xml and then referenced from other resources or code. Each <style> element ❶ has one or more <item> children that define a single setting ❷. Styles are made up of the various View settings: sizes, colors, margins, and such. Styles are very helpful because they facilitate easy reuse and the ability to make changes in one place. Styles are applied in layout XML files by associating a style name with a particular View component, such as style="@style/ intro_blurb" (note that in this case style is not prefixed with the android: namespace; it is a custom local style and not one provided by the platform).

Styles can be taken one step further and used as themes. While a style refers to a set of attributes applied to a single View element, themes refer to a set of attributes being applied to an entire screen. Themes can be defined in exactly the same <style> and <item> structure as styles are. To apply a theme you simply associate a style with an entire Activity, such as: android:theme="@android:style/[stylename]".

Along with styles and themes, Android supports a specific XML structure for defining arrays as a resource as well. Arrays are placed in source in res/values/arrays.xml and are helpful for defining collections of constant values, such as the cuisines we used to pass to our ArrayAdapter back in listing 3.1. Listing 3.10 shows how these arrays are defined in XML.

Listing 3.10 Arrays.xml used for defining cuisines and ratings

```xml
<?xml version="1.0" encoding="utf-8"?>
<resources>
   <array name="cuisines">
      <item>ANY</item>
      <item>American</item>
      <item>Barbeque</item>
      <item>Chinese</item>
      <item>French</item>
```

❶ Define <array> elements

❷ Define array <item> elements

```
        <item>German</item>
        <item>Indian</item>
        <item>Italian</item>
        <item>Mexican</item>
        <item>Thai</item>
        <item>Vegetarian</item>
        <item>Kosher</item>
    </array>
</resources>
```

Arrays are defined as resources using an `<array>` element with a `name` attribute **❶** and include any number of `<item>` child elements **❷** to define each array member. You can access arrays in code using the syntax shown in listing 3.1: `String[] ratings = getResources().getStringArray(R.array.ratings)`.

Raw files and XML are also supported through resources. Using the res/raw and res/xml directories, respectively, you can package these file types with your application and access them through either `Resources.openRawResource(int id)` or `Resources.getXml(int id)`.

Going past simple values for strings, colors, and dimensions and more involved but still straightforward structures for styles, arrays, raw files, and raw XML, the next type of resources we need to explore are animations.

3.3.5   *Providing animations*

Animations are more complicated than other Android resources but are also the most visually impressive. Android allows you to define animations that can rotate, fade, move, or stretch graphics or text. While you don't want to go overboard with a constantly blinking animated shovel, an initial splash or occasional subtle animated effect can really enhance your UI.

Animation XML files are placed in the res/anim source directory. There can be more than one anim file, and, as with layouts, you reference the respective animation you want by name/id. Android supports four types of animations:

- `<alpha>`—Defines fading, from 0.0 to 1.0 (0.0 being transparent)
- `<scale>`—Defines sizing, X and Y (1.0 being no change)
- `<translate>`—Defines motion, X and Y (percentage or absolute)
- `<rotate>`—Defines rotation, pivot from X and Y (degrees)

In addition, Android provides several attributes that can be used with any animation type:

- `duration`—Duration in milliseconds
- `startOffset`—Offset start time in milliseconds
- `interpolator`—Used to define a velocity curve for speed of animation

Listing 3.11 shows a very simple animation that can be used to scale a `View`.

Listing 3.11   Example of an animation defined in an XML resource, scaler.xml

```
<?xml version="1.0" encoding="utf-8"?>                    Use <scale> animation  ❶
<scale xmlns:android="http://schemas.android.com/apk/res/android"   ←┘
```

```
android:fromXScale="0.5"
android:toXScale="2.0"
android:fromYScale="0.5"
android:toYScale="2.0"
android:pivotX="50%"
android:pivotY="50%"
android:startOffset="700"
android:duration="400"
android:fillBefore="false" />
```

In code you can reference and use this animation with any View object (TextView, for example) as follows:

```
view.startAnimation(AnimationUtils.loadAnimation(this, R.anim.scaler));.
```

This will scale ❶ the view element up in size on both the *X* and *Y* axes. Though we do not have any animations in the RestaurantFinder sample application by default, to see this work you can simply add the startAnimation method to any view element in the code and reload the application. Animations can come in handy, so you should be aware of them. We will cover animations and other graphics topics in detail in chapter 9.

With our journey through Android resources now complete, we next need to address the final aspect of RestaurantFinder we have yet to cover, the AndroidManifest.xml manifest file, which is required for every Android application.

3.4 *Understanding the AndroidManifest file*

As you learned in chapter 1, Android requires a manifest file for every application—AndroidManifest.xml. This file, which is placed in the root directory of the project source, describes the application context and any supported activities, services, intent receivers, and/or content providers, as well as permissions. You will learn more about services, intents, and intent receivers in the next chapter and about content providers in chapter 5. For now the manifest for our RestaurantFinder sample application, as shown in listing 3.11, contains only the <application> itself, an <activity> element for each screen, and several <uses-permission> elements.

Listing 3.12 The RestaurantFinder AndroidManifest.xml file

```
<?xml version="1.0" encoding="utf-8"?>                    Include <manifest> declaration ❶
<manifest xmlns:android="http://schemas.android.com/apk/res/android"

  <application android:icon="@drawable/restaurant_icon_trans"
  android:label="@string/app_short_name"
    android:name="RestaurantFinderApplication"            ❷ Include RestaurantFinder-
  android:allowClearUserData="true"                          Application declaration
    android:theme="@android:style/Theme.Black">

    <activity android:name="ReviewCriteria"               ❸ Define Review-
      android:label="@string/app_short_name">                Criteria Activity
      <intent-filter>
        <action android:name="android.intent.action.MAIN" />
        <category
          android:name="android.intent.category.LAUNCHER" />
      </intent-filter>
    </activity>                          Define MAIN LAUNCHER Intent filter ❹
```

```
<activity android:name="ReviewList"                     ❺  Define ReviewList Activity
   android:label="@string/app_name_reviews">
   <intent-filter>                                      ◁──❻  Define custom Intent filter
     <category
        android:name="android.intent.category.DEFAULT" />
        <action
           android:name="com.msi.manning.restaurant.VIEW_LIST" />
   </intent-filter>
</activity>

<activity android:name="ReviewDetail"
   android:label="@string/app_name_review">
   <intent-filter>
     <category
        android:name="android.intent.category.DEFAULT" />
     <action
        android:name="com.msi.manning.restaurant.VIEW_DETAIL" />
   </intent-filter>
</activity>
                                                         Add permissions  ❼
</application>

<uses-permission android:name="android.permission.CALL_PHONE" />
<uses-permission android:name="android.permission.INTERNET" />
</manifest>
```

In the RestaurantFinder descriptor file we first see the root `<manifest>` element declaration, which includes the application's package declaration and the Android namespace ❶. Then we see the `<application>` element with both the name and icon attributes defined ❷. You don't have to include the name attribute here unless you want to extend the default Android `Application` object to provide some global state to your application (which we did to store the `Review` object each screen is operating on). The icon is also optional; if not specified, a system default is used to represent your application on the main menu.

After the application itself is defined, we see the child `<activity>` elements within. These, obviously, define each `Activity` the application supports ❸ (note that the manifest file can use Android resources as well, such as with `@string/app_name`). As was noted when discussing activities in general, one `Activity` in every application is the starting point; this `Activity` has the `<intent-filter>` action `MAIN` and category `LAUNCHER` designation ❹. This tells the Android platform how to start an application from the `Launcher`, meaning this `Activity` will be placed in the main menu on the device.

Past the `ReviewCriteria Activity` we see another `<activity>` designation for `ReviewList` ❺. This `Activity` also includes an `<intent-filter>`, but for our own action, `com.msi.manning.chapter3.VIEW_LIST` ❻. This tells the platform that this `Activity` should be invoked for this "intent." You will learn more about exactly how this works in the next chapter. Last in our manifest we have a `<uses-permission>` ❼ element. This also relates to intents and tells the platform that this application needs the `CALL_PHONE` permission. (We discussed several aspects of security in chapter 2, and we will touch on this in various contexts throughout the book.)

The RestaurantFinder sample application uses a fairly basic manifest file with three activities and a series of intents. This is not a comprehensive example, of course, but all of the elements an Android manifest supports are shown in table 3.4 for reference.

Table 3.4 Supported AndroidManifest.xml elements and their descriptions

Element	Position	Description
`<manifest>`	root	Defines application package and Android namespace
`<uses-permission>`	root	Requests a security permission
`<permission>`	root	Declares a security permission
`<instrumentation>`	root	Declares a test instrumentation component
`<application>`	root	Defines an application, class name, label, icon, or theme (one per manifest)
`<activity>`	child of `<application>`	Defines an `Activity` class
`<intent-filter>`	child of `<activity>`	Declares the `Intents` an `Activity` supports
`<action>`	child of `<intent-filter>`	`Intent` action
`<category>`	child of `<intent-filter>`	`Intent` category
`<data>`	child of `<intent-filter>`	`Intent` MIME type, URI scheme, URI authority, or URI path
`<meta-data>`	child of `<activity>`	General metadata, accessible via ComponentInfo.metaData
`<receiver>`	root	Defines an `IntentReceiver`, responds to `Intents` (also supports `<intent-filter>` children)
`<service>`	root	Defines a background `Service` (also supports `<intent-filter>` children)
`<provider>`	root	Defines a `ContentProvider` to manage persistent data for access by other applications

Wrapping up the description of the manifest file completes our discussion of views, activities, resources, and in general working with UIs in Android.

3.5 Summary

A big part of the Android platform revolves around the UI and the concepts of activities and views. In this chapter we explored these concepts in detail and worked on a sample application to demonstrate them. In relation to activities we addressed the concepts and methods involved, and we covered the all-important lifecycle events the platform uses to manage them. With regard to views we looked at common and custom types, attributes that define layout and appearance, and focus and events.

In addition, we looked at how Android handles various types of resources, from simple types to more involved layouts, arrays, and animations—and how these relate to, and are used within, views and activities. We also explored the AndroidManifest.xml application descriptor and how it brings all these pieces together to define an Android application.

This chapter has provided a good foundation for general Android UI development; next we need to go deeper into the concepts of `Intent` and `IntentReceiver` classes, the communication layer that Android activities and other components use. We will cover these items, along with longer-running `Service` processes and the Android Inter-Process Communication (IPC) system involving the `Binder`, in chapter 4, where we will also complete the RestaurantFinder application.

Intents and services 4

This chapter covers:
- Working with intents and intent filters
- Listening in with broadcast receivers
- Building Services
- Performing Inter-Process Communication and AIDL

The canonical Android application comprises `Activity` and `View` objects on the front end and `Intent` and `Service` objects on the back end. As we discussed in chapter 3, activities are roughly comparable to UI screens, and views are UI components. When a user interacts with a screen, that screen usually represents a task, such as display a list of choices and allow selection, gather information through form input, or display graphics and data. Once each screen is finished with its individual job, it usually hands off to another component to perform the next task.

In Android terms, "hand off to another component" is done with an `Intent`. We introduced this concept and term in chapter 1, and we saw some limited amounts of `Intent`-related code in our examples in chapter 3. In this chapter we are going to expand on the details, including looking more closely at what exactly an `Intent` is and how it is resolved and matched with an `IntentFilter`. Along the way we will complete the RestaurantFinder application we started in chapter 3, finishing up the code and elaborating on the Intent classes involved. RestaurantFinder uses Intent objects internally, to go from Activity to Activity, and also calls on intents from Android built-in applications—to phone a restaurant, map directions to a restaurant, and visit a restaurant review web page.

After we complete the RestaurantFinder application, we will move on to another sample application in this chapter—WeatherReporter. WeatherReporter will make use of the Yahoo! Weather API to retrieve weather data and display it, along with weather alerts, to the user on the Android platform. Through the course of the Weather-Reporter application we will exercise intents in a new way, using a BroadcastReceiver and a Service.

A BroadcastReceiver, as the name implies, also deals with intents but is used to catch broadcasts to any number of interested receivers, rather than to signal a particular action from an Activity. Services are background processes, rather than UI screens, but they are also invoked with a call to action, an Intent.

Lastly in this chapter, in relation to services, we will examine the Android mechanism for making Inter-Process Communication (IPC) possible using Binder objects and the Android Interface Definition Language (AIDL). Android provides a high-performance way for different processes to pass messages among themselves. This is important because every application runs within its own isolated process (for security and performance purposes, owing to the Linux heritage of the platform). To enable communication between components in different processes, something services often need to do, the platform provides a path via a specified IPC approach.

The first thing we need to cover is the basic means to perform an action from within any component; this means focusing on Intent details.

4.1   *Working with Intent classes*

Intent classes are the communications network of the applications on the Android platform. In many ways the Android architecture is similar to larger Service-Oriented Architecture (SOA) approaches in that each Activity makes a type of Intent call to get something done, without knowing exactly what the receiver of the Intent may be.

In an ideal situation you don't care how a particular task gets performed; rather, you care that it is done and is completed to your requirements. That way, you can divide up what you need to get done at a particular time—your *intent*—and concentrate on the problem you are trying to solve, rather than worrying about specific underlying implementation details.

Intent classes are *late binding*, and this is one of the things that makes them a bit different from what you might be used to. This means they are mapped and routed to a component that can handle a specified task at runtime rather than at build or compile time. One Activity tells the platform, "I need a map to Langtry, TX, US," and another component, one the platform determines is capable, handles the request and returns the result. With this approach, individual components are decoupled and can be modified, enhanced, and maintained without requiring changes to a larger application or system.

With that concept and the advantages the design intends in mind, here we will look at exactly how an `Intent` is defined in code, how an `Intent` is invoked by an `Activity,` how `Intent` resolution takes place using `IntentFilter` classes, and some intents that are built into the platform ready for you to take advantage of.

4.1.1 Defining intents

`Intents` are made up of three primary pieces of information—action, categories, and data—and include an additional set of optional elements. An *action* is simply a `String`, as is a *category*, and *data* is defined in the form of a `Uri` object. A `Uri` is a generic URI (as defined by RFC 3986) which includes a scheme, an authority, and optionally a path (you will find out more about these parts in the next section). Table 4.1 lays out all of the components of an `Intent` object.

Table 4.1 `Intent` elements and description

Intent element	Description
Extras	Extra data to pass to the `Intent` that is in the form of a `Bundle`
Component	Specifies an explicit package and class to use for `Intent`, optional, normally inferred from action, type, and categories
Type	Specifies an explicit MIME type (as opposed to being parsed from a URI)
Category	Additional metadata about `Intent` (for example, `android.intent.category.LAUNCHER`)
Data	Data to work with expressed as a URI (for example, `content://contacts/1`)
Action	Fully qualified `String` indicating action (for example, `android.intent.action.MAIN`)

Intent definitions typically express a combination of action, data, and attributes such as category. This designation is used by the system as a sort of language to resolve exactly which class should be used to fill the request.

When a component such as an `Activity` wants to call upon an `Intent`, it can do so in one of two ways:

- Implicit `Intent` invocation
- Explicit `Intent` invocation

An implicit `Intent` invocation is one in which the platform determines which component is the best to run the `Intent`. This happens through a process of `Intent` resolution using the action, data, and categories. We will explore this resolution process in detail in the next section. An explicit `Intent` invocation is one in which the code directly specifies which component should handle the `Intent`. Explicit invocation is done by specifying either the `Class` or `ComponentName` of the receiver (where `ComponentName` is a `String` for the package and a `String` for the class).

To explicitly invoke an Intent, you can use the following form: Intent(Context ctx, Class cls). With this approach you can short-circuit all the Android Intent-resolution wiring and directly pass in an Activity or Service class reference to handle the Intent. While this approach is convenient and fast, and therefore sometimes arguably appropriate, it also introduces tight coupling that may be a disadvantage later.

In listing 4.1 we show the final portion of the ReviewDetail Activity from the RestaurantFinder sample application. This listing shows several implicit Intent invocations. (We began this application in chapter 3; the first half of this class is shown in listing 3.6.)

Listing 4.1   Second portion of the ReviewDetail, demonstrating Intent invocation

```
@Override
public boolean onMenuItemSelected(int featureId, MenuItem item) {
    Intent intent = null;                          ①  Declare an Intent
    switch (item.getItemId()) {
        case MENU_WEB_REVIEW:
            if ((this.link != null) && !this.link.equals("")) {
                intent = new Intent(Intent.ACTION_VIEW,          ②  Set Intent for
                    Uri.parse(this.link));                           web menu item
                startActivity(intent);                  ③  Use
            } else {                                         StartActivity(intent)
                new AlertDialog.Builder(this)
                    setTitle(getResources()
                    .getString(R.string.alert_label))
                    .setMessage(R.string.no_link_message)
                    .setPositiveButton("Continue",
                        new OnClickListener() {
                        public void onClick(DialogInterface dialog,
                            int arg1) {
                        }
                    }).show();
            }
            return true;
        case MENU_MAP_REVIEW:
            if ((this.location.getText() != null)
                    && !this.location.getText().equals("")) {
                intent = new Intent(Intent.ACTION_VIEW,
                    Uri.parse("geo:0,0?q=" +
                    this.location.getText().toString()));     ④  Set Intent for
                startActivity(intent);                            map menu item
            } else {
                new AlertDialog.Builder(this)
                .setTitle(getResources()
                .getString(R.string.alert_label))
                .setMessage(R.string.no_location_message)
                    .setPositiveButton("Continue", new OnClickListener() {
                    public void onClick(DialogInterface dialog,
                        int arg1) {
                    }
                }).show();
            }
```

```
        return true;
    case MENU_CALL_REVIEW:
        if ((this.phone.getText() != null)
                && !this.phone.getText().equals("")
                && !this.phone.getText().equals("NA")) {
            String phoneString =
                parsePhone(this.phone.getText().toString());
            intent = new Intent(Intent.ACTION_CALL,
                Uri.parse("tel:" + phoneString));
            startActivity(intent);
        } else {
            new AlertDialog.Builder(this)
            .setTitle(getResources()
            .getString(R.string.alert_label))
            .setMessage(R.string.no_phone_message)
            .setPositiveButton("Continue", new OnClickListener() {
                public void onClick(DialogInterface dialog,
                    int arg1) {
                }
            }).show();
        }
        return true;
    }
    return super.onMenuItemSelected(featureId, item);
}
```

⑤ Set Intent for call menu item

The `Review` object that the `ReviewDetail` `Activity` displays to the user contains the address and phone number for a restaurant and a link to the full online review. Using this `Activity` the user can choose, through the menu, to display a map with directions to the restaurant, call the restaurant, or view the full review in a web browser. To allow all of these actions to take place, `ReviewDetail` uses built-in Android applications, through implicit `Intent` calls.

First, an `Intent` class instance is initialized to null ❶, so it can later be used by the various menu cases. Then, if the `MENU_WEB_REVIEW` menu button is selected by the user, we create a new instance of the `Intent` variable by passing in an action and some data ❷. For the action we are using the `String` constant `Intent.ACTION_VIEW`. The value of this constant is `android.app.action.VIEW`, a fully qualified `String` including the package so as to be unique. The `Intent` class has a host of constants like this that represent common actions, for example, `Intent.ACTION_EDIT`, `Intent.ACTION_INSERT`, and `Intent.ACTION_DELETE`. Various activities and services use these same values when they declare they support a particular `Intent` (and you can reuse these constants, too, where applicable; see the Android Javadocs for a complete list of what is available: http://code.google.com/android/reference/android/content/Intent.html).

After the action is declared, the data comes into play. In this case we are using `Uri.parse(link)` to specify a `Uri` (where `link` is an HTTP URL). The `parse(String s)` method simply parses the parts of a URI and creates a `Uri` object. This `Uri` is used in the resolution process we will cover next. Basically, the type can be derived from the `Uri`, or else the scheme, authority, and path themselves can be used. This allows the correct component to answer the `startActivity(Intent i)` request ❸ and render the resource identified by the `Uri`. As you can see, we haven't directly declared any particular `Activity` or `Service` for the `Intent`; we are simply saying we want to `VIEW` http://somehost/somepath. This is the late-binding aspect in action. When it comes to a web URL, it's pretty obvious how this works, but the same concept is applied in Android with many other built-in data types (and you can define your own when necessary, as you shall see).

The next menu item `ReviewDetail` handles is for the `MENU_MAP_REVIEW` case, where we see the `Intent` reinitialized to use the `Intent.ACTION_VIEW` again, but this time with a different type of `Uri` being parsed: `"geo:0,0?q="` + `street_address` **4**. This combination of `VIEW` and `geo` scheme invokes a different `Intent`, this time within the built-in maps application. And finally, we see the `MENU_MAP_CALL` case, where the `Intent` is reinitialized again, this time to make a phone call using the `Intent.ACTION_CALL` and the `tel:` `Uri` scheme **5**.

Through those simple statements, our RestaurantFinder application is using implicit `Intent` invocation to allow the user to phone or map the restaurant selected or to view the full review web page. These menu buttons are shown in the screen shot in figure 4.1.

To get the menu buttons on the `ReviewDetail` activity of the RestaurantFinder sample application to work, we did not have to code all the functionality ourselves; we simply had to leverage the existing applications Android provides by telling the platform our intentions. Those last steps complete the RestaurantFinder application, which can now search for reviews, allow the user to select a particular review from a list, display a detailed review, and use additional built-in applications to find out more about a selected restaurant.

You will learn more about all of the built-in apps and action-data pairs in section 4.1.3. Now we turn our focus to more detail on the `Intent`-resolution process, where we will uncover more about `Intent` action and data.

Figure 4.1 The menu buttons on the RestaurantFinder sample application, used for invoking respective intents

4.1.2 *Intent resolution*

Three types of Android components can register to be `Intent` handlers: `Activity`, `BroadcastReceiver`, and `Service`. These components typically register with the platform to be the destination for particular intent types using the `<intent-filter>` element in the AndroidManifest.xml file, as we have seen.

Each `<intent-filter>` element is parsed into an `IntentFilter` object. When a package is installed on the platform, the components within are registered, including the `Intent` filters. Once the platform has a registry of `Intent` filters, it basically knows how to map any `Intent` requests that come in to the correct installed `Activity`, `BroadcastReceiver`, or `Service`.

When an `Intent` is requested, resolution takes place through the registered filters, using the action, data, and categories of the `Intent`. There are two basic rules about matching `Intent` to `IntentFilter` that you should be aware of:

- The action and category must match.
- If specified, the data *type* must match, or the combination of data scheme and authority and path must match.

In the next few sections we will explore these aspects in greater detail, as they are paramount to understanding how `Intent` classes work.

ACTION AND CATEGORIES

The action and category parts are pretty simple. These boil down to `String` objects, one for the action, potential multiples for the categories. If the action is not specified in the `IntentFilter`, it will then match any action coming from an `Intent` (all actions work). With categories, the `IntentFilter` is a superset. An `IntentFilter` can have additional categories beyond what an `Intent` specifies to match but must have at least what the `Intent` specifies. Also, unlike with an action, an `IntentFilter` with no categories will match *only* an `Intent` with no categories (it is not treated as a wildcard). So first, action and category specifications have to match.

Before we move on to the next matching component, data, it's important to understand that data is optional. You can work with action and category alone, and in many cases that suffices. This is, for example, the technique we used in the `ReviewList Activity` we built in chapter 3. There the `IntentFilter` was defined (in the manifest XML), as shown in listing 4.2.

Listing 4.2 Manifest declaration of `ReviewList Activity` with `intent-filter`

```xml
<activity android:name="ReviewList" android:label="@string/app_name">
  <intent-filter>
    <category android:name="android.intent.category.DEFAULT" />
    <action android:name="com.msi.manning.restaurant.VIEW_LIST" />
  </intent-filter>
</activity>
```

To match the filter declared in listing 4.2, we used the following `Intent` in code (where `Constants.INTENT_ACTION_VIEW_LIST` is the `String com.msi.manning.restaurant.VIEW_LIST`):

```java
Intent intent = new Intent(Constants.INTENT_ACTION_VIEW_LIST);
startActivity(intent);
```

NOTE The `DEFAULT` category designation on an `Activity` means that the `Activity` should be present as an option for the default action—center button press—for a particular type of data. This is usually specified in an `IntentFilter`, but it does not typically need to be present in an `Intent` (the filter will still match; categories are a superset).

DATA

After the action and categories are resolved, Intent data comes into play. The data can be either an explicit MIME type or a combination of scheme, authority, and path. Either of these data forms can be derived from a Uri. The Uri shown in figure 4.2 is an example of using scheme, authority, and path.

Figure 4.2   The portions of a URI that are used in Android, showing scheme, authority, and path

As opposed to scheme, authority, and path, using an explicit MIME type within a Uri looks like the following:

```
content://com.google.provider.NotePad/notes
```

You might reasonably ask how this is differentiated from scheme/authority/path, because those elements are really still there. The answer is the content:// scheme. That indicates a type override to the platform. The type itself is defined in the manifest of the package supplying the content provider. We will look at more details concerning content providers later in this chapter.

When IntentFilter classes are defined, they set the boundaries for what they will match in terms of type, scheme, authority, and path. A somewhat convoluted resolution path follows:

1 If scheme is present and type is *not* present, intents with any type will match.
2 If type is present and scheme is *not* present, intents with any scheme will match.
3 If neither scheme nor type is present, only intents with neither scheme nor type will match.
4 If an authority is specified, a scheme must also be specified.
5 If a path is specified, a scheme and authority must also be specified.

The majority of times what you are matching will be fairly straightforward, but as you can see, with these rules and multiple levels of authorities and schemes, it can get complicated. To boil down Intent resolution, think of Intent and IntentFilter as separate pieces of the same puzzle. When you call an Intent in an Android application, the system resolves the Activity or Service (or BroadcastReceiver) to handle your request through this resolution process using the action, categories, and data (type or scheme, authority, and path) provided. The system searches all the pieces of the puzzle it has until it finds one that meshes with the one you have just handed it, and then it snaps those pieces together to make the late-binding connection.

A more involved example of this matching is shown in figure 4.3. There you can see that an IntentFilter is defined with an action, the default category, and a combination of scheme and authority (leaving out the path so that any path will match). An example of an Intent that would match this filter is also shown, in this case using a Uri that is passed in by the next sample application we will build, WeatherReporter.

The IntentFilter shown in figure 4.3 matches with the action, category, and data (extracted from the Uri passed in) of the Intent being used. This Intent and filter come from the next sample application we are going to begin working on, a

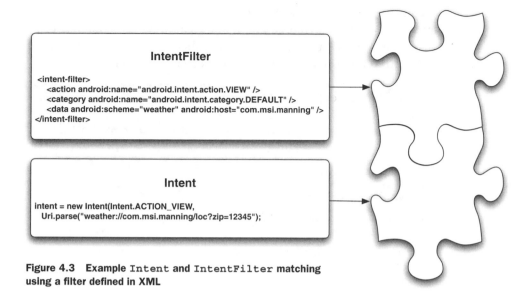

Figure 4.3 Example `Intent` and `IntentFilter` matching using a filter defined in XML

weather-reporting and -alerting application. This application will carry us through the remaining concepts in this chapter and into the next.

4.1.3 *Matching a custom URI*

The concept behind WeatherReporter, the next sample application we will build, is that it will make use of the Yahoo! Weather API to retrieve weather data and display it to the user on the Android platform. Optionally this application will also alert users of severe weather for locations they have indicated they are interested in (based on either the current location of the device or the specified postal code).

Within this project you will see how a custom URI can be defined and registered with a matching `Intent` filter to allow any other application to invoke a weather report through an `Intent`. (Defining and publishing an `Intent` in this way allows other applications to easily use our application.) When complete, the main screen of the WeatherReporter application will look like what is shown in figure 4.4.

Figure 4.4 The main screen in the sample WeatherReporter application showing the weather forecast for the current location and a check box to indicate whether alerts should be enabled

To begin this application we first have to cover basics, such as the manifest file. Although we have already explored manifest files in previous chapters, here we will fill in details for this application, and we will further reinforce how `Intent` filters are defined in XML. The manifest for WeatherReporter is shown in listing 4.3.

Listing 4.3   The Android manifest file for the WeatherReporter application

```xml
<?xml version="1.0" encoding="utf-8"?>
  <manifest xmlns:android="http://schemas.android.com/apk/res/android"
   package="com.msi.manning.weather">
    <application android:icon="@drawable/weather_sun_clouds_120"
      android:label="@string/app_name"
      android:theme="@android:style/Theme.Black"
      android:allowClearUserData="true">

    <activity android:name="ReportViewSavedLocations"
      android:label="@string/app_name_view_saved_locations" />

    <activity android:name="ReportSpecifyLocation"
      android:label=
        "@string/app_name_specify_location" />                 Define ❶
                                                               activities

    <activity android:name="ReportViewDetail"
      android:label="@string/app_name_view_detail">
        <intent-filter>
          <action android:name="android.intent.action.VIEW" />
          <category android:name="android.intent.category.DEFAULT" />
          <data android:scheme="weather"
            android:host="com.msi.manning" />
        </intent-filter>
        <intent-filter>
          <action android:name="android.intent.action.VIEW" />
          <data android:scheme="weather"
            android:host="com.msi.manning" />
        </intent-filter>
        <intent-filter>
          <action android:name="android.intent.action.MAIN" />
          <category android:name=
            "android.intent.category.LAUNCHER" />
        </intent-filter>
    </activity>                                      Define a receiver ❷

    <receiver android:name=".service.WeatherAlertServiceReceiver">
        <intent-filter>
          <action android:name=
            "android.intent.action.BOOT_COMPLETED" />
        </intent-filter>
    </receiver>                                         ❸ Define a
                                                            service
    <service android:name=".service.WeatherAlertService" />

  </application>                          Include necessary permissions ❹

  <uses-permission
   android:name="android.permission.RECEIVE_BOOT_COMPLETED" />
  <uses-permission
   android:name="android.permission.ACCESS_COARSE_LOCATION" />

  <uses-permission android:name=
```

```
    "android.permission.ACCESS_FINE_LOCATION" />
  <uses-permission
    android:name=
  "android.permission.ACCESS_LOCATION_EXTRA_COMMANDS" />
  <uses-permission android:name="android.permission.INTERNET" />
```

Include necessary permissions ❹

```
</manifest>
```

In the WeatherReporter manifest we have three activities defined ❶. The most interesting is the `ReportViewDetail Activity`, which we will show a portion of in listing 4.4. This `Activity` has multiple `Intent` filters defined that match it, including one denoting it is the MAIN LAUNCHER, and one with the weather://com.msi.manning scheme and authority shown in figures 4.2 and 4.3. This is the custom URI our application supports.

You can use any combination of scheme, authority, and path—as we have here—or you can use an explicit MIME type. We will find out more about MIME types and how they are processed in chapter 5, where will look specifically at how to work with data sources and use an Android concept known as a `ContentProvider`.

After these activities we use the `<receiver>` element in the manifest file to refer to a `BroadcastReceiver` class ❷. We will uncover what a `BroadcastReceiver` is all about in section 4.2, but the important part for now is that an `<intent-filter>` is also used here to associate an `Intent`—in this case for the BOOT_COMPLETED action. With this association we are telling the platform to invoke the `WeatherAlertServiceReceiver` class after the boot-up sequence is completed.

In our manifest we also have a `Service` definition ❸. You will see how this `Service` is built, and how it is used with our WeatherReporter application to poll for severe weather alerts in the background, in section 4.3. The last thing in our manifest is a series of permissions the application requires ❹.

With the foundation for our sample application in place via the manifest, the next thing we need to look at is the `onStart` method of main `Activity` WeatherReporter will use, which is shown in listing 4.4. This is where data from the `Uri` that matches the `Intent` filter is parsed and used to display a weather report.

Listing 4.4 `onStart` **method of the** `ReportViewDetail Activity`

```
@Override
public void onStart() {
  super.onStart();
  this.dbHelper = new DBHelper(this);            ◁
  this.deviceZip = WeatherAlertService.deviceLocationZIP;   ◁

  if ((getIntent().getData() != null)
      && (getIntent().getData().getEncodedQuery() != null)
      && (getIntent().getData().getEncodedQuery().length() > 8)) {
    String queryString =
      getIntent().getData().getEncodedQuery();    ◁
    this.reportZip = queryString.substring(4, 9);
    this.useDeviceLocation = false;
  } else {
    this.reportZip = this.deviceZip;
    this.useDeviceLocation = true;
```

❶ **Establish database helper**

❷ **Get device location postal code**

❸ **Parse Intent data**

```
    }
    this.savedLocation = this.dbHelper.get(this.reportZip);
    this.deviceAlertEnabledLocation =
        this.dbHelper.get(DBHelper.DEVICE_ALERT_ENABLED_ZIP);

    if (this.useDeviceLocation) {
        this.currentCheck.setText(R.string.view_checkbox_current);
        if (this.deviceAlertEnabledLocation != null) {
            this.currentCheck.setChecked(true);              ◁───┐  Set status of
        } else {                                             ❹  alert-enabled
            this.currentCheck.setChecked(false);             ◁───┘  check box
        }
    } else {
        this.currentCheck.setText(R.string.view_checkbox_specific);
        if (this.savedLocation != null) {
            if (this.savedLocation.alertenabled == 1) {
                this.currentCheck.setChecked(true);          ◁───┐  Set status of
            } else {                                         ❹  alert-enabled
                this.currentCheck.setChecked(false);         ◁───┘  check box
            }
        }
    }
    loadReport(this.reportZip);    ◁──❺  Load weather report
}
```

The complete ReportViewDetail Activity can be obtained by grabbing the source code in its entirety from http://www.manning.com/UnlockingAndroid. In the portion of the class shown in listing 4.4, the onStart method, we are focusing on parsing data from the Uri passed in as part of the Intent that invokes the Activity.

First in this class snippet we are establishing a database helper object ❶. This will be used to query a local SQLite database that stores user-specified location data. We will show more about how data is handled in general, and the details of this helper class, in chapter 5.

In this method we are also obtaining the postal code of the current device location from a LocationManager in the WeatherAlertService class (defaulting to 94102, San Francisco, CA) ❷. This is significant because it's important to understand that we want our application to be location-aware. We want the location of the device (wherever it is) to be the default weather report and alert location. As the user travels with the phone, this location should automatically be updated. We will cover more about location and LocationManager in chapter 11. For now, note that the device location is returned to us here as a postal code.

After obtaining the device location, we move on to the key aspect of obtaining Uri data from an Intent. We are parsing the Uri passed in to obtain the queryString and embedded postal code to use for the user's specified location ❸. if this location is present, we use it; if not, we default to the device location postal code.

Once we have determined the postal code to use, we move on to set the status of the check box that indicates whether or not alerts should be enabled for the location being displayed ❹. We have two kinds of alerts: one for the device location (wherever that location may be at a given time) and another for the user's specified saved locations.

Finally, we call the `loadReport` method, which is used to make the call out to the Yahoo! Weather API to obtain data, and then we use a `Handler` to send a `Message` to update the needed UI `View` elements ❺. These details are not shown in this code portion, because we are focusing on `Intent` handling in this section, but the pattern is the same one used in previous listings.

The key with this `Activity` is the way it is registered in the manifest to receive weather://com.msi.manning intents and then parses the path of the URI for data. This allows any application to invoke this `Activity` without knowing any details other than the URI. This is the separation-of-responsibilities pattern the Android platform design encourages at work (the late binding).

Now that you've seen the manifest and pertinent details of the main `Activity` class for the WeatherReporter application we will be building in the next few sections, and we have covered a good bit about how `Intent` and `IntentFilter` classes work together to wire up calls between components in general, we will take a look at some of the built-in Android applications that work the same way. These enable you to launch activities by simply passing in the correct URI.

4.1.4 *Using Android-provided activities*

Another way to get a feel for how `Intent` resolution works in Android and how URIs are used is to explore the built-in `Activity` support. Android ships with a very useful set of core applications that provide access via the formats shown in table 4.2.

Table 4.2 Common Android application `Intent` action and `Uri` combinations and the purpose of each

Action	Uri	Description
Intent.ACTION_VIEW	geo:latitude,longitude	Opens the maps application to the specified latitude and longitude
Intent.ACTION_VIEW	geo:0,0?q=street+address	Opens the maps application to the specified address
Intent.ACTION_CALL	tel:phone_number	Opens the phone application and calls the specified number
Intent.ACTION_DIAL	tel:phone_number	Opens the phone application and dials (but does not call) the specified number
Intent.ACTION_DIAL	voicemail:	Opens the phone application and dials (but does not call) the voicemail number
Intent.ACTION_VIEW	http://web_address	Opens the browser application to the specified URL
Intent.ACTION_VIEW	https://web_address	Opens the browser application to the specified URL
Intent.ACTION_WEB_SEARCH	plain_text	Opens the browser application and use Google Search

Using the actions and URIs shown in table 4.2, you can hook into the built-in maps application, phone application, or browser application. These powerful applications are very easy to invoke using the correct `Intent`. We used several of these in the last chapter with our RestaurantFinder application. Android also includes support for another construct, the `ContentProvider`, which also uses a form of a URI to provide access to data. You will learn more about this system, which is what exposes the contacts and media parts of the Android system, in chapter 5.

By comparing the actions and URIs for the built-in Android applications, you can get a feel for the fact that some applications use a `Uri` that is parsed into a type (contacts, media), and others use the scheme, or scheme and authority, or scheme and authority and path—the various ways to match data discussed in section 4.1.2.

With a handle on the basics of resolution and a quick look at built-in intents out of the way, we need to get back to our WeatherReporter sample application. The next thing we will discuss is another usage for the `Intent` concept, namely, using a `BroadcastReceiver`.

4.2   *Listening in with broadcast receivers*

Another way to use an `Intent` involves sending a broadcast to any interested receiver. There are many reasons an application may want to broadcast an event; for example, when an incoming phone call or text message is received. In this section we will take a look at how events are broadcast and how they are captured using a `BroadcastReceiver`.

Here we will continue working through the WeatherReporter sample application we began in the previous section. One of the most important parts of the Weather-Reporter application will be its ability to display alerts to the user when severe weather is in the forecast for a location where the user has indicated interest. We will need a background process that checks the weather and sends any needed alerts. This is where the Android `Service` concept will come into play. We won't be creating the actual `Service` class until section 4.3, but we need a way to get the platform running the `Service` as soon as it boots up, and this is where we will use an `Intent` broadcast.

4.2.1   *Overloading the Intent concept*

As you have seen, `Intent` objects are used to go from `Activity` to `Activity` in an Android application. While this is the main use of intents in Android, it is not the only one. Intents are also used to broadcast events to any configured receiver using one of several methods available from the `Context` class, as shown in table 4.3.

Table 4.3   Methods for broadcasting intents

Method	Description
sendBroadcast(Intent intent)	Simple form for broadcasting an `Intent`.
sendBroadcast(Intent intent, String receiverPermission)	Broadcasts an `Intent` with a permission `String` that receivers must declare to receive the broadcast.

Table 4.3   Methods for broadcasting intents *(continued)*

Method	Description
`sendStickyBroadcast(Intent intent)`	Broadcasts an `Intent` that hangs around a short time after it is sent so that receivers can retrieve data. Applications using this must declare the `BROADCAST_STICKY` permission.
`sendOrderedBroadcast(Intent intent, String receiverPermission)`	Broadcasts an `Intent` call to the receivers one-by-one serially.
`sendOrderedBroadcast(Intent intent, String receiverPermission, BroadcastReceiver resultReceiver, Handler scheduler, int initialCode, String initialData, Bundle initialExtras)`	Broadcasts an `Intent` and gets a response back by implementing your own `BroadcastReceiver` for the broadcast (and passing it in). All receivers can append data that will be returned in the `BroadcastReceiver`. When using this method, the receivers are called serially.

When broadcasting intents you are basically reusing the `Intent` concept to send an event in the background. Though the `Intent` class is used, it is used differently than when invoking foreground `Activity` paths. A broadcast `Intent` does not invoke an `Activity` (though a `BroadcastReceiver` can do so after the event is received, if necessary).

Another important aspect with `Intent` broadcasts is how permissions are handled. When you broadcast an `Intent`, you can optionally specify a permission. Permissions are something we addressed in chapter 1. They basically are `String` declarations that can be used when making a broadcast that require receivers to declare the same permission.

Broadcasting an `Intent` itself is fairly straightforward; you use the `Context` object to throw it on the wire, and interested receivers will catch it. Android provides a set of platform-related `Intent` broadcasts that use this approach. When the time zone on the platform changes, when the device completes booting, or when a package is added or removed, for example, the system broadcasts an event using an `Intent`. Some of the specific `Intent` broadcasts the platform provides are shown in table 4.4.

Table 4.4   Provided Android platform broadcast actions

Action	Description
`ACTION_TIME_TICK`	Sent every minute to indicate that time is ticking
`ACTION_TIME_CHANGED`	Sent when the user changes the time on the device
`ACTION_TIMEZONE_CHANGED`	Sent when the user changes the time zone on the device
`ACTION_BOOT_COMPLETED`	Sent when the platform completes booting
`ACTION_PACKAGE_ADDED`	Sent when a package is added to the platform
`ACTION_PACKAGE_REMOVED`	Sent when a package is removed from the platform
`ACTION_BATTERY_CHANGED`	Sent when the battery charge level or charging state changes

The other half of broadcasting events is the receiving end. To register to receive an `Intent` broadcast, you implement a `BroadcastReceiver`. This is where we are going to implement a receiver that will catch the platform-provided `BOOT_COMPLETED` `Intent` in order to start the weather alert service we will create for the Weather-Reporter application.

4.2.2 *Creating a receiver*

Because the weather alert `Service` we want to create needs to be running in the background whenever the platform itself is running, we need a way to start it when the platform boots. To do this, we will create a `BroadcastReceiver` that listens for the `BOOT_COMPLETED` `Intent` broadcast.

The `BroadcastReceiver` base class provides a series of methods that allow for getting and setting a result code, result data (in the form of a `String`), and an extras `Bundle`. In addition, there are a series of lifecycle-related methods that correspond to the lifecycle events of a receiver; you will learn more about these as we progress through this section.

Associating a `BroadcastReceiver` with an `IntentFilter` can be done in code or in the manifest XML file. Once again the XML usage is often easier and thus more common. This is the way we did it for WeatherReporter in listing 4.3, where we associated the `BOOT_COMPLETED` broadcast with the `WeatherAlertServiceReceiver` class. This class is shown in listing 4.5.

Listing 4.5 The `WeatherAlertServiceReceiver` `BroadcastReceiver` class

```
public class WeatherAlertServiceReceiver extends BroadcastReceiver {

    @Override
    public void onReceive(Context context, Intent intent) {
        if (intent.getAction().equals(Intent.ACTION_BOOT_COMPLETED)) {
            context.startService(new Intent(context,
                WeatherAlertService.class));
        }
    }
}
```

Start WeatherAlertService ❸   **Extend BroadcastReceiver** ❶

Override onReceive ❷

When creating your own `Intent` broadcast receiver you extend the `BroadcastReceiver` class Android provides ❶ and implement the abstract `onReceive(Context c, Intent i)` method ❷. Within this method we are starting the `WeatherAlertService`. This `Service` class, which we will create next, is started using the `Context.startService(Intent i, Bundle b)` method ❸.

Keep in mind that receiver class instances have a very short, specific lifecycle. When the `onReceive(Context c, Intent i)` method is complete, the instance and process that invoked the receiver are no longer needed and may be killed by the system. Because of this, you can't perform any asynchronous operations in a `BroadcastReceiver`, such as binding to a `Service` or showing a dialog. Alternatively, you can start a `Service`, as we have done here, and leave it running in the background. (Binding to a `Service` is different than starting one; we will cover this distinction in the next section.)

Now that our receiver is starting the WeatherAlertService, which will run in the background and warn users of severe weather in the forecast with a Notification-based alert, we need to delve into the realm of the Android Service concept itself.

4.3 Building a Service

In the typical Android application you create Activity classes and move from screen to screen using Intent calls. This is the approach we introduced in chapter 1 and used in other previous chapters. This works for the canonical Android screen-to-screen foreground application but is not applicable for a longer-running background process—for that you need a Service.

The Service we will work with here is the WeatherAlertService we sent an Intent request for in the WeatherAlertServiceReceiver in listing 4.4. This Service sends an alert to the user when there is severe weather in a location in which the user has indicated an interest. This alert will be displayed in any application, in the form of a Notification, by the background Service if severe weather is detected. The notifications we will send are shown in the screen shot in figure 4.5.

Figure 4.5
The Notification-based alert the WeatherAlertService displays to the user when severe weather is detected in the forecast

One key aspect of Android Service classes we need to cover prior to jumping in and implementing one is their dual-purpose nature. Something like the duality of man (you know, the "Jungian Thing"); services lead a double life.

4.3.1 Dual-purpose nature of a Service

In Android a Service is intended to serve two purposes: running a background task or exposing a remotable object for Inter-Process Communication (IPC). We will explore both of these purposes for a Service in turn. Although we are going to build separate Service instances for each purpose, you can also build one Service that serves both purposes, if needed.

A background task is typically a process that does not involve direct user interaction or any type of UI. This of course is a perfect fit for polling for severe weather. As far as exposing a remotable object for IPC, we will see how that works, and why it is necessary, in section 4.4.1. There we will build another Service that walks through creating and exposing a remotable object.

As we have already discussed briefly, and we will explain more about here as we go, a Service can either be started or bound or both. Starting a Service relates to the background task aspect. Once started, a Service runs until it is explicitly stopped (you will learn more about this in section 4.4, where we discuss the overall lifecycle of a Service). Binding to a Service involves using a ServiceConnection object to connect and get a remotable reference.

Creating the WeatherAlertService itself, which serves the first type of Service purpose and enables our background weather checks, is where we will focus next.

4.3.2 *Creating a background task Service*

The WeatherAlertService background task-focused Service, which is started when the device is booted via the BroadcastReceiver previously discussed, is shown in listing 4.6.

Listing 4.6 WeatherAlertService class, used to register locations and send alerts

```
public class WeatherAlertService extends Service {        ◄──❶ Extend Service

   private static final String LOC = "LOC";
   private static final String ZIP = "ZIP";                       ❷ Define
   private static final long ALERT_QUIET_PERIOD = 10000;            constants for
   private static final long ALERT_POLL_INTERVAL = 15000;           polling intervals

   public static String deviceLocationZIP = "94102";

   private Timer timer;
   private DBHelper dbHelper;
   private NotificationManager nm;
                                                       Get locations with ❸
                                                          alerts enabled
   private TimerTask task = new TimerTask() {
      public void run() {
         List<Location> locations = dbHelper.getAllAlertEnabled();   ◄─┘
         for (Location loc : locations) {
            WeatherRecord record = loadRecord(loc.zip);
            if (record.isSevere()) {
               if ((loc.lastalert +
                 WeatherAlertService.ALERT_QUIET_PERIOD)
               < System.currentTimeMillis()) {
                  loc.lastalert = System.currentTimeMillis();
                  dbHelper.update(loc);
                  sendNotification(loc.zip, record);      ◄─┐  Fire alert
               }                                           ❹  if severe
            }
         }
         . . . device location alert block omitted for brevity
      }
   };
   private Handler handler = new Handler() {
      public void handleMessage(Message msg) {
```

```
        notifyFromHandler((String) msg.getData()
          .get(WeatherAlertService.LOC), (String) msg.getData()
          .get(WeatherAlertService.ZIP));
    }
};
```

5 Call notify method from handler

```
@Override
public void onCreate() {
    this.dbHelper = new DBHelper(this);
```

6 Set up database

```
    this.timer = new Timer();
    this.timer.schedule(this.task, 5000,
        WeatherAlertService.ALERT_POLL_INTERVAL);
    this.nm = (NotificationManager)
      getSystemService(Context.NOTIFICATION_SERVICE);
}
```

7 Set up notification manager

```
. . . onStart with LocationManager and LocationListener \
      omitted for brevity

@Override
public void onDestroy() {
    super.onDestroy();
    this.dbHelper.cleanup();
}
```

8 Clean up database connection

```
@Override
public IBinder onBind(Intent intent) {
    return null;
}
```

9 Return null from onBind

```
private WeatherRecord loadRecord(String zip) {
    final YWeatherFetcher ywh = new YWeatherFetcher(zip, true);
    return ywh.getWeather();
}
```

10 Load a weather record

11 Include helper for handler

```
private void notifyFromHandler(String location, String zip) {
    Uri uri = Uri.parse("weather://com.msi.manning/loc?zip=" + zip);
    Intent intent = new Intent(Intent.ACTION_VIEW, uri);
    PendingIntent pendingIntent =
    PendingIntent.getActivity(this, Intent.FLAG_ACTIVITY_NEW_TASK,
        intent, PendingIntent.FLAG_ONE_SHOT);
    final Notification n =
      new Notification(R.drawable.severe_weather_24,
          "Severe Weather Alert!",
        System.currentTimeMillis());
    n.setLatestEventInfo(this, "Severe Weather Alert!",
        location, pendingIntent);
    this.nm.notify(Integer.parseInt(zip), n);
}
```

12 Include helper for notification

```
private void sendNotification(String zip, WeatherRecord record) {
    Message message = Message.obtain();
    Bundle bundle = new Bundle();
    bundle.putString(WeatherAlertService.ZIP, zip);
    bundle.putString(WeatherAlertService.LOC, record.getCity()
      + ", " + record.getRegion());
    message.setData(bundle);
    this.handler.sendMessage(message);
}
}
```

The first thing of note in the WeatherAlertService class is the fact that it extends Service ❶. This is the same approach we have seen with activities and receivers: extend the base class, implement the abstract methods, and override the lifecycle methods as needed.

After the initial class declaration a series of member variables is defined. The first of these are constants that represent intervals for polling for severe weather and a quiet period ❷. These are significant because we have set a very low threshold for polling during development—severe weather alerts will spam the emulator often because of this setting. In production this would be throttled back to once every 6 or 12 hours or such.

Next is a TimerTask variable that we will use to do the polling and get all of the user's saved locations that have alerting enabled, through a database call ❸. We will learn the specifics of using a database in Android in the next chapter, where we will finish out the WeatherReporter application and focus on data; here we are going to stay on track with our Service discussion.

Once we have the saved locations, we parse each one and load the weather report. If the report shows severe weather in the forecast, we update the time of the last alert field and call a helper method to initiate a Notification being sent ❹. After we process the user's saved locations, we get the device's alert location from the database using a special postal code designation. The process of polling and sending an alert is repeated for the device current location—as opposed to saved specific locations—if the user has this feature enabled. The device location itself is obtained via a LocationManager. We have omitted the device location–related details here to stay focused, but complete details on Android location-related facilities are covered in chapter 11.

After our TimerTask is set up, we have a Handler member variable. This variable will be used later, using the same technique as in previous listings, to receive a Message object that is fired from a non-UI-related thread and then react. In this case, when the message is received, we call a helper method that instantiates and displays a Notification ❺.

Beyond our member variables we come to the Service lifecycle methods that we have overridden, starting with onCreate. Inside this method we set up our database helper object ❻ and a NotificationManager ❼. Again, we will cover data in the next chapter. (Alert and notification details are specifically addressed in chapter 8.) After onCreate we see onDestroy, which is where we clean up our database connection ❽. Service classes have these lifecycle methods so we can control how resources are allocated and deallocated, similarly to Activity classes; in section 4.4.5 we will address this in more depth.

After the lifecycle-related methods we implement the required onBind method ❾. This method returns an IBinder, which is generally what other components that call into Service methods use for communication. Service classes, as we discussed in section 4.3.1, can serve two purposes: first to run background processes and second for binding to enable IPC. Our weather alert Service is only performing a background task, not enabling IBinder/Binder-based IPC. Therefore, this class returns a null for onBind. We will delve into the binding and IPC aspect of a Service in section 4.4.

Next we see the implementations of our own helper type methods. First we have loadRecord, which is where we call out to the Yahoo! Weather API via YWeatherFetcher ❿. (How this works in terms of networking specifics will be covered in chapter 6.) Then we have sendNotification, which sets up a Message with location details to pass into our earlier declared Handler ⑪. The way this method uses the handler ensures that processing time to get weather data doesn't hang the main UI thread. Lastly we see the notifyFromHandler method that is invoked from the Handler; this fires off a Notification with Intent objects that will call back into WeatherReporter if the user clicks on the Notification ⑫.

A warning about long-running services

We are starting a Service for our sample application here and then leaving it running in the background. Our service is designed to have a minimal footprint (when the polling is tuned), but in general long-running services are strongly discouraged. If your use case doesn't require it, you should make sure to stop any services you have started when your application exits. If you do require a long-running service, you may want to give the user the option of using it or not (a preference). Services are a bit of a paradox in this sense; they are for background tasks, but background is not intended to mean forever. For more discussion on this topic see the Android developers forum: http://groups.google.com/group/android-developers/browse_thread/thread/fa2848e31636af70.

Now that we have discussed what services are for, have created a Service class, and have previously seen a service started via a BroadcastReceiver, we need to cover a bit more detail about the IPC process in Android and other Service details related to it, such as starting versus binding and lifecycle.

4.4   *Performing Inter-Process Communication*

Communication between application components in different processes is made possible in Android by a specific IPC approach. This, again, is necessary because each application on the platform runs in its own process, and processes are intentionally separated from one another. In order to pass messages and objects between processes, you have to use the Android IPC path.

To begin exploring this path we are first going to build a small, focused sample application to examine the means to generate a remote interface using AIDL, and then we will connect to that interface through a proxy that we will expose using a Service (the other Service purpose). Along the way we will expand on the IBinder and Binder concepts Android uses to pass messages and types during IPC.

4.4.1   *Android Interface Definition Language*

Android provides its own Interface Definition Language that you can use to create IDL files. These files then become the input to the aidl tool, which Android also includes. This tool is used to generate a Java interface and inner Stub class that you can, in turn, use to create a remotely accessible object.

AIDL files have a specific syntax that allows you to define methods, with return types and parameters (you cannot define static fields, unlike with a typical Java interface). In the basic AIDL syntax you define your package, imports, and interface just like you would in Java, as shown in listing 4.7.

Listing 4.7   An example .aidl remote interface definition language file

```
package com.msi.manning.binder;        ◁────❶ Define the package

interface ISimpleMathService {         ◁──❷ Declare the interface name
    int add(int a, int b);
    int subtract(int a, int b);        ❸ Describe a method
    String echo(in String input);
}
```

The package ❶, import statements (of which we have none here), and interface ❷ constructs in AIDL are straightforward—they are analogous to regular Java. When you define methods, you must specify a directional tag for all nonprimitive types with each parameter (in, out, or inout). Primitives are allowed only as in and are therefore treated as in by default (and thus don't need the tag). This directional tag is used by the platform to generate the necessary code for marshaling and unmarshaling instances of your interface across IPC boundaries. It's better to go in only one direction where you can, for performance reasons, so try to use only what you really need.

In this case we have declared an interface named ISimpleMathService that includes methods ❸ that perform addition, subtraction, and echoing a String. This is an oversimplified example, of course, but it does demonstrate the approach.

When using AIDL you also have to be aware that only certain types are allowed; these types are shown in table 4.5.

Once you have defined your interface methods with return types and parameters with directional tags in the AIDL format, you then invoke the aidl tool to generate a

Table 4.5   Android IDL allowed types

Type	Description	Import Required
Java primitives	boolean, byte, short, int, float, double, long, char.	No
String	java.lang.String.	No
CharSequence	java.lang.CharSequence.	No
List	Can be generic; all types used in collection must be one of IDL allowed. Ultimately implemented as an ArrayList.	No
Map	Can be generic, all types used in collection must be one of IDL allowed. Ultimately implemented as a HashMap.	No
Other AIDL interfaces	Any other AIDL-generated interface type.	Yes
Parcelable objects	Objects that implement the Android Parcelable interface (more about this in section 4.4.3).	Yes

Java interface that represents your AIDL specification. From the command line you can invoke `[ANDROID_HOME]/tools/aidl` to see the options and syntax for this tool. Generally you just need to point it at your .aidl file, and it will emit a Java interface of the same name. If you use the Eclipse plug-in, it will automatically invoke the aidl tool for you (it recognizes .aidl files and invokes the tool).

The interface that gets generated through AIDL includes an inner static abstract class named `Stub` that extends `Binder` and implements the outer class interface. This `Stub` class represents the *local* side of your remotable interface. `Stub` also includes an `asInterface(IBinder binder)` method that returns a *remote* version of your interface type. Callers can use this method to get a handle on the remote object and from there invoke remote methods. The AIDL process generates a `Proxy` class (another inner class, this time inside `Stub`) that is used to wire up the plumbing and return to callers from the `asInterface` method. The diagram in figure 4.6 depicts this IPC local/ remote relationship.

Once you have all of the generated parts involved, create a concrete class that extends from `Stub` and implements your interface. You then expose this interface to callers through a `Service`.

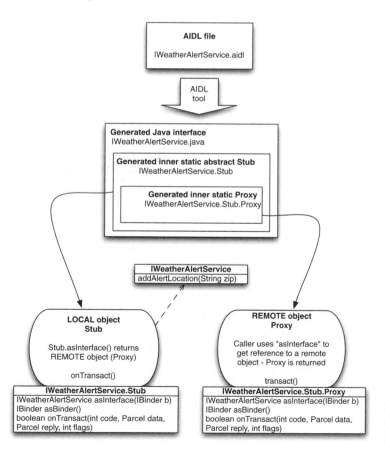

Figure 4.6   Diagram of the Android AIDL process

4.4.2   *Exposing a remote interface*

The glue in all of the moving parts of AIDL that we have discussed up to now is the point where a remote interface is exposed—via a `Service`. In Android parlance, exposing a remote interface through a `Service` is known as *publishing*.

To publish a remote interface you create a class that extends `Service` and returns an `IBinder` through the `onBind(Intent intent)` method within. The `IBinder` that you return here is what clients will use to access a particular remote object. As we discussed in the previous section, the AIDL-generated `Stub` class (which itself extends `Binder`) is usually used to extend from and return an implementation of a remotable interface. This is usually what is returned from a `Service` class's `onBind` method—and hence this is how a remote interface is exposed to any other process that can bind to a `Service`. All of this is shown in listing 4.8, where we implement and publish the `ISimpleMathService` we created in the previous section.

> **Listing 4.8   A `Service` implementation that exposes an `IBinder` remotable object**

```
public class SimpleMathService extends Service {

    private final ISimpleMathService.Stub binder =
      new ISimpleMathService.Stub() {                      Implement the
        public int add(int a, int b) {                ❶   remote interface
            return a + b;
        }
        public int subtract(int a, int b) {
            return a - b;
        }
        public String echo (String input) {
            return "echo " + input;
        }
    };
                                                          Return an IBinder
    @Override                                         ❷  representing the
    public IBinder onBind(Intent intent) {                remotable object
        return this.binder;
    }
}
```

A concrete instance of the generated AIDL Java interface is required to return an `IBinder` to any caller than binds to a `Service`. The way to create an implementation is to implement the `Stub` class that the aidl tool generates ❶. This class, again, implements the AIDL interface and extends `Binder`. Once the `IBinder` is established, it is then simply returned from the `onBind` method ❷.

Now that we have seen where a caller can hook into a `Service` and get a reference to a remotable object, we need to walk through finishing that connection by binding to a `Service` from an `Activity`.

4.4.3   *Binding to a Service*

When an `Activity` class binds to a `Service`, which is done using the `Context.bindService(Intent i, ServiceConnection connection, int flags)` method, the

ServiceConnection object that is passed in is used to send several callbacks, from the Service back to the Activity. One significant callback happens when the binding process completes. This callback comes in the form of the onServiceConnected (ComponentName className, IBinder binder) method. The platform automatically injects the IBinder onBind result (from the Service being bound to) into this method, making this object available to the caller. We show how this works in code in listing 4.9.

Listing 4.9   Binding to a `Service` within an `Activity`

```
public class ActivityExample extends Activity {     ❶ Define remote interface type variable

    private ISimpleMathService service;             ◀
    private boolean bound;        ◀─❷ Define bound state boolean
    . . . View element declarations omitted for brevity

    private ServiceConnection connection = new ServiceConnection() {
        public void onServiceConnected(ComponentName className,
            IBinder iservice) {              ◀─❹ React to onServiceConnected callback
            service = ISimpleMathService.Stub.asInterface(iservice);   ◀
            Toast.makeText(ActivityExample.this,
                "connected to Service", Toast.LENGTH_SHORT).show();
            bound = true;
            }
        public void onServiceDisconnected(ComponentName className) {    ◀
            service = null;
            Toast.makeText(ActivityExample.this,
                "disconnected from Service", Toast.LENGTH_SHORT).show();
            bound = false;
        }
    };

    @Override
    public void onCreate(Bundle icicle) {
        . . . View element inflation omitted for brevity

        this.addButton.setOnClickListener(new OnClickListener() {
            public void onClick(View v) {
                try {
                    int result = service.add(
                        Integer.parseInt(inputa.getText().toString()),
                        Integer.parseInt(inputb.getText().toString()));    ◀
                    output.setText(String.valueOf(result));
                } catch (DeadObjectException e) {
                    Log.e("ActivityExample", "error", e);
                } catch (RemoteException e) {
                    Log.e("ActivityExample", "error", e);
                }
            }
        });

        . . . subtractButton, similar to addButton, omitted for brevity
    }
    @Override
    public void onStart() {
        super.onStart();
```

❸ Include ServiceConnection implementation

❺ Establish remote interface type

❻ React to onServiceDisconnected callback

❼ Use remote object for operations

```
    if (!bound) {
       this.bindService(
            new Intent(ActivityExample.this,
               SimpleMathService.class),
            connection,
            Context.BIND_AUTO_CREATE);      ◁——❽ Perform binding
       }
    }

    @Override
    public void onPause() {
       super.onPause();
       if (bound) {
          bound = false;
          this.unbindService(connection);   ◁——❾ Perform unbinding
       }
    }
}
```

In order to use the remotable `ISimpleMathService` we defined in AIDL, we declare a variable of the generated Java interface type ❶. Along with this `service` variable, we include a `boolean` to keep track of the current state of the binding ❷.

We next see the `ServiceConnection` object ❸, which is essential to the binding process. This object is used with `Context` methods to bind and unbind. When a `Service` is bound, the `onServiceConnected` callback is fired ❹. Within this callback the remote `IBinder` reference is returned and can be assigned to the remotable type ❺. After the connection-related callback there is a similar `onServiceDisconnected` callback that is fired when a `Service` is unbound ❻.

Once the connection is established and the remote `IBinder` is in place, it can be used to perform the operations it defines ❼. Here we are using the add, subtract, and echo methods we created in AIDL in listing 4.7.

With this class we see the `Activity` lifecycle methods that are now familiar. In `onStart` we establish the binding using `bindService` ❽, and in `onPause` we use `unbindService` ❾. A `Service` that is bound but not started can itself be cleaned up by the system to free up resources. If we don't unbind these, resources might unnecessarily hang around.

A `Service`, as you have seen and will learn more about next, is invoked using an `Intent`. Here again, explicit or implicit `Intent` invocation can be used. Significantly, any application (with the correct permissions) can call into a `Service` and bind to it, returning the `IBinder` to perform operations—it need not be an `Activity` in the same application as the `Service` (this is how applications in different processes communicate).

That brings us to the difference between starting a `Service` and binding to one and what the implications are for each usage.

4.4.4 *Starting versus binding*

Again, `Services` serve two purposes in Android, and you can use them as you have now seen in two corresponding ways:

- Starting—`Context.startService(Intent service, Bundle b)`
- Binding—`Context.bindService(Intent service, ServiceConnection c, int flag)`

Starting a `Service` tells the platform to launch it in the background and keep it running, without any particular connection to any other `Activity` or application. We used the `WeatherReportService` in this manner to run in the background and issue severe weather alerts.

Binding to a `Service`, as we did with our sample `SimpleMathService`, is how you get a handle to a remote object and call methods defined there from an `Activity`. As we have discussed, because every Android application is running in its own process, using a bound `Service` (which returns an `IBinder` through `ServiceConnection`) is how you pass data between processes.

Marshaling and unmarshaling remotable objects across process boundaries is fairly complicated. This is the reason the AIDL process has so many moving parts. Fortunately you don't generally have to deal with all of the internals; you can instead stick to a simple recipe that will enable you to create and use remotable objects:

1 Define your interface using AIDL, in the form of an [INTERFACE_NAME].aidl file; see listing 4.7.
2 Generate a Java interface for your .aidl file (automatic in Eclipse).
3 Extend from the generated `[INTERFACE_NAME].Stub` class and implement your interface methods; see listing 4.8.
4 Expose your interface to clients through a `Service` and the `Service` `onBind(Intent i)` method; see listing 4.8.
5 Bind to your `Service` with a `ServiceConnection` to get a handle to the remotable object, and use it; see listing 4.9.

Another important aspect of the `Service` concept to be aware of, and one that is affected by whether or not a `Service` is bound or started or both, is the lifecycle.

4.4.5 *Service lifecycle*

Along with overall application lifecycle that we introduced in chapter 2 and the `Activity` lifecycle that we discussed in detail in chapter 3, services also have their own well-defined process phases. Which parts of the `Service` lifecycle are invoked is affected by how the `Service` is being used: started, bound, or both.

SERVICE-STARTED LIFECYCLE

If a `Service` is started by `Context.startService(Intent service, Bundle b)`, as shown in listing 4.5, it runs in the background whether or not anything is bound to it. In this case, if it is needed, the `Service` `onCreate()` method will be called, and then the `onStart(int id, Bundle args)` method will be called. If a `Service` is started more than once, the `onStart(int id, Bundle args)` method will be called multiple times, but additional instances of the `Service` will not be created (still needs only one stop call).

The Service will continue to run in the background until it is explicitly stopped by the Context.stopService() method or its own stopSelf() method. You should also keep in mind that the platform may kill services if resources are running low, so your application needs to be able to react accordingly (restart a service automatically, function without it, and the like).

SERVICE-BOUND LIFECYCLE

If a Service is bound by an Activity calling Context.bindService(Intent service, ServiceConnection connection, int flags), as shown in listing 4.9, it will run as long as the connection is established. An Activity establishes the connection using the Context and is responsible for closing it as well.

When a Service is only bound in this manner and not also started, its onCreate() method is invoked, but onStart(int id, Bundle args) is *not* used. In these cases the Service is eligible to be stopped and cleaned up by the platform when no longer bound.

SERVICE-STARTED AND -BOUND LIFECYCLE

If a Service is both started and bound, which is allowable, it will basically keep running in the background, similarly to the started lifecycle. The only real difference is the lifecycle itself. Because of the starting and binding, both onStart(int id, Bundle args) and onCreate() will be called.

CLEANING UP WHEN A SERVICE STOPS

When a Service is stopped, either explicitly after having been started or implicitly when there are no more bound connections (and it was not started), the onDestroy() method is invoked. Inside onDestroy() every Service should perform final cleanup, stopping any spawned threads and the like.

Now that we have shown how a Service is implemented, how one can be used both in terms of starting and binding, and what the lifecycle looks like, we need to take a closer look at details of remotable data types when using Android IPC and IDL.

4.4.6   *Binder and Parcelable*

The IBinder interface is the base of the remoting protocol in Android. As you have seen, you don't implement this interface directly; rather you typically use AIDL to generate an interface that contains a Stub Binder implementation.

The key to the IBinder and Binder–enabling IPC, once the interfaces are defined and implemented, is the IBinder.transact() method and corresponding Binder.onTransact() method. Though you don't typically work with these internal methods directly, they are the backbone of the remoting process. Each method you define using AIDL is handled synchronously through the transaction process (enabling the same semantics as if the method were local).

All of the objects you pass in and out, through the interface methods you define using AIDL, use the transact process. These objects must be Parcelable in order to be able to be placed inside a Parcel and moved across the local/remote process barrier in the Binder transaction methods.

The only time you need to worry about something being Parcelable is when you want to send a custom object through Android IPC. If you use the default allowable types in your interface definition files—primitives, String, CharSequence, List, and Map—everything is automatically handled. If you need to use something beyond those, only then do you need to implement Parcelable.

The Android documentation describes what methods you need to implement to create a Parcelable class. The only tricky part of doing this is remembering to create an .aidl file for each Parcelable interface. These .aidl files are different from those you use to define Binder classes themselves; for these you need to remember *not* to generate from the aidl tool. Trying to use the aidl tool won't work, and it isn't intended to work. The documentation states these files are used "like a header in C," and so they are not intended to be processed by the aidl tool.

Also, when considering creation of your own Parcelable types, make sure you really need them. Passing complex objects across the IPC boundary in an embedded environment is an expensive operation and should be avoided if possible (not to mention that manually creating these types is fairly tedious).

Rounding out our IPC discussion with a quick overview of Parcelable completes our tour of Android Intent and Service usage.

4.5   *Summary*

In this chapter we covered a broad swath of Android territory. We first focused on the Intent abstraction, defining what intents are, how they are resolved using Intent-Filter objects, and what some built-in platform-provided Intent handlers are. We also addressed explicit Intent invocation versus implicit Intent invocation and the reasons you might choose one type over another. In that discussion we completed the RestaurantFinder sample application.

After we covered the basics of Intent classes, we moved on to a new sample application, WeatherReporter. Within the scope of this application, we explored the concept of a BroadcastReceiver and an Android Service. We used the receiver to start the Service, and we designed the Service to send notification alerts for severe weather events. Along with Service implementation details we covered the difference between starting and binding services and the moving parts behind the Android IPC system, which uses the Android IDL process.

Through looking at all these components in several complete examples, you should now have a good idea of the basic foundation of these concepts. In the next chapter we will build on this foundation a bit further by looking at the various means Android provides to retrieve and store data, including using preferences, the file system, databases, and creating a ContentProvider.

5

Storing and retrieving data

Anytime you are developing software, one of the most common and basic constructs you have to deal with is the means to store and retrieve data. It's all about the data after all. Though there are many ways to pipe data into and out of various languages and technologies, there are typically only a few ways to persist it: in memory structures, the filesystem, databases, and network services.

Like other technologies, Android has its own concepts for getting and sharing data in applications, yet these concepts are ultimately implemented using familiar approaches (for the most part). Android provides access to the filesystem, has support for a local relational database through SQLite, and includes a Shared-Preferences object and preferences system that allows you to store simple key-value pairs within applications.

In this chapter we are going to take a tour of each of the local data-related mechanisms (we will examine the network possibilities in chapter 6). We will start with preferences and create a small sample application to exercise those concepts. From there we will create another sample application to examine using the filesystem to store data, both internal to our application and external using the platform's SD card support. Then we will look at creating and accessing a database. To do this we will take a closer look at some of the code and concepts from the WeatherReporter application we created in chapter 4, which uses SQLite.

Beyond the basics, Android also includes its own construct that allows applications to share data through a clever URI-based approach called a `ContentProvider`. This technique combines several other Android concepts, such as the URI-based style of intents and the `Cursor` result set seen in SQLite, to make data accessible across different applications. To demonstrate how this works we will create another small sample application that uses built-in providers, then we will walk through the steps required to create a `ContentProvider` on our own.

We begin with the easiest form of data storage and retrieval Android provides, preferences.

5.1 Using preferences

When moving from `Activity` to `Activity` in Android it is very handy to be able to save some global application state in a `SharedPreferences` object. Here we will discuss how you can set data into a preferences object and how you can later retrieve it. Also, we will discuss how to make preferences private to your application or accessible to other applications on the same device.

5.1.1 Working with SharedPreferences

You access a `SharedPreferences` object through the `Context` you are working in. Many Android classes have a reference to, or themselves extend from, `Context`. For example, `Activity` and `Service` both extend `Context`.

`Context` includes a `getSharedPreferences(String name, int accessMode)` method that allows you to get a preferences handle. The name you specify indicates the file that backs the preferences you are interested in. If no such file exists when you try to get preferences, one is automatically created using the passed-in name. The access mode refers to what permissions you want to allow.

Listing 5.1 is an example `Activity` that demonstrates allowing the user to enter input and then storing that data through `SharedPreferences` objects with different access modes.

Listing 5.1 Storing `SharedPreferences` using different modes

```
package com.msi.manning.chapter5.prefs;

// imports omitted for brevity

public class SharedPrefTestInput extends Activity {
```

```
public static final String PREFS_PRIVATE = "PREFS_PRIVATE";
public static final String PREFS_WORLD_READ = "PREFS_WORLD_READABLE";
public static final String PREFS_WORLD_WRITE = "PREFS_WORLD_WRITABLE";
public static final String PREFS_WORLD_READ_WRITE =
  "PREFS_WORLD_READABLE_WRITABLE";

public static final String KEY_PRIVATE = "KEY_PRIVATE";
public static final String KEY_WORLD_READ = "KEY_WORLD_READ";
public static final String KEY_WORLD_WRITE = "KEY_WORLD_WRITE";
public static final String KEY_WORLD_READ_WRITE =
  "KEY_WORLD_READ_WRITE";

. . . view element variable declarations omitted for brevity

private SharedPreferences prefsPrivate;
private SharedPreferences prefsWorldRead;
private SharedPreferences prefsWorldWrite;
private SharedPreferences prefsWorldReadWrite;
```

❶ **Declare SharedPreferences variables**

```
@Override
public void onCreate(Bundle icicle) {

.. view inflation omitted for brevity

   this.button.setOnClickListener(new OnClickListener() {
      public void onClick(final View v) {
         boolean valid = validate();
         if (valid) {
            prefsPrivate =
             getSharedPreferences(
               SharedPrefTestInput.PREFS_PRIVATE,
               Context.MODE_PRIVATE);
            prefsWorldRead =
              getSharedPreferences(
                SharedPrefTestInput.PREFS_WORLD_READ,
               Context.MODE_WORLD_READABLE);
            prefsWorldWrite =
             getSharedPreferences(
               SharedPrefTestInput.PREFS_WORLD_WRITE,
               Context.MODE_WORLD_WRITEABLE);
            prefsWorldReadWrite =
             getSharedPreferences(
               SharedPrefTestInput.PREFS_WORLD_READ_WRITE,
               Context.MODE_WORLD_READABLE
               + Context.MODE_WORLD_WRITEABLE);

            Editor prefsPrivateEditor =
              prefsPrivate.edit();
            Editor prefsWorldReadEditor =
              prefsWorldRead.edit();
            Editor prefsWorldWriteEditor =
              prefsWorldWrite.edit();
            Editor prefsWorldReadWriteEditor =
              prefsWorldReadWrite.edit();

            prefsPrivateEditor.putString(
              SharedPrefTestInput.KEY_PRIVATE,
```

❸ **Use different modes**

❷ **Use Context. getShared-Preferences for references**

❹ **Get SharedPreferences Editor**

```
                inputPrivate.getText.toString());        ◁─┐
            prefsWorldReadEditor.putString(                 │
              SharedPrefTestInput.KEY_WORLD_READ,           │
                inputWorldRead.getText().toString());   ◁─┤
                                                            │   ❺ Store values
            prefsWorldWriteEditor.putString(                │      with editor
              SharedPrefTestInput.KEY_WORLD_WRITE,          │
                inputWorldWrite.getText().toString());  ◁─┤
            prefsWorldReadWriteEditor.putString(            │
              SharedPrefTestInput.KEY_WORLD_READ_WRITE,     │
                inputWorldReadWrite.getText().toString()); ◁─┘

            prefsPrivateEditor.commit();          ❻ Commit changes
            prefsWorldReadEditor.commit();           with editoreferences
            prefsWorldWriteEditor.commit();          variables
            prefsWorldReadWriteEditor.commit();

            Intent intent =
              new Intent(SharedPrefTestInput.this,
                SharedPrefTestOutput.class);
            startActivity(intent);
          }
        }
      });
    }

  . . . validate omitted for brevity

}
```

Once you have a SharedPreferences variable ❶, you may assign a reference through the Context ❷. Note that for each SharedPreferences object we are getting, we are using a different constant value for the access mode, and in some cases we are even adding modes (modes are of int type) ❸. Modes specify whether or not the preferences should be private, world readable, world writable, or a combination.

After you have preferences, you can then get an Editor handle in order to start manipulating values ❹. With the Editor you can set String, boolean, float, int, and long types as key-value pairs ❺. This limited set of types can be restrictive, and it is why we extended the Context in chapter 3 to store some application state in the form of a complex object rather than using preferences. Even with this restriction, though, often preferences are adequate, and as you can see they are simple to use.

After you have stored data with an Editor, which creates an in-memory Map, you have to remember to call commit() to persist it to the preferences backing file ❻. After data is committed, you can get it from a SharedPreferences object even easier than storing it. Listing 5.2 is an example Activity from the same application (same package) that gets and displays the data that was stored in listing 5.1.

Listing 5.2 Getting SharedPreferences data stored in the same application

```
package com.msi.manning.chapter5.prefs;

// imports omitted for brevity
```

```
public class SharedPrefTestOutput extends Activity {

    . . . view element variable declarations omitted for brevity

    private SharedPreferences prefsPrivate;              ❶ Declare
    private SharedPreferences prefsWorldRead;              SharedPreferences
    private SharedPreferences prefsWorldWrite;            variables
    private SharedPreferences prefsWorldReadWrite;

    . . . onCreate omitted for brevity

    @Override
    public void onStart() {
        super.onStart();
        this.prefsPrivate =
          getSharedPreferences(SharedPrefTestInput.PREFS_PRIVATE,
            Context.MODE_PRIVATE);
        this.prefsWorldRead =
          getSharedPreferences(SharedPrefTestInput.PREFS_WORLD_READ,
            Context.MODE_WORLD_READABLE);
        this.prefsWorldWrite =
          getSharedPreferences(SharedPrefTestInput.PREFS_WORLD_WRITE,
            Context.MODE_WORLD_WRITEABLE);
        this.prefsWorldReadWrite =

        getSharedPreferences(
          SharedPrefTestInput.PREFS_WORLD_READ_WRITE,
          Context.MODE_WORLD_READABLE
          + Context.MODE_WORLD_WRITEABLE);

        this.outputPrivate.setText(this.prefsPrivate.getString(
          SharedPrefTestInput.KEY_PRIVATE, "NA"));
        this.outputWorldRead.setText(this.prefsWorldRead.getString(
          SharedPrefTestInput.KEY_WORLD_READ, "NA"));
        this.outputWorldWrite.setText(this.prefsWorldWrite.getString(
          SharedPrefTestInput.KEY_WORLD_WRITE, "NA"));
        this.outputWorldReadWrite.setText(this.prefsWorldReadWrite.getString(
          SharedPrefTestInput.KEY_WORLD_READ_WRITE,
          "NA"));
    }
}
```

Assign ❷
SharedPreferences
variables

Get values ❸

To get SharedPreferences values that we have previously stored, we again declare variables ❶ and assign references ❷. Once these are in place, we can simply get values using methods such as getString(String key, String default) ❸.

So, as you can see, setting and getting preferences is very straightforward. The only potential flies in the ointment are the access modes, which we will focus on next.

5.1.2 *Preference access permissions*

SharedPreferences can be opened or created with any combination of several Context mode constants. Because these values are int types, they can be added together, as we did in listings 5.1 and 5.2, to combine permissions. The supported mode constants are as follows:

- Context.MODE_PRIVATE *(value 0)*
- Context.MODE_WORLD_READABLE *(value 1)*
- Context.MODE_WORLD_WRITEABLE *(value 2)*

These modes allow you to finely tune who has access to what preference. If we take a look at the filesystem on the emulator, after having created SharedPreferences objects (which themselves create XML files to persist the data), we can see how this works using a Linux-based filesystem.

Figure 5.1 is a screen shot of the Android Eclipse plug-in File Explorer view; it shows the Linux-level permissions for the SharedPreferences XML files that were created in listing 5.1 (these were automatically created for us when we used SharedPreferences).

The quick and dirty version of how Linux file permissions work is that each file (or directory) has a type and three sets of permissions represented by a drwxrwxrwx notation. The first character indicates the type (d means directory, - means regular file type, and symbolic links and other things can be represented using the type as well). After the type, the three sets of rwx represent read, write, and/or execute permissions for user, group, and other, in that order. So looking at this notation we can tell which files are accessible by the user they are owned by, or by the group they belong to, or by other.

Directories with the other x permission

Directory permissions can be confusing. The important thing to remember with regard to Android, though, is that each package directory is created with the other x permission. This means anyone can search and list the files in the directory. This, in turn, means that Android packages have directory-level access to one another's files—from there the file-level access determines file permissions.

SharedPreferences XML files are placed in the /data/data/PACKAGE_NAME/ shared_prefs path on the filesystem. Every application or package (each .apk file) has its own user ID (unless you use sharedUserId in the manifest, which allows you to share the user ID, but that's a special exception). When an application creates files (including SharedPreferences), they are owned by that application's user ID. To allow other applications to access these files, the other permissions have to be set (as

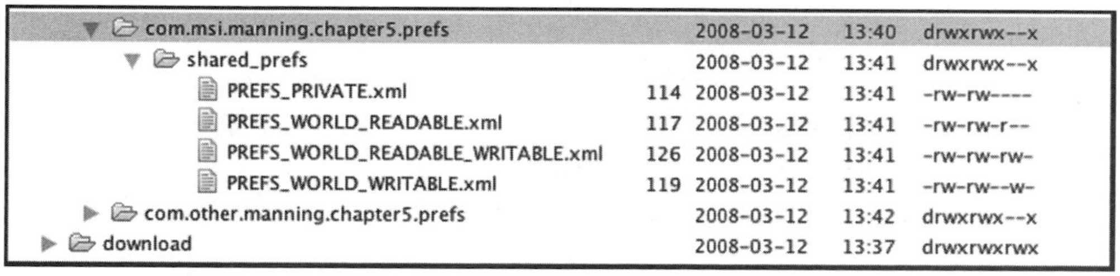

▼ 🗁 com.msi.manning.chapter5.prefs		2008-03-12	13:40	drwxrwx--x
▼ 🗁 shared_prefs		2008-03-12	13:41	drwxrwx--x
📄 PREFS_PRIVATE.xml	114	2008-03-12	13:41	-rw-rw----
📄 PREFS_WORLD_READABLE.xml	117	2008-03-12	13:41	-rw-rw-r--
📄 PREFS_WORLD_READABLE_WRITABLE.xml	126	2008-03-12	13:41	-rw-rw-rw-
📄 PREFS_WORLD_WRITABLE.xml	119	2008-03-12	13:41	-rw-rw-w-
▶ 🗁 com.other.manning.chapter5.prefs		2008-03-12	13:42	drwxrwx--x
▶ 🗁 download		2008-03-12	13:37	drwxrwxrwx

Figure 5.1 The Android File Explorer view showing preferences file permissions

shown in figure 5.2, where one of our preferences files has no outside permissions, one of our files is world-readable, one is world-readable and -writable, and one is world-writable).

The tricky part with getting access to the files of one application from another, even when they have accessible permissions, is the starting path. The path is built from the Context. So, to get files from another application you have to know and use that application's Context. An example of this is shown in listing 5.3, where we get the SharedPreferences we set in listing 5.1 again, this time from a different application (different .apk and different package).

Listing 5.3 Getting `SharedPreferences` data stored in a different application

```
package com.other.manning.chapter5.prefs;        ← ① Use a different package

. . . imports omitted for brevity

public class SharedPrefTestOtherOutput extends Activity {

    . . . constants and variable declarations omitted for brevity

    . . . onCreate omitted for brevity

    @Override
    public void onStart() {
      super.onStart();
      Context otherAppsContext = null;
      try {
        otherAppsContext =
          createPackageContext("com.msi.manning.chapter5.prefs",
            Context.MODE_WORLD_WRITEABLE);        ←
      } catch (NameNotFoundException e) {         ② Get another
        // log and or handle                         application's context
      }

      this.prefsPrivate =
       otherAppsContext.getSharedPreferences(
         SharedPrefTestOtherOutput.PREFS_PRIVATE, 0);        ←
      this.prefsWorldRead =
       otherAppsContext.getSharedPreferences(
         SharedPrefTestOtherOutput.PREFS_WORLD_READ, 0);     ←
      this.prefsWorldWrite =                          Use ③
       otherAppsContext.getSharedPreferences(   otherAppsContext
         SharedPrefTestOtherOutput.PREFS_WORLD_WRITE, 0);    ←
      this.prefsWorldReadWrite =
       otherAppsContext.getSharedPreferences(
         SharedPrefTestOtherOutput.PREFS_WORLD_READ_WRITE, 0);  ←

      this.outputPrivate.setText(
         this.prefsPrivate.getString(
           SharedPrefTestOtherOutput.KEY_PRIVATE, "NA"));
      this.outputWorldRead.setText(
        this.prefsWorldRead.getString(
          SharedPrefTestOtherOutput.KEY_WORLD_READ, "NA"));
      this.outputWorldWrite.setText(
        this.prefsWorldWrite.getString(
          SharedPrefTestOtherOutput.KEY_WORLD_WRITE, "NA"));
```

```
        this.outputWorldReadWrite.setText(
          this.prefsWorldReadWrite.getString(
            SharedPrefTestOtherOutput.KEY_WORLD_READ_WRITE,"NA"));
    }
}
```

To get to the SharedPreferences one application has defined from another application in a different package ❶, we must use the createPackageContext(String context-Name, int mode) method ❷. Once we have a reference to the other application's Context, we can use the same names for the SharedPreferences objects the other application created (we do have to know the names) to access those preferences ❸.

With these examples we now have one application that sets and gets Shared-Preferences and a second application (in a different package, with a different .apk file) that gets the preferences set by the first. The composite screen shot shown in figure 5.2 demonstrates what this looks like (where NA is the preferences we could not access from the second application, due to permissions).

Figure 5.2 Two separate applications getting and setting SharedPreferences

The way `SharedPreferences` are backed by XML files on the Android filesystem and use permission modes leads us to the next method of storing and retrieving data, the filesystem itself.

5.2   *Using the filesystem*

As you have seen, Android has a filesystem that is based on Linux and supports mode-based permissions. There are several ways you can access this filesystem. You can create and read files from within applications, you can access raw files that are included as resources, and you can work with specially compiled custom XML files. In this section we will take a tour of each approach.

5.2.1   *Creating files*

You can easily create files in Android and have them stored in the filesystem under the data path for the application in which you are working. Listing 5.4 demonstrates how you get a `FileOutputStream` handle and how you write to it to create a file.

Listing 5.4   Creating a file in Android from an `Activity`

```java
public class CreateFile extends Activity {

   private EditText createInput;
   private Button createButton;

   @Override
   public void onCreate(Bundle icicle) {
      super.onCreate(icicle);
      this.setContentView(R.layout.create_file);

      this.createInput =
        (EditText) this.findViewById(R.id.create_input);
      this.createButton =
        (Button) this.findViewById(R.id.create_button);

      this.createButton.setOnClickListener(new OnClickListener() {
         public void onClick(final View v) {
            FileOutputStream fos = null;
            try {
               fos = openFileOutput("filename.txt",         ❶ Use
                Context.MODE_PRIVATE);                          openFileOutput
               fos.write(createInput.getText().toString().getBytes());   ⬅
            } catch (FileNotFoundException e) {
               Log.e("CreateFile", e.getLocalizedMessage());    Write data
            } catch (IOException e)                             to stream ❷
   {

               Log.e("CreateFile", e.getLocalizedMessage());
            } finally {
               if (fos != null) {
                  try {
                     fos.flush();              ❸ Flush and
                     fos.close();                 close stream
                  } catch (IOException e) {
                     // swallow
```

```
                }
              }
            }
            startActivity(
              new Intent(CreateFile.this, ReadFile.class));
          }
        });
      }
    }
```

Android provides a convenience method on `Context` to get a `FileOutputStream` reference, `openFileOutput(String name, int mode)` ❶. Using this method you can create a stream to a file. That file will ultimately be stored at the data/data/ [PACKAGE_NAME]/files/file.name path on the platform. Once you have the stream, you can write to it as you would with typical Java ❷. After you have finished with a stream you have to remember to flush it and close it to cleanup ❸.

Reading from a file within an application context (that is, within the package path of the application) is also very simple; in the next section we will show how this can be done.

5.2.2 *Accessing files*

Similarly to `openFileOutput`, the `Context` also has a convenience `openFileInput` method. This method can be used to access a file on the filesystem and read it in, as shown in listing 5.5.

Listing 5.5 Accessing an existing file in Android from an `Activity`

```
public class ReadFile extends Activity {
    private TextView readOutput;
    private Button gotoReadResource;

    @Override
    public void onCreate(Bundle icicle) {
        super.onCreate(icicle);
        this.setContentView(R.layout.read_file);

        this.readOutput =
          (TextView) this.findViewById(R.id.read_output);

        FileInputStream fis = null;
        try {
            fis = this.openFileInput("filename.txt");      ❶ Use openFileInput
            byte[] reader = new byte[fis.available()];          for stream
            while (fis.read(reader) != -1) {}              ❷ Read data
            this.readOutput.setText(new String(reader));      from stream
        } catch (IOException e) {
            Log.e("ReadFile", e.getMessage(), e);
        } finally {
            if (fis != null) {
                try {                                     ❸ Clean up when
                    fis.close();                              finished
                } catch (IOException e) {
```

```
            // swallow
        }
    }
}

. . . goto next Activity via startActivity omitted for brevity
  }
}
```

Getting a `FileInputStream`, in order to read in a file from the filesystem, is the mirror opposite of getting a `FileOutputStream`. For input you use `openFileInput(String name, int mode)` to get the stream ❶, and then you read in the file as with standard Java ❷ (in this case we are filling the byte `reader` byte array). Once you have finished, you need to close the stream properly to avoid hanging onto resources ❸.

   With `openFileOutput` and `openFileInput` you can write to and read from any file within the files directory of the application package within which you are working. Also, much like the access modes and permissions we discussed in the previous sections, you can access files across different applications if the permissions allow it and if you know the full path to the file (you know the package to establish the path from the other application's context).

Running a bundle of apps with the same user ID

Though it is the exception rather than rule, there are times when setting the user ID your application runs as can be extremely useful (most of the time it's fine to allow the platform to select a unique ID for you). For instance, if you have multiple applications that need to store data among one another, but you also want that data to not be accessible outside that group of applications, you may want to set the permissions to private and share the UID to allow access. You can allow a shared UID by using the sharedUserId attribute in your manifest: `android:sharedUserId="YourFancyID"`.

Along with creating files from within your application, you can push and pull files to the platform, using the adb (Android Debug Bridge) tool (which you met in chapters 1 and 2). You can optionally put such files in the directory for your application; once they are there you can read these files just like you would any other file. Keep in mind, though, outside of development-related use you won't usually be pushing and pulling files. Rather you will be creating and reading files from within the application or working with files that are included with an application as a raw resource, as you will see next.

5.2.3   *Files as raw resources*

If you want to include raw files with your application of any form, you can do so using the res/raw resources location. We discussed resources in general in chapter 3, but we did not drill down into raw files there, so we could group this data storage and access approach with others here. When you place a file in the res/raw location, it is not compiled by the platform but is available as a *raw* resource, as shown in listing 5.6.

Listing 5.6   Accessing a noncompiled raw file from res/raw

```
public class ReadRawResourceFile extends Activity {

   private TextView readOutput;
   private Button gotoReadXMLResource;

   @Override
   public void onCreate(Bundle icicle) {
      super.onCreate(icicle);
      this.setContentView(R.layout.read_rawresource_file);

      this.readOutput =
        (TextView) this.findViewById(R.id.readrawres_output);

      Resources resources = this.getResources();          ❶ Hold raw resource
      InputStream is = null;                                  with InputStream
      try {
         is = resources.openRawResource(R.raw.people);          Use getResources().
         byte[] reader = new byte[is.available()];          ❷ openRawResource()
         while (is.read(reader) != -1) {}
         this.readOutput.setText(new String(reader));
      } catch (IOException e) {
         Log.e("ReadRawResourceFile", e.getMessage(), e);
      } finally {
         if (is != null) {
            try {
               is.close();
            } catch (IOException e) {
               // swallow
            }
         }
      }

      . . . goto next Activity via startActivity omitted for brevity

   }
}
```

Getting raw resources is very similar to getting files. You get a handle to an Input-
Stream, and you can use that stream to assign to a raw reference later ❶. You call
Context.getResources() to get the Resources reference for your current application's context, and then you call openRawResource(int id) to link to the particular
item you want ❷. The id will automatically be available from the R class if you place
your asset in the res/raw directory. Raw resources don't have to be text files, even
though that's what we are using here. They can be images, documents—you name it.

The significance with raw resources is that they are not precompiled by the platform, and they can refer to any type of raw file. The last type of file resource we need
to discuss is the res/xml type—which is compiled by the platform into an efficient
binary type that you need to access in a special manner.

5.2.4   *XML file resources*

The terms can get confusing when talking about XML resources in Android circles. This
is because *XML resources* can mean resources in general that are defined in XML, such as
layout files, styles, arrays, and the like, or it can specifically mean res/xml XML files.

In this section we will be dealing with res/xml XML files. These files are treated a bit differently than other Android resources. They are different from raw files in that you don't use a stream to access them because they are compiled into an efficient binary form when deployed, and they are different from other resources in that they can be of any custom XML structure that you desire.

To demonstrate this concept we are going to use an XML file that defines multiple <person> elements and uses attributes for firstname and lastname—people.xml. We will then grab this resource and display the elements within it on screen in last-name, first-name order, as shown in figure 5.3.

Our data file for this process, which we will place in res/xml in source, is shown in listing 5.7.

Figure 5.3   The example `ReadXMLResource-File` **Activity created in listing 5.8, which reads a res/xml resource file**

Listing 5.7   A custom XML file included in res/xml

```xml
<people>
    <person firstname="John" lastname="Ford" />
    <person firstname="Alfred" lastname="Hitchcock" />
    <person firstname="Stanley" lastname="Kubrick" />
    <person firstname="Wes" lastname="Anderson" />
</people>
```

Once a file is in the res/xml path, it will be automatically picked up by the platform (if you are using Eclipse) and compiled into a resource asset. This asset can then be accessed in code by parsing the binary XML format Android supports, as shown in listing 5.8.

Listing 5.8   Accessing a compiled XML resource from res/xml

```java
public class ReadXMLResourceFile extends Activity {

    private TextView readOutput;

    @Override
    public void onCreate(Bundle icicle) {
        super.onCreate(icicle);
        this.setContentView(R.layout.read_xmlresource_file);

        this.readOutput = (TextView)
          this.findViewById(R.id.readxmlres_output);

        XmlPullParser parser = this.getResources().getXml(R.xml.people);
        StringBuffer sb = new StringBuffer();

        try {
            while (parser.next() != XmlPullParser.END_DOCUMENT) {
```

1 Parse XML with XMLPullParser

2 Walking the XML tree

```
                    String name = parser.getName();
                    String first = null;
                    String last = null;
                    if ((name != null) && name.equals("person")) {     ❸  Get attributeCount
                        int size = parser.getAttributeCount();    ◁─┘      for element
                        for (int i = 0; i < size; i++) {
                            String attrName =
                              parser.getAttributeName(i);         ◁─┐
                            String attrValue =                       ❹  Get attribute
                              parser.getAttributeValue(i);       ◁─┘     name and value
                            if ((attrName != null)
                              && attrName.equals("firstname")) {
                                first = attrValue;
                            } else if ((attrName != null)
                              && attrName.equals("lastname")) {
                                last = attrValue;
                            }
                        }
                        if ((first != null) && (last != null)) {
                            sb.append(last + ", " + first + "\n");
                        }
                    }
                }
              this.readOutput.setText(sb.toString());
            } catch (Exception e) {
              Log.e("ReadXMLResourceFile", e.getMessage(), e);
            }

            . . . goto next Activity via startActivity omitted for brevity
        }
    }
```

To process a binary XML resource you use an XmlPullParser ❶. This class can walk though the XML tree SAX style. The parser provides an event type represented by an int for each element it encounters, such as DOCDECL, COMMENT, START_DOCUMENT, START_TAG, END_TAG, END_DOCUMENT, and so on. Using the next() method you can retrieve the current event type value and compare it to event constants in the class ❷. Each element encountered has a name, a text value, and an optional set of attributes. You can walk through the document as we are here by getting the attributeCount ❸ for each item and grabbing the name and value ❹. We are traversing the nodes of a resource-based XML file here with a pull parser; you will see more types of XML parsing in later examples. (SAX is specifically covered in chapter 13.)

Apart from local file storage on the device filesystem, you have another option that is more appropriate for certain types of content, writing to an external SD card filesystem.

5.2.5 *External storage via an SD card*

One of the advantages the Android platform provides over some other similar device competitors is that it offers access to an available Secure Digital (SD) flash memory card. Ultimately, it is possible that not every Android device will have an SD card, but the good news is that if the device does have it, the platform supports it and provides an easy way for you to use it.

SD cards and the emulator

In order to work with an SD card image in the Android Emulator, you will first need to use the mksdcard tool provided to set up your SD image file (you will find this executable in the tools directory of the SDK). After you have created the file, you will need to start the emulator with the -sdcard <path_to_file> option in order to have the SD image mounted.

Using the SD card makes a lot of sense if you are dealing with large files or when you don't necessarily need to have permanent secure access to certain files. Obviously, if you are working with image data, audio files, or the like, you will want to store these on the SD card. The built-in internal filesystem is stored on the system memory, which is limited on a small mobile device—you don't typically want to throw snapshots of Grandma on the device itself if you have other options (like an SD card). On the other hand, for application-specialized data that you do need to be permanent and for which you are concerned about secure access, you should use the internal filesystem (or an internal database).

The SD card is impermanent (the user can remove it), and SD card support on most devices, including Android-powered devices, supports the FAT (File Allocation Table) filesystem. That's important to remember because it will help you keep in mind that the SD card doesn't have the access modes and permissions that come from the Linux filesystem.

Using the SD card when you need it is fairly basic. The standard java.io.File and related objects can be used to create and read (and remove) files on the /sdcard path (assuming that path is available, which you do need to check, also using the standard File methods). Listing 5.9 is an example of checking that the /sdcard path is present, creating another subdirectory therein, then writing and subsequently reading file data at that location.

Listing 5.9   Using standard java.io.File techniques with an SD card

```java
public class ReadWriteSDCardFile extends Activity {

    private TextView readOutput;

    @Override
    public void onCreate(Bundle icicle) {
        super.onCreate(icicle);
        this.setContentView(R.layout.read_write_sdcard_file);

        this.readOutput = (TextView)
            this.findViewById(R.id.readwritesd_output);

        String fileName = "testfile-"
            + System.currentTimeMillis() + ".txt";     ◁——❶ Establish filename
```

```
File sdDir = new File("/sdcard/");
if (sdDir.exists() && sdDir.canWrite()) {
    File uadDir = new File(sdDir.getAbsolutePath()
        + "/unlocking_android");
    uadDir.mkdir();
    if (uadDir.exists() && uadDir.canWrite()) {
        File file = new File(uadDir.getAbsolutePath()
            + "/" + fileName);
        try {
            file.createNewFile();
        } catch (IOException e) {
            // log and or handle
        }

        if (file.exists() && file.canWrite()) {
            FileOutputStream fos = null;
            try {
                fos = new FileOutputStream(file);
                fos.write("I fear you speak upon the rack,"
                    + "where men enforced do speak "
                    + "anything.".getBytes());
            } catch (FileNotFoundException e) {
                Log.e(ReadWriteSDCardFile.LOGTAG, "ERROR", e);
            } catch (IOException e) {
                Log.e(ReadWriteSDCardFile.LOGTAG, "ERROR", e);
            } finally {
                if (fos != null) {
                    try {
                        fos.flush();
                        fos.close();
                    } catch (IOException e) {
                        // swallow
                    }
                }
            }
        } else {
            // log and or handle - error writing to file
        }

    } else {
        // log and or handle -
        // unable to write to /sdcard/unlocking_android
    }
} else {
    Log.e("ReadWriteSDCardFile.LOGTAG",
        "ERROR /sdcard path not available (did you create "
            + " an SD image with the mksdcard tool,"
            + " and start emulator with -sdcard "
            + <path_to_file> option?");
}

File rFile =
 new File("/sdcard/unlocking_android/" + fileName);
if (rFile.exists() && rFile.canRead()) {
    FileInputStream fis = null;
    try {
        fis = new FileInputStream(rFile);
```

2 Get /sdcard directory reference

3 Instantiate File for path

4 Use mkdir() to create directory

5 Get reference to File

6 Create file

7 Write with FileInputStream

8 Use new File object for reading

```
        byte[] reader = new byte[fis.available()];      ⟵┐    Read with
        while (fis.read(reader) != -1) {                  ⑨   FileOutputStream
        }
        this.readOutput.setText(new String(reader));
    } catch (IOException e) {
        // log and or handle
    } finally {
        if (fis != null) {
            try {
                fis.close();
            } catch (IOException e) {
                // swallow
            }
        }
    }
} else {
    this.readOutput.setText(
      "Unable to read/write sdcard file, see logcat output");
}
  }
}
```

The first thing we need to do in the ReadWriteSDCardFile class is to establish a file-name for the file we want to create ❶. We have done this by appending a timestamp so as to create a unique file each time this example application is run. After we have the filename, we create a File object reference to the /sdcard directory ❷. From there we create a File reference to a new subdirectory, /sdcard/unlocking_android ❸ (in Java both files and directories can be represented by the File object). After we have the sub-directory reference we call mkdir() to ensure it is created if it does not already exist ❹.

With the structure we need in place, we follow a similar pattern for the actual file. We instantiate a reference File object ❺, and we call createFile() to create a file on the filesystem ❻. Once we have the File, and we know it exists and we are allowed to write to it (recall files on the sdcard will be world writable by default because it's using a FAT filesystem), we then use a FileInputStream to write some data into the file ❼.

After we create the file and have data in it, we create another File object with the full path to read the data back ❽. Yes, we could use the same File object handle that we had when creating the file, but for the purposes of the example we wanted to explicitly demonstrate starting with a fresh File. With the File reference we then create a FileOutputStream and read back the data that was earlier stored in the file ❾.

As you can see, working with files on the SD card is pretty much standard java.io.File fare. This does entail a good bit of boilerplate Java code to make a robust solution, with permissions and error checking every step of the way and log-ging about what is happening, but it is still simple and powerful. If you need to do a lot of File handling, you will probably want to create some simple local utilities for wrapping the mundane tasks so you don't have to repeat them over and over again (opening files, writing to them, creating them, and so on). You may want to look at using or porting something like the Apache commons.io package, which includes a FileUtils class that handles these types of tasks and more.

The SD card example completes our exploration in this section, where we have seen that there are various ways to store different types of file data on the Android platform. If you have static elements that are predefined you can use res/raw, if you have XML files you can use res/xml. You can also work directly with the filesystem by creating, modifying, and retrieving data in files (either in the local internal filesystem or on the SD card if available).

Another way to deal with data, one that may be more appropriate for many situations (such as when you need to share relational data across applications), is through the use of a database.

5.3 *Persisting data to a database*

One nice convenience that the Android platform provides is the fact that a relational database is built in. SQLite doesn't have all of the features of larger client/server database products, but it does cover just about anything you might need for local data storage, while being easy to deal with and quick.

In this section we are going to cover working with the built-in SQLite database system, from creating and querying a database to upgrading and working with the sqlite3 tool that is available in the Android Debug Bridge (adb) shell. Once again we will do this in the context of the WeatherReporter application we began in chapter 4. This application uses a database to store the user's saved locations and persists user preferences for each location. The screen shot shown in figure 5.4 displays this saved data for the user to select from; when the user selects a location, data is retrieved from the database and a location weather report is shown.

To see how this comes together we will begin with what it takes to create the database Weather-Reporter uses.

Figure 5.4   The WeatherReporter Saved Locations screen, which pulls data from a SQLite database

5.3.1 *Building and accessing a database*

To use SQLite you have to know a bit about SQL usage in general. If you need to brush up on the background of the basic commands—CREATE, INSERT, UPDATE, DELETE, and SELECT—then you may want to take a quick look at the SQLite documentation (http://www.sqlite.org/lang.html).

For our purposes we are going to jump right in and build a database helper class that our application will use. We are creating a helper class so that the details concerning creating and upgrading our database, opening and closing connections, and running through specific queries are all encapsulated in one place and not otherwise exposed or repeated in our application code. This is so our `Activity` and `Service` classes can later use simple `get` and `insert` methods, with specific bean objects representing our model, or `Collections` rather than database-specific abstractions (such as the Android `Cursor` object that represents a query result set). You can think of this class as a miniature Data Access Layer (DAL).

The first part of our `DBHelper` class, which includes a few inner classes you will learn about, is shown in listing 5.10.

Listing 5.10 Portion of the `DBHelper` class showing the `DBOpenHelper` inner class

```java
public class DBHelper {

    public static final String DEVICE_ALERT_ENABLED_ZIP = "DAEZ99";
    public static final String DB_NAME = "w_alert";
    public static final String DB_TABLE = "w_alert_loc";         Use constants for  ❶
    public static final int DB_VERSION = 3;                      database properties

    private static final String CLASSNAME = DBHelper.class.getSimpleName();
    private static final String[] COLS = new String[]
      { "_id", "zip", "city", "region", "lastalert", "alertenabled" };

    private SQLiteDatabase db;
    private final DBOpenHelper dbOpenHelper;

    public static class Location {          Define inner  ❷
        public long id;                     Location bean
        public long lastalert;
        public int alertenabled;
        public String zip;
        public String city;
        public String region;

        . . . Location constructors and toString omitted for brevity
    }

    private static class DBOpenHelper extends        Define inner  ❸
        SQLiteOpenHelper {                           DBOpenHelper class

        private static final String DB_CREATE = "CREATE TABLE "
            + DBHelper.DB_TABLE                                        Define SQL  ❹
            + " (_id INTEGER PRIMARY KEY, zip TEXT UNIQUE NOT NULL,"   query for
            + "city TEXT, region TEXT, lastalert INTEGER, "           database
            + "alertenabled INTEGER);";                               creation

        public DBOpenHelper(Context context, String dbName, int version) {
            super(context, DBHelper.DB_NAME, null, DBHelper.DB_VERSION);
        }

        @Override                                       Override helper  ❺
        public void onCreate(SQLiteDatabase db) {        callbacks
            try {
                db.execSQL(DBOpenHelper.DB_CREATE);
            } catch (SQLException e) {
```

```
        Log.e(Constants.LOGTAG, DBHelper.CLASSNAME, e);
    }
}

@Override
public void onOpen(SQLiteDatabase db) {
    super.onOpen(db);
}

@Override
public void onUpgrade(SQLiteDatabase db, int oldVersion,
    int newVersion) {
    db.execSQL("DROP TABLE IF EXISTS " + DBHelper.DB_TABLE);
    this.onCreate(db);
}
}
```

5 Override helper callbacks

Within our DBHelper class we first have a series of constants that define important static values relating to the database we want to work with, such as database name, database version, and table name **1**. Then we show several of the most important parts of the database helper class that we have created for the WeatherReporter application, the inner classes.

The first inner class is a simple Location bean that is used to represent a user's selected location to save **2**. This class intentionally does not have accessors and mutators, because these add overhead and we don't really need them when we will use this bean only within our application (we won't expose it). The second inner class is a SQLiteOpenHelper implementation **3**.

Our DBOpenHelper inner class extends SQLiteOpenHelper, which is a class that Android provides to help with creating, upgrading, and opening databases. Within this class we are including a String that represents the CREATE query we will use to build our database table; this shows the exact columns and types our table will have **4**. The data types we are using are fairly self-explanatory; most of the time you will use INTEGER and TEXT types, as we have (if you need more information about the other types SQLite supports, please see the documentation: http://www.sqlite.org/datatype3.html). Also within DBOpenHelper we are implementing several key SQLite-OpenHelper callback methods, notably onCreate and onUpgrade (onOpen is also supported, but we aren't using it) **5**. We will explain how these callbacks come into play and why this class is so helpful in the second part of our DBHelper (the outer class), which is shown in listing 5.11.

Listing 5.11 Portion of the DBHelper class showing convenience methods

```
public DBHelper(Context context) {
    this.dbOpenHelper = new DBOpenHelper(context, "WR_DATA", 1);
    this.establishDb();
}
private void establishDb() {
    if (this.db == null) {
```

2 Provide establishDb

Create DBOpenHelper instance 1

```
            this.db = this.dbOpenHelper.getWritableDatabase();
        }
    }

    public void cleanup() {          ◄─┐    Provide cleanup
        if (this.db != null) {          ❸   method
            this.db.close();
            this.db = null;
        }
    }

    public void insert(Location location) {              ◄────────────────┐
        ContentValues values = new ContentValues();
        values.put("zip", location.zip);
        values.put("city", location.city);
        values.put("region", location.region);
        values.put("lastalert", location.lastalert);
        values.put("alertenabled", location.alertenabled);
        this.db.insert(DBHelper.DB_TABLE, null, values);
    }

    public void update(Location location) {              ◄──────┤
        ContentValues values = new ContentValues();              Provide ❹
        values.put("zip", location.zip);                      convenience
        values.put("city", location.city);                 insert, update,
        values.put("region", location.region);                 delete, get
        values.put("lastalert", location.lastalert);
        values.put("alertenabled", location.alertenabled);
        this.db.update(DBHelper.DB_TABLE, values, "_id=" + location.id, null);
    }

    public void delete(long id) {                        ◄────────┤
        this.db.delete(DBHelper.DB_TABLE, "_id=" + id, null);
    }

    public void delete(String zip) {                     ◄────────┤
        this.db.delete(DBHelper.DB_TABLE, "zip='" + zip + "'", null);
    }

    public Location get(String zip) {                    ◄────────┘
        Cursor c = null;
        Location location = null;
        try {
            c = this.db.query(true, DBHelper.DB_TABLE, DBHelper.COLS,
                "zip = '" + zip + "'", null, null, null, null,
                    null);
            if (c.getCount() > 0) {
                c.moveToFirst();
                location = new Location();
                location.id = c.getLong(0);
                location.zip = c.getString(1);
                location.city = c.getString(2);
                location.region = c.getString(3);
                location.lastalert = c.getLong(4);
                location.alertenabled = c.getInt(5);
            }
        } catch (SQLException e) {
```

```
            Log.v(Constants.LOGTAG, DBHelper.CLASSNAME, e);
      } finally {
         if (c != null && !c.isClosed()) {
            c.close();
         }
      }
      return location;
   }
   public List<Location> getAll() {
      ArrayList<Location> ret = new ArrayList<Location>();
      Cursor c = null;
      try {
         c = this.db.query(DBHelper.DB_TABLE, DBHelper.COLS, null,
           null, null, null, null);
         int numRows = c.getCount();
         c.moveToFirst();
         for (int i = 0; i < numRows; ++i) {
            Location location = new Location();
            location.id = c.getLong(0);
            location.zip = c.getString(1);
            location.city = c.getString(2);
            location.region = c.getString(3);
            location.lastalert = c.getLong(4);
            location.alertenabled = c.getInt(5);
            if (!location.zip.equals(DBHelper.DEVICE_ALERT_ENABLED_ZIP)) {
               ret.add(location);
            }
            c.moveToNext();
         }
      } catch (SQLException e) {
         Log.v(Constants.LOGTAG, DBHelper.CLASSNAME, e);
      } finally {
         if (c != null && !c.isClosed()) {
            c.close();
         }
      }
      return ret;
   }

   . . . getAllAlertEnabled omitted for brevity
}
```

❺ Provide additional get methods

Our DBHelper class contains a member-level variable reference to a SQLiteDatabase object, as we saw in listing 5.10 (the first half of this class). This object is the Android database workhorse. It is used to open database connections, to execute SQL statements, and more.

Then the DBOpenHelper inner class we also saw in the first part of the DBHelper class listing is instantiated inside the constructor ❶. From there the dbOpenHelper is used, inside the establishDb method if the db reference is null, to call openDatabase with the current Context, database name, and database version ❷. This establishes db as an instance of SQLiteDatabase through DBOpenHelper.

Although you can also just open a database connection directly on your own, using the open helper in this way invokes the provided callbacks and makes the process easier. With this technique, when we try to open our database connection, it is automatically created or upgraded (or just returned), if necessary, through our DBOpenHelper. While using a DBOpenHelper entails extra steps up front, once you have it in place it is extremely handy when you need to modify your table structure (you can simply increment your version and do what you need to do in the onUpgrade callback—without this you would have to manually alter and/or remove and re-create your existing structure).

Another important thing to provide in a helper class like this is a cleanup method ❸. This method is used by callers who can invoke it when they pause, in order to close connections and free up resources.

After the cleanup method we then see the raw SQL convenience methods that encapsulate the operations our helper provides. In this class we have methods to insert, update, delete and get data ❹. We also have a few additional specialized get and get all methods ❺. Within these methods you get a feel for how the db object is used to run queries. The SQLiteDatabase class itself has many convenience methods, such as insert, update, and delete—which we are wrapping—and it provides direct query access that returns a Cursor over a result set.

> **Databases are package private**
>
> Unlike the SharedPreferences we saw earlier, you can't make a database WORLD_READABLE. Each database is accessible only by the package in which it was created—this means accessible only to the process that created it. If you need to pass data across processes, you can use AIDL/Binder (as in chapter 4) or create a ContentProvider (as we will discuss next), but you can't use a database directly across the process/package boundary.

Typically you can get a lot of mileage and utility from basic steps relating to the SQLiteDatabase class, as we have here, and by using it you can create a very useful and fast data-storage mechanism for your Android applications. The final thing we need to discuss with regard to databases is the sqlite3 tool, which you can use to manipulate data outside your application.

5.3.2   *Using the sqlite3 tool*

When you create a database for an application in Android, the files for that database are created on the device in the /data/data/[PACKAGE_NAME]/database/db.name location. These files are SQLite proprietary, but there is a way to manipulate, dump, restore, and otherwise work with your databases through these files in the ADB shell—the sqlite3 tool.

This tool is accessible through the shell; you can get to it by issuing the following commands on the command line (remember to use your own package name; here we are using the package name for the WeatherReporter sample application):

```
cd [ANDROID_HOME]/tools
adb shell
sqlite3 /data/data/com.msi.manning.chapter4/databases/w_alert.db
```

Once you are in the shell prompt (you have the #), you can then issue sqlite3 commands; .help should get you started (if you need more, see the tool's documentation: http://www.sqlite.org/sqlite.html). From the tool you can issue basic commands, such as SELECT or INSERT, or you can go further and CREATE or ALTER tables. This tool comes in handy for basic poking around and troubleshooting and to .dump and .load data. As with many command-line SQL tools, it takes some time to get used to the format, but there is no better way to back up or load your data. (If you need that facility—in most cases with mobile development you really shouldn't have a huge database. Keep in mind that this tool is available only through the development shell; it's not something you will be able to use to load a real application with data.)

Now that we have shown how to use the SQLite support provided in Android, from creating and accessing tables to store data, to investigating databases with the provided tools in the shell, the next thing we need to cover is the last aspect of handling data on the platform, and that is building and using a ContentProvider.

5.4 *Working with ContentProvider classes*

A ContentProvider is used in Android to share data between different applications. We have already discussed the fact that each application runs in its own process (normally), and data and files stored there are not accessible by other applications by default. We have explained that you can make preferences and files available across application boundaries with the correct permissions and if each application knows the context/path. Nevertheless, that is a limited solution for related applications that already know details about one another. In contrast, with a ContentProvider you can publish and expose a particular data type for other applications to use to query, add, update, and delete, and those applications don't need to have any prior knowledge of paths or resources or even know who or what is providing the content.

The canonical ContentProvider example in Android is the contacts list—the list of name, address, and phone information stored in the phone. You can access this data from any application using a specific URI, content://contacts/people/, and a series of methods provided by the Activity and ContentResolver classes to retrieve and store data. You will learn more about ContentResolver as we explore provider details. One other data-related concept that a ContentProvider brings along with it is the Cursor, the same object we used previously when dealing with SQLite database result sets. Cursor is also returned by the provider query methods you will learn about shortly.

In this section we are going to build several small sample applications to help us look at all of the ContentProvider angles. First we will build a single Activity-based application, which we are calling ProviderExplorer, that will work with the built-in contacts database to query, add, update, and delete data. Then we will create another application that implements its own ContentProvider and includes a similar explorer-type

ContentProvider leaks a Cursor

Returning a `Cursor` is one of the quirks of a `ContentProvider`. Exposing a `Cursor` from a `ContentProvider` is a fairly "leaky" abstraction, and it makes for an inconsistent API, as you shall learn. Cursor is part of the `android.database` package, which implies you are working with database records and binds you to certain database concepts when you get results. Yet the entire idea behind a `ContentProvider` is supposed to be that it is backend agnostic. That is to say you should be able to implement a `ContentProvider` and not use a database to get and store data within it if the situation warrants (the current Android documentation contradicts itself on this point; in one place it says not using a database is possible, and in another it says it is not). Currently, regardless of the merits or demerits, you will need to learn to deal with `Cursor`-based results and SQL constructs when working with `ContentProvider` calls.

`Activity` to manipulate that data as well. Along with covering these fundamentals, we will discuss other built-in providers on the platform beyond contacts.

The ProviderExplorer application we are going to build here will ultimately have one large scrollable screen, which is depicted in figure 5.5. Keep in mind that we are focusing on covering all the bases in one `Activity`—exposing all of the `ContentProvider`

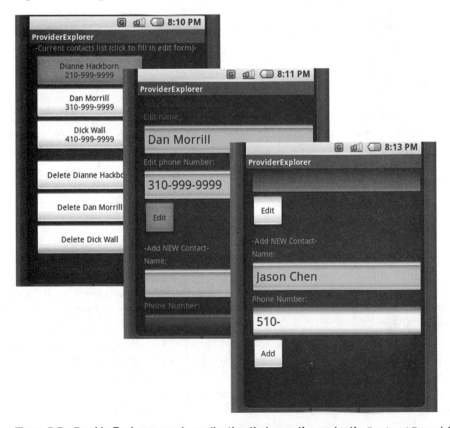

Figure 5.5   ProviderExplorer sample application that uses the contact's `ContentProvider`

operations in a single place—rather than on aesthetics or usability (this application is downright ugly, but that's intentional—at least this time).

To begin we will explore the syntax of URIs and the combinations and paths used to perform different types of operations with the `ContentProvider` and `Content-Resolver` classes.

5.4.1 *Understanding URI representations and manipulating records*

Each `ContentProvider` is required to expose a unique `CONTENT_URI` that is used to identify the content type it will handle. This URI is used in one of two forms, singular or plural, as shown in table 5.1, to query data.

Table 5.1 `ContentProvider` **URI variations for different purposes**

URI	Purpose
content://contacts/people/	Return `List` of all people from provider registered to handle content://contacts
content://contacts/people/1	Return or manipulate single person with ID 1 from provider registered to handle content://contacts

The URI concept comes into play whether or not you are querying data or adding or deleting it, as you shall see. To get familiar with this process we will take a look at the basic CRUD data-manipulation methods and see how they are carried out with the contacts database and respective URIs.

We will step through each task to highlight the details: create, read, update, and delete. To do this concisely we will build one `Activity` in the ProviderExplorer example application that performs all of these actions. In the next few sections we will take a look at different parts of this `Activity` to focus on each task.

The first thing we need to do is set up a bit of scaffolding for the contacts provider we will be using; this is done in the first portion of listing 5.12, the start of the `ProviderExplorer` class.

Listing 5.12 Start of `Activity` that sets up needed inner classes

```
public class ProviderExplorer extends Activity {
    private EditText addName;
    private EditText addPhoneNumber;
    private EditText editName;
    private EditText editPhoneNumber;
    private Button addContact;
    private Button editContact;

    private long contactId;                    ❶ Include inner
                                                  Contact bean
    private class Contact {
        public long id;
        public String name;
        public String phoneNumber;

        public Contact(long id, String name, String phoneNumber) {
```

```
      this.id = id;
      this.name = name;
      this.phoneNumber = phoneNumber;
   }

   @Override
   public String toString() {
      return this.name + "\n" + this.phoneNumber;
   }
}
private class ContactButton extends Button {          ❷ Extend Button with
   public Contact contact;                              ContactButton

   public ContactButton(Context ctx, Contact contact) {
      super(ctx);
      this.contact = contact;
   }
}

@Override
public void onCreate(Bundle icicle) {
   super.onCreate(icicle);
   this.setContentView(R.layout.provider_explorer);

   this.addName = (EditText) this.findViewById(R.id.add_name);
   this.addPhoneNumber =
     (EditText) this.findViewById(R.id.add_phone_number);
   this.editName =
     (EditText) this.findViewById(R.id.edit_name);
   this.editPhoneNumber =
     (EditText) this.findViewById(R.id.edit_phone_number);

   this.addContact =
     (Button) this.findViewById(R.id.add_contact_button);
   this.addContact.setOnClickListener(new OnClickListener() {
      public void onClick(final View v) {
         ProviderExplorer.this.addContact();
      }
   });
   this.editContact =
     (Button) this.findViewById(R.id.edit_contact_button);
   this.editContact.setOnClickListener(new OnClickListener() {
      public void onClick(final View v) {
         ProviderExplorer.this.editContact();
      }
   });
}
```

Call addContact and editContact ❹   ❸ **Create anonymous click listeners**

To start out the ProviderExplorer Activity we are creating a simple inner bean class to represent a Contact record (this is not a comprehensive representation, but it does capture the fields we are interested in here) ❶. Then we include another inner class to represent a ContactButton ❷. This class extends Button and includes a reference to a particular Contact.

After we have the add and edit buttons established, we create anonymous OnClickListener implementations ❸ that call the respective add and edit methods when a button is clicked ❹.

That rounds out the setup-related tasks for `ProviderExplorer`. The next thing we need to implement is the `onStart` method, which adds more buttons dynamically for populating edit data and deleting data. This is shown in listing 5.13.

Listing 5.13 onStart portion of the ProviderExplorer `Activity`

```
@Override
public void onStart() {
   super.onStart();
   List<Contact> contacts = this.getContacts();          ←——    ① Get list of
                                                                    contacts
   LinearLayout.LayoutParams params =
     new LinearLayout.LayoutParams(200,
       android.view.ViewGroup.LayoutParams.WRAP_CONTENT);

   if (contacts != null) {
     LinearLayout editLayout =
       (LinearLayout)
         this.findViewById(R.id.edit_buttons_layout);      ←┐
     LinearLayout deleteLayout =                             │    ② Create
       (LinearLayout)                                              dynamic
         this.findViewById(R.id.delete_buttons_layout);    ←┘    layouts
     params.setMargins(10, 0, 0, 0);

     for (Contact c : contacts) {

       ContactButton contactEditButton =
         new ContactButton(this, c);                         ←┐
       contactEditButton.setText(c.toString());               │
       editLayout.addView(contactEditButton, params);         │
       contactEditButton.setOnClickListener(new OnClickListener() {
         public void onClick(final View v) {                  │
           ContactButton view = (ContactButton) v;            │
           editName.setText(view.contact.name);               │
           editPhoneNumber.setText(view.contact.phoneNumber); │
           contactId = view.contact.id;                       │
         }                                                     │
       });                                          Create dynamic ③
                                                        buttons
       ContactButton contactDeleteButton =                    │
         new ContactButton(this, c);                         ←┘
       contactDeleteButton.setText("Delete " + c.name);
       deleteLayout.addView(contactDeleteButton, params);
       contactDeleteButton.setOnClickListener(new OnClickListener() {
         public void onClick(final View v) {
           ContactButton view = (ContactButton) v;
           contactId = view.contact.id;
           deleteContact();
         }
       });
     }
   } else {
     LinearLayout layout =
       (LinearLayout)
         this.findViewById(R.id.edit_buttons_layout);
     TextView empty = new TextView(this);
     empty.setText("No current contacts");
```

```
        layout.addView(empty, params);
    }
}
```

The onStart method makes a call to the getContacts method ❶. This method, which you will see in listing 5.14, returns a List of current Contact objects from the Android contacts database. Once we have the current contacts, we loop through them and dynamically create a layout in code for edit and delete, respectively ❷. After we have the layout within it, we create a few view objects, including a ContactButton to populate an edit form and a button to delete a record ❸. Each button is then manually added to its respective LinearLayout we have referenced through R.java.

Once our onStart method is in place, we have a View to display all the current contacts and all of the buttons, static and dynamic, that we need in order to be able to add, edit, and delete contact data. From there we need to implement the methods to perform these actions—this is where we will use a ContentResolver and other related classes.

Initially we need to populate our display of current contacts, and to do that we need to query for (read) data.

QUERYING DATA

The Activity class has a managedQuery method that is used to make calls into registered ContentProvider classes. When we create our own ContentProvider in section 5.5.3, we will show how a provider is registered with the platform; for now we are going to focus on calling existing providers. Each provider is required to advertise (or *publish*, in Android terms) the CONTENT_URI it supports. To query the contacts provider, as we are doing in listing 5.14, we have to know this URI and then get a Cursor by calling managedQuery.

Listing 5.14   Query details for `ContentProvider` **in the ProviderExplorer** `Activity`

```
private List<Contact> getContacts() {
    List<Contact> results = null;
    long id = 0L;
    String name = null;
    String phoneNumber = null;
    String[] projection = new String[]
      { Contacts.People._ID,                    ❶ Make        ❷ Get
        Contacts.People.NAME,                      projection     ContentResolver
        Contacts.People.NUMBER };                                 reference
    ContentResolver resolver = this.getContentResolver();
    Cursor cur = resolver.query(Contacts.People.CONTENT_URI,     ❸ Get Cursor
        projection, null, null,                                     from
            Contacts.People.DEFAULT_SORT_ORDER);                    resolver
    while (cur.moveToNext()) {
        if (results == null) {                          ❹ Walk results and
            results = new ArrayList<Contact>();            populate data
        }
        id = cur.getLong(cur.getColumnIndex(BaseColumns._ID));
        name = cur.getString(cur.getColumnIndex(PeopleColumns.NAME));
        phoneNumber =
          cur.getString(cur.getColumnIndex(PhonesColumns.NUMBER));
```

```
        results.add(new Contact(id, name, phoneNumber));
    }
    return results;
}
```

The Android contacts database is really a composite of several types of data. A contact includes details of a person (name, company, photo, and the like), one or more phone numbers (each of which has a number, type, label, and such), and other information. A `ContentProvider` typically supplies all the details of the URI and the types it supports as constants in a class. In the `android.provider` package, there is `Contacts` class that corresponds to the contacts provider. This class has nested inner classes that represent `People` and `Phones`. In additional inner classes in those, there are constants that represent fields or columns of data for each type. This structure with all the inner classes can be mind bending at times, but the bottom line is that `Contacts` data ends up in multiple tables, and the values you need to query and manipulate this data come from the inner classes for each type.

The columns we will be using to get and set data are defined in these classes. Here we are going to work with only the people and phones parts of contacts. We start by creating a projection of the columns we want to return as a `String` array ❶. Then we get a reference to the `ContentResolver` we will use ❷. Using the resolver, we obtain a `Cursor` object ❸. Once we have the `Cursor`, which represents the rows in the data we have returned, we iterate over it to create our contact objects ❹.

Managed Cursor

To obtain a `Cursor` reference you can also use the `managedQuery` method of the `Activity` class. A managed `Cursor` is automatically cleaned up when your `Activity` pauses, and it is also restarted when it starts. It is a `Cursor` instance that has its state maintained by the platform in conjunction with the `Activity` lifecycle. This is very helpful, in most cases. If you just need to retrieve data within an `Activity`, you will want to use a managed `Cursor` as opposed to a `ContentResolver`. (We are not using one in the last example, because there we need to do more than retrieve data, and we want to focus on the provider/resolver components.)

The `query` method on the `ContentResolver` class also lets you pass in additional arguments to narrow the results. Specifically, where we passed `null, null` in listing 5.14, you can alternatively pass in a filter to narrow the rows you want to return in the form of an SQL `WHERE` clause and optional replacement tokens for that `Where` clause (injected at each ?). This is somewhat typical SQL usage, so it's easy to work with. The downside comes when you aren't using a database to back your `ContentProvider`. This is where the abstraction leaks like a sieve—though it might be possible to not use a database for a data source, you still have to handle SQL statements in your provider implementation, and you must require that anyone who uses your provider also has to deal with SQL constructs.

Now that we have covered how to query for data to return results, we look at inserting new data—adding a row.

INSERTING DATA

In listing 5.15 we show the next part of the `ProviderExplorer` class, the `addContact` method. This is used with the add form elements in our `Activity` to insert a new row of data into the contacts-related tables.

Listing 5.15   Insert details for `ContentProvider` in the `ProviderExplorer` `Activity`

```
private void addContact() {
    ContentResolver resolver = this.getContentResolver();        Get
    ContentValues values = new ContentValues();                  ContentResolver
                                                                 ❶ handle

    values.put(Contacts.People.NAME,
      this.addName.getText().toString());
    Uri personUri =                                              Use ContentValues
      Contacts.People.createPersonInMyContactsGroup(           ❷ for query values
        resolver, values);
                                                                 Use Contacts helper
    values.clear();                                            ❸ to create person
    Uri phoneUri = Uri.withAppendedPath(personUri,
      Contacts.People.Phones.CONTENT_DIRECTORY);
    values.put(Contacts.Phones.TYPE, Phones.TYPE_MOBILE);        Append person
    values.put(Contacts.Phones.NUMBER,                         ❹ Uri for phone Uri
      this.addPhoneNumber.getText().toString());

    resolver.insert(phoneUri, values);      ❺ Insert data using resolver

    this.startActivity(new Intent(this, ProviderExplorer.class));
}
```

The first thing to see in the `addContact` method is that we are getting a `ContentResolver` reference ❶ and using a `ContentValues` object to map column names with values ❷. This is an Android-specific type of map object. After we have our variables in place, we use the special `createPersonInMyContactsGroup` helper method on the `Contacts.People` class to both insert a record and return the `Uri` ❸. This method uses the resolver for us, under the covers, and performs an insert. The `Contacts` class structure has a few helper methods sprinkled throughout (see the Javadocs). These are used to cut down on the amount of code you have to know and write to perform common tasks, such as adding a contact to the My Contacts group (the built-in group that the phone displays by default in the contacts app).

After we have created a new contact `People` record, we append new data to that existing `Uri` in order to create a phone record associated with the same person ❹. This is a nice touch that the API provides. You can often append and/or build onto an existing `Uri` in order to access different aspects of the data structure. After we have the `Uri` and have reset and updated the values object, we directly insert a phone record this time, using the `ContentResolver` insert method (no helper for this one) ❺.

After adding data, we need to look at how to update or edit existing data.

UPDATING DATA

To update a row of data you first obtain a `Cursor` row reference to it and then use the update-related `Cursor` methods. This is shown in listing 5.16.

Listing 5.16   Update details for `ContentProvider` in the `ProviderExplorer Activity`

```
private void editContact() {
   ContentResolver resolver = this.getContentResolver();
   ContentValues values = new ContentValues();

   Uri personUri = Contacts.People.CONTENT_URI.buildUpon()      ❶ Append to an
     .appendPath(Long.toString(this.contactId)).build();          existing Uri

   values.put(Contacts.People.NAME,                             ❷ Update values
     this.editName.getText().toString());                         to change data
   resolver.update(personUri, values, null, null);             Call
                                                             ❸ resolver.update
   values.clear();
   Uri phoneUri = Uri.withAppendedPath(personUri,
     Contacts.People.Phones.CONTENT_DIRECTORY + "/1");           After updated,
   values.put(Contacts.Phones.NUMBER,                         ❹ get Uri
     this.editPhoneNumber.getText().toString());
   resolver.update(phoneUri, values, null, null);

   this.startActivity(new Intent(this, ProviderExplorer.class));
}
```

In updating data, we start with the standard `People.CONTENT_URI` and append a specific ID path to it using `UriBuilder` ❶. `UriBuilder` is a very helpful class that uses the builder pattern to allow you to construct and access the components of a `Uri` object. After we have the URI ready, we update the values data ❷ and call `resolver.update` to make the update happen ❸. As you can see, the update process when using a `ContentResolver` is pretty much the same as the create process—with the noted exception that the `update` method allows you to again pass in a `WHERE` clause and replacement tokens (SQL style).

For this example, after we have updated the person's name, we need to once again obtain the correct `Uri` to also update the associated phone record. We do this by again appending additional `Uri` path data to an object we already have, and we slap on the specific ID we want ❹. Outside of example purposes there would be more work to do here in order to determine which phone record for the contact needs to be updated (here we are using ID 1 as a shortcut).

Although we are updating only single records based on a specific URI, keep in mind that you can update a set of records using the nonspecific form of the URI and the `WHERE` clause.

Lastly, in our look at manipulating data through a `ContentProvider`, we need to implement our `delete` method.

DELETING DATA

To delete data we will return to the `ContentResolver` object we used to insert data. This time we will call the `delete` method, as seen in listing 5.17.

Listing 5.17   Delete details for `ContentProvider` in the `ProviderExplorer` `Activity`

```
private void deleteContact() {
    Uri personUri = Contacts.People.CONTENT_URI;
    personUri = personUri.buildUpon().
        appendPath(Long.toString(contactId)).build();       ❶  Use UriBuilder
    getContentResolver().delete(personUri, null, null);          to append path

    startActivity(new Intent(this, ProviderExplorer.class));
    }
}
                                    Call getContentResolver.delete  ❷
```

The delete concept is pretty simple, once you have the rest of the process in hand. Again we use the `UriBuilder` approach to set up a `Uri` for a specific record ❶, and then we obtain a `ContentResolver` reference, this time inline with our `delete` method call ❷.

What if the content changes after the fact?

When you use a `ContentProvider`, which by definition is accessible by any application on the system, and you make a query, you are getting only the current state of the data back. The data could change after your call, so how do you stay up to date? To be notified when a `Cursor` changes, you can use the `ContentObserver` API. `ContentObserver` supports a set of callbacks that are invoked when data changes. `Cursor` has `register` and `unregister` methods for `ContentObserver` objects.

After having seen how the built-in contacts provider works, you may also want to check out the `android.provider` package in the Javadocs, as it lists more built-in providers. Now that we have covered a bit about using a built-in provider and have the CRUD fundamentals under our belt, we will look at the other side of the coin—creating a `ContentProvider`.

5.4.2   *Creating a ContentProvider*

In this section we are going to build a provider that will handle data responsibilities for a generic `Widget` object we will define. This object is simple, with a name, type, category, and other members, and intentionally generic, so we can focus on the *how* here and not the *why*. (The reasons why you might implement a provider in real life are many; for the purposes of this example, our type will be the mythical `Widget`.)

To create a `ContentProvider` extend that class and implement the required abstract methods. We will show how this is done specifically in a moment. Before getting to that, it is a good idea to first define a provider constants class that defines the `CONTENT_URI` and `MIME_TYPE` your provider will support. In addition, you can place the column names your provider will handle here in one class (or you can use multiple nested inner classes as the built-in contacts system does—we find a flatter approach to be easier to understand).

DEFINING A CONTENT_URI AND MIME_TYPE

In listing 5.18, as a prerequisite to extending the `ContentProvider` class for a custom provider, we have defined needed constants for our `Widget` type.

Listing 5.18 WidgetProvider constants, including columns and URI

```
public final class Widget implements BaseColumns {        ◄─── ① Extend BaseColumns

    public static final String MIME_DIR_PREFIX =
      "vnd.android.cursor.dir";                          ◄───
    public static final String MIME_ITEM_PREFIX =           ② Define MIME prefix
      "vnd.android.cursor.item";                              for multiple items
    public static final String MIME_ITEM = "vnd.msi.widget"; ◄───
    public static final String MIME_TYPE_SINGLE =                            Define
      MIME_ITEM_PREFIX + "/" + MIME_ITEM;         Define MIME                 MIME
    public static final String MIME_TYPE_MULTIPLE =    type    ④             prefix
      MIME_DIR_PREFIX + "/" + MIME_ITEM;          ◄───                        for
                                                                             single
                               Define authority ⑤            ③ item
    public static final String AUTHORITY =
      "com.msi.manning.chapter5.Widget";          ◄───     ⑥ Define path for
    public static final String PATH_SINGLE = "widgets/#";  ◄───  single item
    public static final String PATH_MULTIPLE = "widgets";  ◄───
    public static final Uri CONTENT_URI =              ⑦ Define path for
      Uri.parse("content://" + AUTHORITY + "/" + PATH_MULTIPLE);  ◄───  multiple items

    public static final String DEFAULT_SORT_ORDER = "updated DESC";

    public static final String NAME = "name";    Define  ⑨          Define
    public static final String TYPE = "type";    columns            ultimate
    public static final String CATEGORY = "category";             CONTENT_URI  ⑧
    public static final String CREATED = "created";
    public static final String UPDATED = "updated";
}
```

In our `Widget`-related provider constants class we first extend the `BaseColumns` class from Android ①. This gives our class a few base constants such as `_ID`. Next we define the `MIME_TYPE` prefix for a set of multiple items ② and a single item ③. This is outlined in the Android documentation; the convention is that `vnd.android.cursor.dir` represents multiple items, and `vnd.android.cursor.item` represents a single item. Thereafter we define a specific MIME item and combine it with the single and multiple paths to create two `MIME_TYPE` representations ④.

Once we have the MIME details out of the way, we define the authority ⑤ and path for both single ⑥ and multiple ⑦ items that will be used in the `CONTENT_URI` callers we will pass in to use our provider. The multiple-item URI is ultimately the one that callers will start from and the one we publish (they can append specific items from there) ⑧.

After taking care of all the other details, we define column names that represent the variable types in our `Widget` object, which are also going to fields in the database table we will use ⑨. Callers will use these constants to get and set specific fields. That leads us to the next part of the process, extending `ContentProvider`.

EXTENDING CONTENTPROVIDER

In listing 5.19 we show the beginning of our ContentProvider implementation class, WidgetProvider. In this part of the class we do some housekeeping relating to the database we will use and the URI we are supporting.

> **Listing 5.19   The first portion of the WidgetProvider ContentProvider**

```java
public class WidgetProvider extends ContentProvider {            ①  Extend ContentProvider

    private static final String CLASSNAME =
        WidgetProvider.class.getSimpleName();
    private static final int WIDGETS = 1;
    private static final int WIDGET = 2;                          ②  Define database
    public static final String DB_NAME = "widgets_db";              constants
    public static final String DB_TABLE = "widget";
    public static final int DB_VERSION = 1;

    private static UriMatcher URI_MATCHER = null;               ③  Use UriMatcher
    private static HashMap<String, String> PROJECTION_MAP;
                                                                   ④  Include
    private SQLiteDatabase db;        Use SQLiteDatabase              projection Map
                               ⑤  reference
    static {
        WidgetProvider.URI_MATCHER = new UriMatcher(UriMatcher.NO_MATCH);
        WidgetProvider.URI_MATCHER.addURI(Widget.AUTHORITY,
          Widget.PATH_MULTIPLE, WidgetProvider.WIDGETS);
        WidgetProvider.URI_MATCHER.addURI(Widget.AUTHORITY,
          Widget.PATH_SINGLE, WidgetProvider.WIDGET);

        WidgetProvider.PROJECTION_MAP = new HashMap<String, String>();
        WidgetProvider.PROJECTION_MAP.put(BaseColumns._ID, "_id");
        WidgetProvider.PROJECTION_MAP.put(Widget.NAME, "name");
        WidgetProvider.PROJECTION_MAP.put(Widget.TYPE, "type");
        WidgetProvider.PROJECTION_MAP.put(Widget.CATEGORY, "category");
        WidgetProvider.PROJECTION_MAP.put(Widget.CREATED, "created");
        WidgetProvider.PROJECTION_MAP.put(Widget.UPDATED, "updated");
    }

    private static class DBOpenHelper extends SQLiteOpenHelper {
        private static final String DB_CREATE = "CREATE TABLE "
            + WidgetProvider.DB_TABLE
            + " (_id INTEGER PRIMARY KEY, name TEXT UNIQUE NOT NULL,"
              + "type TEXT, category TEXT, updated INTEGER, created"
              + "INTEGER);";                           Create and
                                                       open database  ⑥
        public DBOpenHelper(Context context) {
            super(context, WidgetProvider.DB_NAME, null,
              WidgetProvider.DB_VERSION);
        }

        @Override
        public void onCreate(SQLiteDatabase db) {
            try {
                db.execSQL(DBOpenHelper.DB_CREATE);
            } catch (SQLException e) {
                // log and or handle
            }
```

```
      }
      @Override
      public void onOpen(SQLiteDatabase db) {
      }

      @Override
      public void onUpgrade(SQLiteDatabase db, int oldVersion,
        int newVersion) {
        db.execSQL("DROP TABLE IF EXISTS "
          + WidgetProvider.DB_TABLE);
        this.onCreate(db);
      }
    }

    @Override                              ❼  Override onCreate
    public boolean onCreate() {    ◄──┘
      DBOpenHelper dbHelper = new DBOpenHelper(this.getContext());
      this.db = dbHelper.getWritableDatabase();

      if (this.db == null) {
        return false;
      } else {
        return true;
      }
    }

    @Override                                         ❽  Implement
    public String getType(Uri uri) {      ◄──┘           getType method
      switch (WidgetProvider.URI_MATCHER.match(uri)) {
      case WIDGETS:
        return Widget.MIME_TYPE_MULTIPLE;
      case WIDGET:
        return Widget.MIME_TYPE_SINGLE;
      default:
        throw new IllegalArgumentException("Unknown URI " + uri);
      }
    }
```

Our provider extends ContentProvider, which defines the methods we will need to implement ❶. Then we use several database-related constants to define the database name and table we will use ❷. After that we include a UriMatcher ❸, which we will use when matching types in a moment, and a projection Map for field names ❹.

We include a reference to a SQLiteDatabase object; this is what we will use to store and retrieve the data that our provider handles ❺. This database is created, opened, and upgraded using a SQLiteOpenHelper in an inner class ❻. We have used this helper pattern before, when we worked directly with the database in listing 5.14. The onCreate method of our provider is where the open helper is used to set up the database reference ❼.

After our setup-related steps we come to the first method a ContentProvider requires us to implement, getType ❽. This method is used by the provider to resolve each passed-in Uri to determine if it is supported and if so which type of data the current call is requesting (a single item or the entire set). The MIME_TYPE String we return here is based on the constants we defined in our Widget class.

The next steps we need to cover are the remaining required methods to implement to satisfy the ContentProvider contract. These methods, which are shown in listing 5.20, correspond to the CRUD-related activities used with the contacts provider in the previous section: query, insert, update, and delete.

Listing 5.20 The second portion of the WidgetProvider ContentProvider

```
@Override
public Cursor query(Uri uri, String[] projection,
  String selection, String[] selectionArgs,
    String sortOrder) {
    SQLiteQueryBuilder queryBuilder = new SQLiteQueryBuilder();
    String orderBy = null;

    switch (WidgetProvider.URI_MATCHER.match(uri)) {
    case WIDGETS:
       queryBuilder.setTables(WidgetProvider.DB_TABLE);
       queryBuilder.setProjectionMap(WidgetProvider.PROJECTION_MAP);
       break;
    case WIDGET:
       queryBuilder.setTables(WidgetProvider.DB_TABLE);
       queryBuilder.appendWhere("_id="
        + uri.getPathSegments().get(1));
       break;
    default:
       throw new IllegalArgumentException("Unknown URI " + uri);
    }

    if (TextUtils.isEmpty(sortOrder)) {
       orderBy = Widget.DEFAULT_SORT_ORDER;
    } else {
       orderBy = sortOrder;
    }

    Cursor c = queryBuilder.query(this.db, projection,
       selection, selectionArgs, null, null,
       orderBy);
    c.setNotificationUri(
      this.getContext().getContentResolver(), uri);
    return c;
}

@Override
public Uri insert(Uri uri, ContentValues initialValues) {
    long rowId = 0L;
    ContentValues values = null;
    if (initialValues != null) {
      values = new ContentValues(initialValues);
    } else {
      values = new ContentValues();
    }

    if (WidgetProvider.URI_MATCHER.match(uri) !=
      WidgetProvider.WIDGETS) {
      throw new IllegalArgumentException("Unknown URI " + uri);
```

① Use query builder

② Set up query based on URI

③ Perform query to get Cursor

④ Set notification Uri on Cursor

⑤ Use ContentValues in insert method

```
    }
    Long now = System.currentTimeMillis();

    . . . omit defaulting of values for brevity

    rowId = this.db.insert(WidgetProvider.DB_TABLE, "widget_hack",
      values);
    if (rowId > 0) {
      Uri result = ContentUris.withAppendedId(Widget.CONTENT_URI,
        rowId);
      this.getContext().getContentResolver().notifyChange(result,
        null);
      return result;
    }
    throw new SQLException("Failed to insert row into " + uri);
  }

  @Override
  public int update(Uri uri, ContentValues values, String selection,
    String[] selectionArgs) {
    int count = 0;
    switch (WidgetProvider.URI_MATCHER.match(uri)) {
    case WIDGETS:
      count = this.db.update(WidgetProvider.DB_TABLE, values,
        selection, selectionArgs);
      break;
    case WIDGET:
      String segment = uri.getPathSegments().get(1);
      String where = "";
      if (!TextUtils.isEmpty(selection)) {
        where = " AND (" + selection + ")";
      }
      count = this.db.update(WidgetProvider.DB_TABLE, values,
          "_id=" + segment + where, selectionArgs);
      break;
    default:
      throw new IllegalArgumentException("Unknown URI " + uri);
    }
    this.getContext().getContentResolver().notifyChange(uri, null);
    return count;
  }

  @Override
  public int delete(
  Uri uri, String selection, String[] selectionArgs) {
    int count;

    switch (WidgetProvider.URI_MATCHER.match(uri)) {
    case WIDGETS:
      count = this.db.delete(WidgetProvider.DB_TABLE, selection,
        selectionArgs);
      break;
    case WIDGET:
      String segment = uri.getPathSegments().get(1);
      String where = "";
      if (!TextUtils.isEmpty(selection)) {
```

⑥ Call database insert

Get Uri to return ⑦

⑧ Notify listeners data was inserted

⑨ Provide update method

⑩ Provide delete method

```
            where = " AND (" + selection + ")";
        }
        count = this.db.delete(WidgetProvider.DB_TABLE,
            "_id=" + segment + where, selectionArgs);
        break;
    default:
        throw new IllegalArgumentException("Unknown URI " + uri);
    }
    this.getContext().getContentResolver().notifyChange(uri, null);
    return count;
    }
}
```

In the last part of our WidgetProvider class we show how the ContentProvider methods are implemented. These are the same methods but a different provider that we called earlier in our ProviderExplorer example.

First we use a SQLQueryBuilder inside the query method to append the projection map passed in ❶ and any SQL clauses, along with the correct URI based on our matcher ❷, before we make the actual query and get a handle on a Cursor to return ❸.

At the end of the query method we use the setNotificationUri method to set the returned Uri to be watched for changes ❹. This is an event-based mechanism that can be used to keep track of when Cursor data items are changed, regardless of how changes are made.

Next we see the insert method, where the passed-in ContentValues object is validated and populated with default values if not present ❺. After the values are ready, we call the database insert method ❻ and get the resulting Uri to return with the appended ID of the new record ❼. After the insert is complete, another notification system is in use, this time for ContentResolver. Here, since we have made a data change, we are informing the ContentResolver what happened so that any registered listeners can be updated ❽.

After the insert method is complete, we come to the update ❾ and delete methods ❿. These repeat many of the concepts we have already used. First they match the Uri passed in to a single element or the set, then they call the respective update and delete methods on the database object. Again, at the end of these methods we notify listeners that the data has changed.

Implementing the needed provider methods completes our class. This provider, which now serves the Widget data type, can be used from any application to query, insert, update, or delete data, once we have registered it as a provider with the platform. This is done using the application manifest, which we will look at next.

PROVIDER MANIFESTS

In order for the platform to be aware of the content providers that are available and what data types they represent, they must be defined in an application manifest file and installed on the platform. The manifest for our provider is shown in listing 5.21.

Listing 5.21 WidgetProvider AndroidManifest.xml file

```xml
<?xml version="1.0" encoding="utf-8"?>
<manifest xmlns:android="http://schemas.android.com/apk/res/android"
   package="com.msi.manning.chapter5.widget">
   <application android:icon="@drawable/icon"
      android:label="@string/app_short_name">
      <activity android:name=".WidgetExplorer"
         android:label="@string/app_name">
         <intent-filter>
            <action android:name="android.intent.action.MAIN" />
            <category android:name="android.intent.category.LAUNCHER" />
         </intent-filter>
      </activity>

      <provider android:name="WidgetProvider"
         android:authorities=
            "com.msi.manning.chapter5.Widget" />
   </application>
</manifest>
```

❶ Use provider element to define class and authority

The significant part of the manifest concerning content provider support is the `<provider>` element ❶. This is used to define the class that implements the provider and associate a particular authority with that class.

> **Additional ContentProvider manifest properties**
>
> The properties of a `ContentProvider`, which are configurable in the manifest, are capable of configuring several important settings beyond the basics, such as specific permissions, initialization order, multiprocess capability, and more. While most `ContentProvider` implementations won't be required to delve into these details, they are still good to be aware of. For complete and up-to-date `ContentProvider` properties, see the following Android documentation page: http://code.google.com/android/reference/android/R.styleable.html - AndroidManifestProvider.

A completed project that is capable of inserting, retrieving, updating, and deleting records rounds out our exploration of using and building `ContentProvider` classes. And with that, we have also now demonstrated many of the ways to store and retrieve data on the Android platform.

5.5 *Summary*

From a simple `SharedPreferences` mechanism that saves data backed by files to file storage itself, databases, and finally the concept of a `ContentProvider`, Android provides myriad ways for applications to retrieve and store data.

As we discussed in this chapter, several of these means are intended to be used across application and process boundaries, and several aren't. Here we showed that `SharedPreferences` can be created with a permissions mode, allowing the flexibility to keep things private, or can be shared globally with read-only or read-write permissions.

Preferences are stored as simple XML files in a specific path on the device per application, as are other file resources you can create and read yourself. The filesystem, which we also looked at in this chapter, is good for handling some levels of application-local state and data persistence but not appropriate for more broad-reaching goals.

After filesystem access, the next level of storage Android provides is a relational database system based on SQLite. This system is lightweight, speedy, and very capable, but again, as you saw here, it is intended only for local data persistence within a single application. Beyond storing and retrieving data locally you can still use a database, but you need to expose an interface through a `Service` (as we explained in chapter 4) or a `ContentProvider`. Providers, which we covered in this chapter, expose data types and operations through a URI-based approach.

In this chapter we examined each of the data paths available to an Android application. We did this by using several small, focused sample applications to utilize preferences and the filesystem, and we looked at more of the WeatherReporter sample application that we began in the last chapter. This Android application uses a SQLite database to access and persist data.

Expanding our Android horizons beyond data and beyond foundational concepts we have already looked at in earlier chapters, such as views, intents, and services, we will move on to general networking in the next chapter. There we will cover networking basics and the networking APIs Android provides, and we will expand on the data concepts we have covered here to include the network itself as a data source.

Networking
and web services

This chapter covers:

- Networking basics
- Determining network status
- Using the network to retrieve and store data
- Working with web services

Every mobile provider supports voice and data networks of one or more types. The interesting part with an Android-enabled device is really the data network, along with the power to link the data available on the network to interesting applications. Those applications can then be built with the open Intent- and Service-based approach you learned about in previous chapters. That approach combines built-in (or custom) intents, such as fully capable web browsing, with access to hardware components, such as a 3D graphics subsystem, a GPS receiver, a camera, removable storage, and more. This combination of open platform, hardware capability, software architecture, and access to network data makes Android so compelling.

This is not to say that the voice network is not also important (and we will cover telephony explicitly in chapter 7), but rather it is simply an admittance that voice is almost a commodity, and data is where we will focus when talk about the *network*.

In terms of the data network, Android provides access in several ways: mobile Internet Protocol (IP) networks, Wi-Fi, and Bluetooth. Here we are going to concentrate on getting our Android applications to communicate using IP network data, with several different approaches. We will cover a bit of networking background, and then we will deal with Android specifics as we explore communication with the network using sockets and higher-level protocols such as Hypertext Transfer Protocol (HTTP).

Android provides a portion of the `java.net` package and the `org.apache.http-client` package to support basic networking. Other related packages such as `android.net` address internal networking details and general connectivity properties. We will encounter all of these packages as we progress though networking scenarios in this chapter.

In terms of connectivity properties, we will look at using the `ConnectivityManager` class to determine when the network connection is active and what type of connection it is (mobile or Wi-Fi). From there we will make use of the network in various ways with sample applications.

One caveat to this networking chapter is that we won't be digging into the details concerning the Android Wi-Fi or Bluetooth APIs. Bluetooth is an important technology for close-range wireless networking between devices, but the related Android APIs are not yet finalized (even in the 1.0 SDK). Bluetooth is supported on Android devices, but in a limited capacity at present, and is not available in the Android Emulator. Wi-Fi, on the other hand, does have a good existing API but also doesn't have an emulation layer. Because the emulator doesn't distinguish the type of network you are using and doesn't know anything about either Bluetooth or Wi-Fi, and because we think the importance lies more in how you use the network, we are not going to cover these APIs. If you want more information on the Wi-Fi APIs please see the Android documentation (http:// code.google.com/android/reference/android/net/wifi/package-summary.html).

Getting back to what we will address here, the aptly named sample application for this chapter, NetworkExplorer, will look at ways to communicate with the network in Android and will include some handy utilities. Ultimately this application will have multiple screens that exercise different networking techniques, as shown in figure 6.1.

After we cover general IP networking with regard to Android, we will discuss turning the server side into a more robust API itself by using *web services*. On this topic we will work with Plain Old XML over HTTP (POX) and Representational State Transfer (REST). And, we will discuss the Simple Object Access Protocol (SOAP). We will address the pros and cons of the various approaches and why you might want to choose one method over another for an Android client.

Before we delve into the details of networked Android applications, we will begin with an overview of networking basics. If you are already well versed in general networking, you can certainly skip ahead to section 6.2, but it is important to have this foundation if you think you need it, and we promise to keep it short.

Figure 6.1 The NetworkExplorer application we will build to cover networking topics

6.1 An overview of networking

A group of interconnected computers is a *network*. Over time, networking has grown from something that was once available only to governments and large organizations to the almost ubiquitous and truly amazing internet. Though the concept is simple—allow computers to communicate—networking does involve some advanced technology. We won't get into great detail here, though we will cover the core tenets as a background to the general networking we will do in the remainder of this chapter.

6.1.1 Networking basics

A large percentage of the time the APIs you will use to program Android applications will abstract the underlying network details. This is good. The APIs and the network protocols themselves are designed so that you can focus on your application and not worry about routing and reliable packet delivery and so on.

Nevertheless, it helps to have some understanding of the way a network works so that you can better design and troubleshoot your applications. To that end, here we are going to blaze through some general networking concepts, with a Transmission Control Protocol/Internet Protocol (TCP/IP) bent. We will begin with nodes, layers, and protocols.

NODES

The basic idea behind a network is that data is sent between connected devices with particular addresses. Connections can be made over wire, over radio waves, and so on. Each addressed device is known as a *node*. A node can be a mainframe, a PC, a fancy toaster, or any other device with a network stack and connectivity, such as an Android-enabled handheld.

LAYERS AND PROTOCOLS

Protocols are a predefined and agreed-upon set of rules for communication. Protocols are often layered on top of one another because they handle different levels of responsibility. For example, in the TCP/IP stack, which is used for the majority of web traffic of all kinds and with Android, the main layers are:

- The Link Layer (including physical device address resolution protocols such as ARP and RARP and more)
- The Internet Layer (including IP itself, which has multiple versions, and the ping protocol, ICMP, among others)
- The Transport Layer (where different types of delivery protocols such as TCP and UDP are found)
- The Application Layer (which includes familiar protocols such as HTTP, FTP, SMTP, IMAP, POP, DNS, SSH, and SOAP)

Layers are an abstraction of the different levels of a network protocol stack. The lowest level, the Link Layer, is concerned with physical devices and physical addresses. The next level, the Internet Layer, is concerned with addressing and general data details. After that, the Transport Layer is concerned with delivery details. And, finally, the top-level Application Layer protocols, which make use of the stack beneath them, are application specific for sending files or email or viewing web pages.

IP

IP is in charge of the addressing system and delivering data in small chunks known as *packets*. Packets, known in IP terms as *datagrams*, define how much data can go in each chunk, where the boundaries for payload versus header information are, and the like. IP addresses tell where each packet is from (its source) and where it's going (its destination).

IP addresses come in different sizes depending on the version of the protocol being used, but by far the most common at present is the 32-bit address. 32-bit IP addresses (IPv4) are typically written using a decimal notation that separates the 32 bits into four sections, each representing 8 bits (an octet), such as 74.125.45.100.

Certain IP address classes have special roles and meaning. For example, 127 always identifies a *loopback* or local address on every machine; this class does not communicate with any other devices (it can be used internally, on a single machine only). Addresses that begin with 10 or 192 are *not routable*, meaning they can communicate with other devices on the same local network segment but cannot connect to other segments. Every address on a particular network segment must be unique or collisions may occur and it gets ugly.

The routing of packets on an IP network—how packets traverse the network and go from one segment to another—is handled by *routers*. Routers speak to each other using IP addresses and other IP-related information.

TCP AND UDP

TCP and UDP are different types of delivery protocols that are commonly used with TCP/IP. TCP is reliable, and UDP is fire and forget. What does this mean? It means that TCP includes extra data to guarantee the order of packets and to send back an acknowledgment once a packet is received (the common analogy is certified mail: the sender gets a receipt that shows the letter was delivered and signed for and therefore knows the recipient got the message). UDP, on the other hand, doesn't provide any ordering or acknowledgment (it's more like a regular letter: it's cheaper and faster to send, but you basically hope the recipient gets it—you don't know for sure).

APPLICATION PROTOCOLS

Once a packet is sent and delivered, an application takes over. To send an email message, for example, SMTP defines a rigorous set of procedures that have to take place. You have to say hello in a particular way and introduce yourself; then you have to supply from and to information, followed by a message body in a particular format. Similarly, HTTP defines the set of rules for the internet—which methods are allowed (GET, POST, PUT, DELETE) and how the overall request/response system works between a client and a server.

When working with Android, and Java-related APIs in general, you won't typically need to delve into the details of any of the lower-level protocols, but you may need to know the major differences we have outlined here for troubleshooting, and you will need to be well versed in IP addressing. In addition, you should also know a bit more about clients and servers and how connections are established using ports.

6.1.2 *Clients and servers*

Anyone who has ever used a web browser is familiar with the client/server computing model. Data, in one format or another, is stored on a centralized, powerful server. Clients then connect to that server using a designated protocol (such as HTTP) to retrieve the data and work with it.

This pattern is of course much older than the web, and it has been applied for everything from completely dumb terminals connecting to mainframes to modern desktop applications that connect to a server for only a portion of their purpose (such as with iTunes, which is primarily a media organizer and player but also has a store where customers can connect to the server to get new content). In any case, the concept is the same: the client makes a type of request to the server and the server responds. This is the same model that the majority of Android applications, at least those that use a server side at all, generally follow (Android applications typically end up as the client).

In order to handle many client requests, often for different purposes, coming in nearly simultaneously to a single IP address, modern server operating systems use the concept of *ports*. Ports are not physical; they are simply a representation of a particular area of the computer's memory. A server can "listen" on multiple designated ports at a single address; for example, one port for sending email, one port for web traffic, two ports for file transfer, and so on. Every computer with an IP address also supports a range of thousands of ports to enable multiple "conversations" to happen at the same time.

Ports are divided into three ranges:

- *Well Known Ports*—0 through 1023
- *Registered Ports*—1024 through 49151
- *Dynamic and/or Private Ports*—49152 through 65535

The Well Known Ports are all published and are just that, well known. HTTP is port 80 (and HTTP Secure, or HTTPS, is port 443), FTP is ports 20 (control) and 21 (data), SSH is port 22, SMTP is port 25, and so on.

Beyond the Well Known Ports, the Registered Ports are still controlled and published but for more specific purposes. Often these ports are used for a particular application or company; for example, MySQL is port 3306 (by default). For a complete list of Well Known and Registered Ports, see the ICANN port-numbers document: http://www.iana.org/assignments/port-numbers.

The Dynamic or Private Ports are intentionally unregistered because they are used by the TCP/IP stack to facilitate communication. These ports are dynamically registered on each computer and used in the conversation. Dynamic port 49500, for example, might be used to handle sending a request to a web server and dealing with the response. Once the conversation is over, the port is reclaimed and can be reused, locally, for any other data transfer.

Clients and servers therefore communicate as nodes with addresses, using ports, on a network that supports various protocols. The protocols involved with Android are based on the IP network the platform is designed to participate in and involve the TCP/IP family. Before we can build a full-on client/server Android application using the network, we need to handle the prerequisite task of determining the state of the connection.

6.2   *Checking the network status*

Android provides a host of utilities to determine the device configuration and the status of various services, including the network. You will typically use the ConnectivityManager class to determine whether there is network connectivity and to get notifications of network changes. Listing 6.1, a portion of the main Activity in the NetworkExplorer application, demonstrates basic usage of the ConnectivityManager.

> **Listing 6.1 The** `onStart` **method of the NetworkExplorer main** `Activity`

```
@Override
public void onStart() {
    super.onStart();

    ConnectivityManager cMgr =  (ConnectivityManager)
  this.getSystemService(Context.CONNECTIVITY_SERVICE);
    NetworkInfo netInfo = cMgr.getActiveNetworkInfo();
    this.status.setText(netInfo.toString());
}
```

❶ Obtain manager from Context

Get ❷ NetworkInfo

This short and sweet example shows that you can get a handle to the `Connectivity-Manager` through the context's `getSystemService` method by passing the `CONNECTIVITY_SERVICE` constant ❶. Once you have the manager, you can obtain network information via the `NetworkInfo` object ❷. The `toString` method of the `NetworkInfo` object returns the output shown in figure 6.2.

Of course you won't normally just display the `String` output from `Network-Info`, but this does give you a quick glance at what is available. More often you will use the `isAvailable` or `isConnected` methods (which return a `boolean` value),

Figure 6.2 The output of the NetworkInfo toString method.

or you will directly query the `NetworkInfo.State` using the `getState` method. `NetworkInfo.State` is an `enum` that defines the coarse state of the connection, the possible values are: `CONNECTED`, `CONNECTING`, `DISCONNECTED`, and `DISCONNECTING`. The `NetworkInfo` object also provides access to more detailed information but you won't normally need more than the basic state (unless of course you have a special use case, such as if you are writing a network state management application).

Once you know that you are connected, either via mobile or Wi-Fi, you can use the IP network. For the purposes of our NetworkExplorer application, we are going to start with the most rudimentary IP connection, a raw socket, and work our way up to HTTP and web services.

6.3 *Communicating with a server socket*

A server socket is a stream that you can read or write raw bytes to, at a specified IP address and port. This lets you deal with data and not worry about media types, packet sizes, and so on. This is yet another network abstraction intended to make the job of the programmer a bit easier. The philosophy that sockets take on, that everything should look like file I/O to the developer, comes from the POSIX family of standards and has been adopted by most major operating systems in use today.

We will move on to higher levels of network communication in a bit, but first we will start with a raw socket. For that we need a server listening on a particular port. The `EchoServer` code shown in listing 6.2 fits the bill. This isn't an Android-specific class; rather it's just an oversimplified server that can run on any host machine with Java. We'll later connect to it from an Android client.

Listing 6.2   A simple echo server for demonstrating socket usage

```java
public final class EchoServer extends Thread {

    private static final int PORT = 8889;

    private EchoServer() {}

    public static void main(String args[]) {
        EchoServer echoServer = new EchoServer();
        if (echoServer != null) {
            echoServer.start();
        }
    }

    public void run() {                             ① Implement run to start
        try {
            ServerSocket server = new ServerSocket(PORT, 1);   ② Use java.net.ServerSocket

            while (true) {
                Socket client = server.accept();
                System.out.println("Client connected");        ③ Use java.net.Socket for each client

                while (true) {

                    BufferedReader reader =
                        new BufferedReader(new InputStreamReader(   ④ Read input with BufferedReader
                        client.getInputStream()));
                    System.out.println("Read from client");
                    String textLine = reader.readLine() + "\n";

                    if (textLine.equalsIgnoreCase("EXIT\n")) {
                        System.out.println("EXIT invoked, closing client");
                        break;                                  ⑤ EXIT, break the loop
                    }

                    BufferedWriter writer = new BufferedWriter(
                        new OutputStreamWriter(
                        client.getOutputStream()));             ⑥ Send echo with BufferedWriter
                    System.out.println("Echo input to client");
                    writer.write("ECHO from server: "
                        + textLine, 0, textLine.length() + 18);
                    writer.flush();
                }
                client.close();
            }
        } catch (IOException e) {
            System.err.println(e);
        }
    }
}
```

The EchoServer class we are using is fairly basic Java I/O. It extends Thread and implements run ①, so that each client that connects can be handled in its own context. Then we use a ServerSocket ② to listen on a defined port. Each client is then an implementation of a `Socket` ❸. The client input is fed into a `BufferedReader` that each line is read from ❹. The only special consideration this simple server has is that if the input is `EXIT`, it breaks the loops and exits ❺. If the input does not prompt an exit, the server echoes the input back to the client's `OuputStream` with a `BufferedWriter` ❻.

This is a good, albeit intentionally very basic, representation of what a server does. It handles input, usually in a separate thread, then responds to the client based on the input. To try out this server before using Android, you can telnet to the specified port (after the server is running, of course) and type some input; if all is well it will echo the output.

To run the server you need to invoke it locally with Java. It has a main method, so it will run on its own; start it from the command line or from your IDE. Be aware that when you connect to a server from the emulator, this or any other, you need to connect to the IP address of the host you run the server process on, not the loopback (not 127.0.0.1). The emulator thinks of itself as 127.0.0.1, so use the non-loopback address of the server host when you attempt to connect from Android. (You can find out the IP address of the machine you are on from the command line by entering `ifconfig` on Linux or Mac and `ipconfig` on Windows.)

The client portion of this example is where NetworkExplorer itself begins, with the `callSocket` method of the `SimpleSocket Activity` shown in listing 6.3.

Listing 6.3 An Android client invoking a raw socket server resource, the echo server

```
public class SimpleSocket extends Activity {

   . . . View variable declarations omitted for brevity

   @Override
   public void onCreate(final Bundle icicle) {
      super.onCreate(icicle);
      this.setContentView(R.layout.simple_socket);

      . . . View inflation omitted for brevity

      this.socketButton.setOnClickListener(new OnClickListener() {

         public void onClick(final View v) {
            socketOutput.setText("");
            String output = callSocket(
              ipAddress.getText().toString(),
              port.getText().toString(),
              socketInput.getText().toString());        ❶ Use callSocket
            socketOutput.setText(output);        ❷ Set view output
         }
      });
   }

   private String callSocket(String ip, String port, String socketData) {
      Socket socket = null;
      BufferedWriter writer = null;
      BufferedReader reader = null;
      String output = null;
```

❶ Use callSocket method

❷ Set view output

```
try {
    socket = new Socket(ip, Integer.parseInt(port));        ◄──┐   Create client
    writer = new BufferedWriter(                               ❸   Socket
      new OutputStreamWriter(
        socket.getOutputStream()));        ◄──❹  Establish BufferedWriter for input
    reader = new BufferedReader(
      new InputStreamReader(
        socket.getInputStream()));         ◄──❺  Establish BufferedReader for output

    String input = socketData;
    writer.write(input + "\n", 0, input.length() + 1);    ◄──┐  Write to
    writer.flush();                                          ❻  socket

    output = reader.readLine();        ◄──┐  Get socket
    this.socketOutput.setText(output);    ❼  output

    // send EXIT and close
    writer.write("EXIT\n", 0, 5);
    writer.flush();
. . . catches and reader, writer, and socket closes omitted for brevity
. . . onCreate omitted for brevity

    return output;
}
```

Here we use the onCreate method to call a private helper callSocket method ❶ and set the output to a TextView ❷. Within the callSocket method we create a Socket to represent the client side of our connection ❸, and we establish a writer for the input ❹ and a reader for the output ❺. With the housekeeping taken care of, we then write to the socket ❻, which communicates with the server, and get the output value to return ❼.

A socket is probably the lowest-level networking usage in Android you will encounter. Using a raw socket, while abstracted a great deal, still leaves many of the details up to you (especially server-side details, threading, and queuing). Although you may run up against situations in which either you have to use a raw socket (the server side is already built) or you elect to use one for one reason or another, higher-level solutions such as leveraging HTTP normally have decided advantages.

6.4   *Working with HTTP*

As we discussed in the previous section, you can use a raw socket to transfer IP data to and from a server with Android. This is an important approach to be aware of so that you know you have that option and so that you understand a bit about the underlying details. Nevertheless, you may want to avoid this technique where possible and instead take advantage of existing server products to send your data. The most common way to do this is to use a web server and leverage HTTP.

Here we are going to take a look at making HTTP requests from an Android client and sending them to an HTTP server. We will let the HTTP server handle all the socket details, and we will focus on our client Android application.

The HTTP protocol itself is fairly involved. If you are unfamiliar with it and or want the complete details, they are readily available via RFCs (such as for version 1.1:

http://www.w3.org/Protocols/rfc2616/rfc2616.html). The short story is that the protocol is stateless and involves several different methods that allow users to make *requests* to servers, and those servers return *responses*. The entire web is, of course, based on HTTP. Beyond the most basic concepts, there are ways to pass data into and out of requests and responses and to authenticate with servers. Here we are going to use some of the most common methods and concepts to talk to network resources from Android applications.

To begin we will retrieve data using HTTP GET requests to a simple HTML page using the standard java.net API. From there we will look at using the Android-included Apache HttpClient API. After we use HttpClient directly to get a feel for it, we will also make a helper class, HttpRequestHelper, that we can use to simplify the process and encapsulate the details. This class—and the Apache networking API in general—has a few advantages over rolling your own networking with java.net, as we shall see. Once the helper class is in place, we will use it to make additional HTTP and HTTPS requests, both GET and POST, and we will look at basic authentication.

Our first HTTP request will be an HTTP GET call using a HttpUrlConnection.

6.4.1 Simple HTTP and java.net

The most basic HTTP request method is a GET. In this type of request any data that is sent is embedded in the URL using the query string. The next class in our NetworkExplorer application, which is shown in listing 6.4, has an Activity that demonstrates this.

Listing 6.4 The SimpleGet Activity showing java.net.UrlConnection

```
public class SimpleGet extends Activity {

    . . . other portions of onCreate omitted for brevity

        this.getButton.setOnClickListener(new OnClickListener() {
            public void onClick(View v) {
                getOutput.setText("");
                String output =
                    getHttpResponse(getInput.getText().toString());   ◀─┐
                if (output != null) {                          Invoke  │
                    getOutput.setText(output);           getHttpResponse│ ❶
                }                                               method ─┘
            }
        });
    };
    . . .

    private String getHttpResponse(String location) {
        String result = null;
        URL url = null;

        try {                              ❷  Construct URL
            url = new URL(location);       ◀─    object
        } catch (MalformedURLException e) {
            // log and or handle
        }
```

```
if (url != null) {                                            ❸ Open
    try {                                                        connection using
        HttpURLConnection urlConn =                              HttpURLConnection
            (HttpURLConnection) url.openConnection();   ◁┘
        BufferedReader in =
            new BufferedReader(
                new InputStreamReader(                   ❹ Create BufferedReader
                    urlConn.getInputStream()));   ◁┘        for output
        String inputLine;

        int lineCount = 0; // limit lines for example
        while ((lineCount < 10)
            && ((inputLine = in.readLine()) != null)) {   ◁──❺ Read data
            lineCount++;
            result += "\n" + inputLine;      ◁──❻ Append to result
        }

        in.close();                    ❼ Close reader
        urlConn.disconnect();             and connection
    } catch (IOException e) {
        // log and or handle
    }
} else {
    // log and or handle
}
return result;
    }
}
```

In order to get an HTTP response and show the first few lines of it in our `SimpleGet` class, we are calling a `getHttpResponse` method that we have built ❶. Within this method we construct a `java.net.URL` object ❷, which takes care of many of the details for us, and then we open a connection to a server using an `HttpURLConnection` ❸.

We then use a `BufferedReader` ❹ to read data from the connection one line at a time ❺. Keep in mind that as we are doing this, we are using the same thread as the UI and therefore blocking the UI. This isn't a good idea. We are doing this here only to demonstrate the network operation; we will explain more about how to use a separate thread for this shortly. Once we have the data, we append it to the result `String` that our method returns ❻, and we close the reader and the connection ❼. Using the plain and simple java.net support that has been ported to Android this way provides quick and dirty access to HTTP network resources.

Communicating with HTTP this way is fairly easy, but it can quickly get cumbersome when you need to do more than just retrieve simple data, and, as noted, the blocking nature of the call is bad form. We could get around some of the problems with this approach on our own by spawning separate threads and keeping track of them and by writing our own small framework/API structure around that concept for each HTTP request, but we don't have to. Fortunately, Android provides another set of APIs in the form of the Apache HttpClient library that abstract the java.net classes further and that are designed to offer more robust HTTP support and help handle the separate-thread issue.

6.4.2 *Robust HTTP with HttpClient*

To get started with HttpClient we are going to look at using core classes to perform HTTP GET and POST method requests. Here we will concentrate on making network requests in a Thread separate from the UI, using a combination of the Apache ResponseHandler and Android Handler (for different but related purposes, as we shall see). Listing 6.5 shows our first example of using the HttpClient API.

Listing 6.5 Apache HttpClient with Android `Handler` and Apache `ResponseHandler`

```
. . . .
private final Handler handler = new Handler() {          ◁──  ❶ Create Android
    public void handleMessage(Message msg) {                    Handler
        progressDialog.dismiss();
        String bundleResult =
          msg.getData().getString("RESPONSE");          ❷ Use Handler
        output.setText(bundleResult);                      to update UI
    }
};

. . . onCreate omitted for brevity

private void performRequest() {                              ❸ Create
    final ResponseHandler<String> responseHandler =            ResponseHandler
      new ResponseHandler<String>() {            ◁             for asynchronous
        public String handleResponse(HttpResponse response) {  ◁  HTTP
            StatusLine status = response.getStatusLine();
            HttpEntity entity = response.getEntity();     Implement
            String result = null;                         onResponse
            try {                                         callback  ❹
                result = StringUtils.inputStreamToString(
                  entity.getContent());           ◁── Get HTTP response
                Message message = handler.obtainMessage(); ❺ payload
                Bundle bundle = new Bundle();
                bundle.putString("RESPONSE", result);
                message.setData(bundle);
                handler.sendMessage(message);
            } catch (IOException e) {
                // log and or handle
            }
            return result;
        }
    };

    this.progressDialog =
      ProgressDialog.show(this, "working . . .",
        "performing HTTP request");

    new Thread() {                  ◁──  Use a separate
        public void run() {               Thread for HTTP call
            try {
                DefaultHttpClient client = new DefaultHttpClient();
                HttpGet httpMethod =                    Create
                  new HttpGet(                          HttpGet
                    urlChooser.getSelectedItem().toString());  ◁── object
```

```
        client.execute(
          httpMethod, responseHandler);        ◁──  Execute HTTP
      } catch (ClientProtocolException e) {         with HttpClient
        // log and or handle
      } catch (IOException e) {
        // log and or handle
      }
    }
  }.start();
}
```

The first thing we do in our initial `HttpClient` example is create a `Handler` that we can send messages to from other threads **❶**. This is the same technique we have used in previous examples, and it is used to allow background tasks to send `Message` objects to hook back into the main UI thread **❷**. After we create an Android `Handler`, we also create an Apache `ResponseHandler` **❸**. This class can be used with `HttpClient` HTTP requests to pass in as a callback point. When an HTTP request that is fired by `HttpClient` completes, it will call the `onResponse` method (if a `ResponseHandler` is used) **❹**. When the response does come in, we then get the payload using the `HttpEntity` the API returns **❺**. This in effect allows the HTTP call to be made in an asynchronous manner—we don't have to block and wait the entire time between when the request is fired and when it completes. The relationship of the request, response, `Handler`, `Response-Handler`, and separate threads is diagrammed in figure 6.3.

Now that you have seen `HttpClient` at work and understand the basic approach, the next thing we will do is encapsulate a few of the details into a convenient helper class so that we can call it over and over without having to repeat a lot of the setup.

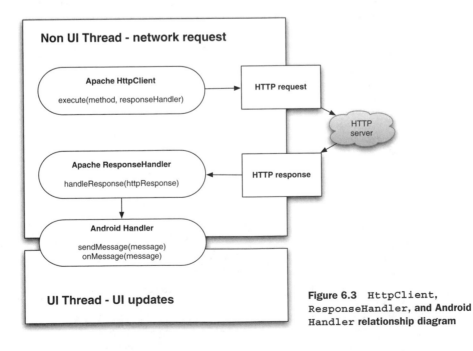

Figure 6.3 `HttpClient`, `ResponseHandler`, and Android `Handler` **relationship diagram**

6.4.3 *Creating an HTTP and HTTPS helper*

The next `Activity` in our NetworkExplorer application, which is shown in listing 6.6, is a lot more straightforward and pure Android focused than our other HTTP-related classes up to this point. This is made possible by the helper class we mentioned previously, which hides some of the complexity (we will examine the helper class itself after we look at this first class that uses it).

Listing 6.6 Using Apache `HttpClient` via a custom `HttpRequestHelper`

```
public class ApacheHTTPViaHelper extends Activity {

    . . . other member variables omitted for brevity

    private final Handler handler = new Handler() {          ①  Create a
        public void handleMessage(Message msg) {                 Handler
            progressDialog.dismiss();
            String bundleResult = msg.getData().getString("RESPONSE");
            output.setText(bundleResult);
        }                                                    ②  Update UI
    };                                                          from Handler

    @Override
    public void onCreate(final Bundle icicle) {
        super.onCreate(icicle);

        . . . view inflation and setup omitted for brevity

        this.button.setOnClickListener(new OnClickListener() {
            public void onClick(final View v) {
                output.setText("");
                performRequest(                              ③  Call local
                    urlChooser.getSelectedItem().toString());    performRequest
            }
        });
    };

    . . . onPause omitted for brevity

    private void performRequest(String url) {

        final ResponseHandler<String> responseHandler -
            HTTPRequestHelper.getResponseHandlerInstance(  ④  Get ResponseHandler
                this.handler);                                 from RequestHelper

        this.progressDialog =
            ProgressDialog.show(this, "working . . .",
                "performing HTTP request");

        new Thread() {
            public void run() {
                HTTPRequestHelper helper = new          ⑤  Instantiate RequestHelper
                HTTPRequestHelper(responseHandler);         with ResponseHandler
                helper.performGet(url, null, null, null);
            }                                            ⑥  Perform HTTP
        }.start();                                          via helper
    }
}
```

First in this class we create another `Handler` ❶, and from within it we simply update a UI `TextView` based on data in the `Message` ❷. Further in the code, in the `onCreate` method, we call a local `performRequest` method when the "go" button is clicked, and we pass a selected `String` representing a URL ❸.

Inside the `performRequest` method we use a static convenience method to return an `HttpClient ResponseHandler`, passing in our Android `Handler`, which it will use ❹. We will examine the helper class next to get a look at exactly how this works, but the important part for now is that the `ResponseHandler` is created for us by the static method. With the `ResponseHandler` instance taken care of, we instantiate an `HttpRequestHelper` instance ❺ and use it to make a simple HTTP `GET` call (passing in only the `String` URL) ❻. Similar to our previous example, when the request completes, the `Response-Handler` will fire the `onResponse` method, and therein our `Handler` will be sent a `Mes-sage` completing the process.

The example `Activity` in listing 6.6 is fairly clean and simple, and it's asynchronous and doesn't block the UI thread. The heavy lifting is taken care of by `HttpClient` itself and by the setup our custom `HttpRequestHelper` makes possible. The first part of the all-important `HttpRequestHelper`, which we will explore in three sections, is shown in listing 6.7.

Listing 6.7   The first part of the `HttpRequestHelper` class

```
public class HTTPRequestHelper {

    private static final int POST_TYPE = 1;
    private static final int GET_TYPE = 2;
    private static final String CONTENT_TYPE = "Content-Type";
    public static final String MIME_FORM_ENCODED =
      "application/x-www-form-urlencoded";
    public static final String MIME_TEXT_PLAIN = "text/plain";          Require  ❶
                                                               ResponseHandler
                                                                  to construct
    private final ResponseHandler<String> responseHandler;

    public HTTPRequestHelper(ResponseHandler<String> responseHandler) {
        this.responseHandler = responseHandler;
    }

    public void performGet(String url, String user, String pass,
        final Map<String, String> additionalHeaders) {              Provide
        performRequest(null, url, user, pass,                        simple GET
          additionalHeaders, null, HTTPRequestHelper.GET_TYPE);   ❷ method
    }

    public void performPost(String contentType, String url,
      String user, String pass,
      Map<String, String> additionalHeaders,            ❸ Provide simple
      Map<String, String> params) {                        POST methods
        performRequest(contentType, url, user, pass,
          additionalHeaders, params, HTTPRequestHelper.POST_TYPE);
    }

    public void performPost(String url, String user, String pass,
      Map<String, String> additionalHeaders,
```

```
      Map<String, String> params) {
        performRequest(HTTPRequestHelper.MIME_FORM_ENCODED,          ❸ Provide simple
          url, user, pass,                                              POST methods
            additionalHeaders, params, HTTPRequestHelper.POST_TYPE);
   }
   private void performRequest(
      String contentType,
      String url,
      String user,
      String pass,
      Map<String, String> headers,              ❹ Handle combinations
      Map<String, String> params,                  in private method
      int requestType) {
                                                                      ❺ Instantiate
      DefaultHttpClient client = new DefaultHttpClient();               DefaultHttpClient

      if ((user != null) && (pass != null)) {
        client.getCredentialsProvider().setCredentials(
          AuthScope.ANY,                                         ❻ Add credentials
          new UsernamePasswordCredentials(user, pass));             if needed
      }

      final Map<String, String> sendHeaders =
        new HashMap<String, String>();
      if ((headers != null) && (headers.size() > 0)) {
        sendHeaders.putAll(headers);
      }
      if (requestType == HTTPRequestHelper.POST_TYPE) {
        sendHeaders.put(HTTPRequestHelper.CONTENT_TYPE, contentType);
      }
      if (sendHeaders.size() > 0) {
        client.addRequestInterceptor(            ❼ Use Interceptor for
          new HttpRequestInterceptor() {             request headers
            public void process(
              final HttpRequest request, final HttpContext context)
                throws HttpException, IOException {
                  for (String key : sendHeaders.keySet()) {
                    if (!request.containsHeader(key)) {
                      request.addHeader(key,
                        sendHeaders.get(key));
                  }
                }
              }
            }
          });
      }

      . . . POST and GET execution in listing 6.8
  }
```

The first thing of note in the HttpRequestHelper class is that a ResponseHandler is
required to be passed in as part of the constructor ❶. This ResponseHandler will be
used when the HttpClient request is ultimately invoked. After the constructor, we see
a public HTTP GET-related method ❷ and several different public HTTP POST-related
methods ❸. Each of these methods is a wrapper around the private performRequest
method that can handle all the HTTP options ❹. The performRequest method

supports a content-type header value, URL, username, password, `Map` of additional headers, similar `Map` of request parameters, and request method type.

Inside the `performRequest` method a `DefaultHttpClient` is instantiated ❺. Next, we check to see if the user and pass method parameters are present, and if so we set the request credentials with a `UsernamePasswordCredentials` type (`HttpClient` supports several types of credentials, see the Javadocs for details) ❻. At the same time we set the credentials, we also set an `AuthScope`. The scope represents which server, port, authentication realm, and authentication scheme the credentials supplied are applicable for.

You can set these as fine or coarse grained as you want; we are using the default `ANY` scope that matches anything. What we notably have not set in all of this is the specific authentication scheme to use. `HttpClient` supports various schemes, including basic authentication, digest authentication, and a Windows-specific NTLM scheme. Basic authentication, meaning simple username/password challenge from the server, is the default. (Also, if you need to, you can use a preemptive form login for form-based authentication—just submit the form you need and get the token or session ID and so on.)

After the security is out of the way, we use an `HttpRequestInterceptor` to add HTTP headers ❼. Headers are name/value pairs, so this is pretty easy. Once we have all of these properties that apply regardless of our request method type, we then add further settings that are specific to the method. Listing 6.8, the second part of our helper class, shows the POST- and GET-specific settings and the execute method.

Listing 6.8 The second part of the `HttpRequestHelper` class

```
. . .

if (requestType == HTTPRequestHelper.POST_TYPE) {        ❶ Handle POST
  HttpPost method = new HttpPost(url);                       requests
  List<NameValuePair> nvps = null;
  if ((params != null) && (params.size() > 0)) {          ❷ Create HttpPost
    nvps = new ArrayList<NameValuePair>();                    object
    for (String key : params.keySet()) {
      nvps.add(new BasicNameValuePair(key,
        params.get(key)));                                  ❸ Add name/value
    }                                                          parameters
  }
  if (nvps != null) {
    try {
      method.setEntity(
        new UrlEncodedFormEntity(nvps, HTTP.UTF_8));
    } catch (UnsupportedEncodingException e) {
      // log and or handle
    }
  }                                    ❹ Call execute
  execute(client, method);                method
} else if (requestType == HTTPRequestHelper.GET_TYPE) {
  HttpGet method = new HttpGet(url);
  execute(client, method);
```

```
    }

  . . .

  private void execute(HttpClient client, HttpRequestBase method) {
    BasicHttpResponse errorResponse =
      new BasicHttpResponse(
        new ProtocolVersion("HTTP_ERROR", 1, 1),
          500, "ERROR");
    try {
        client.execute(method, this.responseHandler);
    } catch (Exception e) {
        errorResponse.setReasonPhrase(e.getMessage());
        try {
          this.responseHandler.handleResponse(errorResponse);
        } catch (Exception ex) {
          // log and or handle
        }
    }
  }
}
```

❺ Set up an error handler

❻ Call HttpClient execute

When the specified request is a POST type ❶, we create an HttpPost object to deal with it ❷. Then we add POST request parameters, which are another set of name/value pairs and are built with the BasicNameValuePair object ❸. After adding the parameters we are ready to perform the request, which we do with our local private execute method using the method object and the client ❹.

Our execute method sets up an error response handler (we want to return a response, error or not, so we set this up in case) ❺ and wraps the HttpClient execute method, which requires a method object (either POST or GET in our case, preestablished) and a ResponseHandler as input ❻. If we don't get an exception when we invoke HttpClient execute, all is well and the response details are placed into the ResponseHandler. If we do get an exception, we populate the error handler and pass it through to the ResponseHandler.

We call the local private execute method with the established details for either a POST or a GET request. The GET method is handled similarly to the POST, but we don't set parameters (with GET requests we expect parameters encoded in the URL itself). Right now our class supports only POST and GET (which cover 98 percent of the requests we generally need), but it certainly could be easily expanded to support other HTTP method types.

The final part of the request helper class, shown in listing 6.9, takes us back to the first example that used the helper, as it outlines exactly what the convenience getResponseHandlerInstance method returns (constructing our helper requires a ResponseHandler, and this method returns a default one).

Listing 6.9 The final part of the HttpRequestHelper class

```
public static ResponseHandler<String>
  getResponseHandlerInstance(final Handler handler) {
    final ResponseHandler<String> responseHandler =
      new ResponseHandler<String>() {
```

❶ Require Handler parameter

```
public String handleResponse(final HttpResponse response) {
    Message message = handler.obtainMessage();
    Bundle bundle = new Bundle();
    StatusLine status = response.getStatusLine();
    HttpEntity entity = response.getEntity();
    String result = null;
    if (entity != null) {
        try {
            result = StringUtils.inputStreamToString(
              entity.getContent());
            bundle.putString(
                "RESPONSE", result);
            message.setData(bundle);
            handler.sendMessage(message);
        } catch (IOException e) {
            bundle.putString("
              RESPONSE", "Error - " + e.getMessage());
            message.setData(bundle);
            handler.sendMessage(message);
        }
    } else {
        bundle.putString("RESPONSE", "Error - "
          + response.getStatusLine().getReasonPhrase());
        message.setData(bundle);
        handler.sendMessage(message);
    }
    return result;
}
};
    return responseHandler;
    }
}
```

❷ Get response content as String

◁— **Put result value into Bundle**

◁— **Set Bundle as data into Message**

◁— **Send Message via Handler**

As we discuss the `getResponseHandlerInstance` method of our helper, we should note that although we find it helpful, it's entirely optional. You can still make use of the helper class without using this method. To do so, construct your own Response-Handler and pass it in to the helper constructor—which is a perfectly plausible case. The `getResponseHandlerInstance` method builds a convenient default Response-Handler that hooks in a `Handler` via a parameter ❶ and parses the response as a String ❷. The response `String` is sent back to the caller using the `Handler  Bundle` and `Message` pattern we have seen used time and time again to pass messages between threads in our Android screens.

With the gory `HttpRequestHelper` details out of the way, and having already explored basic usage, we will next turn to more involved uses of this class in the context of web service calls.

6.5   *Web services*

The term *web services* means many different things depending on the source and the audience. To some it's a nebulous marketing term that is never pinned down; to others it's a very rigid and specific set of protocols and standards. We are going to tackle it as a general concept, without defining it to death, but not leaving it entirely undefined either.

Web services is a means of exposing an API over a technology-neutral network endpoint. It's a means to call a remote method or operation not tied to a specific platform or vendor and get a result. By this definition POX over the network POX is included, so is REST, and so is SOAP—and really so is any other method of exposing operations and data on the wire in a neutral manner.

POX, REST, and SOAP are by far the most common web services around, so they are where we will focus in this section. Each provides a general guideline for accessing data and exposing operations, each in a more rigorous manner than the previous, respectively. POX basically exposes chunks of XML over the wire, usually over HTTP. REST is a bit more detailed in that it uses the concept of *resources* to define data and then manipulates them with different HTTP methods using a URL-style approach (much like the Android `Intent` system in general, which we have explored in previous chapters). SOAP is the most formal of them all, imposing strict rules about types of data, transport mechanisms, and security.

All of these approaches have advantages and disadvantages, and these differences are amplified on a mobile platform like Android. Though we can't possibly cover all the details here, we will touch on the differences as we discuss each of these concepts. We will examine the use of a POX approach to return recent posts from the del.icio.us API, and we will then look at using REST with the Google Data AtomPub API. Up first is what is probably the most ubiquitous type of web service in use on the internet today, and therefore one you will come across again and again when connecting Android applications—POX.

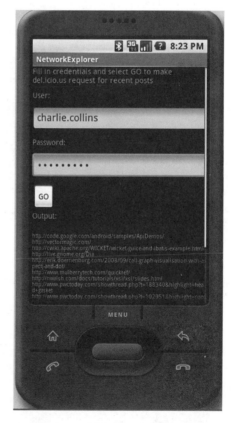

6.5.1 POX—Putting it together with HTTP and XML

To work with POX we are going to make network calls to the popular del.icio.us online social bookmarking site. We will specify a username and password to log in to an HTTPS resource and return a list of recent posts, or *bookmarks*. This service returns raw XML data, and we will then parse it into a JavaBean-style class and display it as shown in figure 6.4.

Figure 6.4 The del.icio.us recent posts screen from the NetworkExplorer application

Listing 6.10 shows the del.icio.us login and HTTPS POST Activity code from our NetworkExplorer application.

Listing 6.10   The del.icio.us HTTPS POX API with authentication from an Activity

```
public class DeliciousRecentPosts extends Activity {

   private static final String CLASSTAG =
      DeliciousRecentPosts.class.getSimpleName();
   private static final String URL_GET_POSTS_RECENT =          ❶ Include
      "https://api.del.icio.us/v1/posts/recent?";                 del.icio.us URL

   . . . member var declarations for user, pass, output,
        and button (Views) omitted for brevity,              ❷ Provide Handler
                                                                to update UI
   private final Handler handler = new Handler() {
      public void handleMessage(final Message msg) {
         progressDialog.dismiss();
         String bundleResult = msg.getData().getString("RESPONSE");
         output.setText(parseXMLResult(bundleResult));
      }
   };

   @Override
   public void onCreate(final Bundle icicle) {
      super.onCreate(icicle);
      this.setContentView(R.layout.delicious_posts);

      . . . inflate views omitted for brevity

      this.button.setOnClickListener(new OnClickListener() {
         public void onClick(final View v) {
            output.setText("");
            performRequest(user.getText().toString(),
               pass.getText().toString());                   ❸ Call local performRequest
         }                                                      with user and passttpClient
      });                                                       execute
   };

   . . . onPause omitted for brevity

   private void performRequest(String user, String pass) {
      this.progressDialog = ProgressDialog.show(this,
         "working . . .", "performing HTTP post to del.icio.us");

      final ResponseHandler<String> responseHandler =
         HTTPRequestHelper.getResponseHandlerInstance(this.handler);

      new Thread() {
         public void run() {
            HTTPRequestHelper helper =
               new HTTPRequestHelper(responseHandler);
            helper.performPost(URL_GET_POSTS_RECENT,          ❹ Use helper
               user, pass, null, null);                          for HTTP
         }
      }.start();
   }
                                                             ❺ Parse XML
   private String parseXMLResult(String xmlString) {            String result
      StringBuilder result = new StringBuilder();
```

```
try {

    SAXParserFactory spf = SAXParserFactory.newInstance();
    SAXParser sp = spf.newSAXParser();
    XMLReader xr = sp.getXMLReader();
    DeliciousHandler handler = new DeliciousHandler();
    xr.setContentHandler(handler);
    xr.parse(new InputSource(new StringReader(xmlString)));

    List<DeliciousPost> posts = handler.getPosts();
    for (DeliciousPost p : posts) {
        result.append("\n" + p.getHref());
    }
} catch (Exception e) {
    // log and or handle
}
    return result.toString();
}
```

To utilize a POX service we need to know a little bit about it, beginning with the URL endpoint ❶. To call the del.icio.us service we will again use a `Handler` to update the UI ❷, and we will use the `HttpRequestHelper` we previously built and walked through in the last section. In this example we again have many fewer lines of code than if we did not use the helper (lines of code we would likely be repeating in different `Activity` classes). With the helper instantiated we call the `performRequest` method with a username and password ❸. This method, via the helper, will log in to del.icio.us and return an XML chunk representing the most recently bookmarked items ❹. To turn the raw XML into useful types we then also include a `parseXMLResult` method ❺. Parsing XML is a subject in its own right, and therefore we will cover it in more detail in chapter 13, but the short takeaway with this method is that we walk the XML structure with a parser and return our own `DeliciousPost` data beans for each record. That's it—that's using POX to read data over HTTPS.

Building on the addition of XML to HTTP, above and beyond POX, is the REST architectural principle, which we will explore next.

6.5.2 *REST*

While we look at REST, we will also try to pull in another useful concept in terms of Android development: working with the various Google Data APIs (http://code.google.com/apis/gdata/). We used the GDATA APIs for our RestaurantFinder review information in chapter 3, but there we didn't authenticate, and we didn't get into the details of networking or REST. Here we will uncover the details as we perform two distinct tasks: authenticate and retrieve a Google `ClientLogin` token and retrieve the Google Contacts data for a specified user. Keep in mind that as we work with the GDATA APIs in any capacity, we will be using a REST-style API.

The main concepts with REST are that you specify resources in a URI form and you use different protocol methods to perform different actions. The Atom Publishing Protocol (AtomPub) defines a REST-style protocol, and the GDATA APIs are an implementation of AtomPub (with some Google extensions). As noted, the entire `Intent`

approach of the Android platform is a lot like REST. A URI such as content://
contacts/1 is in the REST style. It includes a path that identifies the type of data and a
particular resource (contact number 1).

That URI does not say what to do with contact 1, however. In REST terms that's
where the method of the protocol comes into the picture. For HTTP purposes REST
utilizes various methods to perform different tasks: POST (create, update, or in special
cases delete), GET (read), PUT (create, replace), and DELETE (delete). True HTTP REST
implementations use all the HTTP method types and resources to construct APIs.

In the real world you will find very few true REST implementations. It is much more
common to see a REST-style API. That means an API that doesn't typically use the HTTP
DELETE method (many servers, proxies, and so on have trouble with DELETE) and over-
loads the more common GET and POST methods with different URLs for different tasks
(by encoding a bit about what is to be done in the URL, or as a header or parameter,
rather than relying strictly on the method). In fact, though many people refer to the
GDATA APIs as REST, they are technically only REST-like, not true REST. That's not necessarily a bad thing; the idea is ease of use of the API rather than pattern purity. All in
all, REST is a very popular architecture or style, because it's easy yet powerful.

Listing 6.11 is a quick example that focuses on the network aspects of authentication with GDATA to obtain a ClientLogin token and using that token with a subsequent REST-style request to obtain Contacts data by including an email address as a
resource.

Listing 6.11   Using the Google Contacts AtomPub API with authentication

```
public class GoogleClientLogin extends Activity {
    private static final String URL_GET_GTOKEN =
      "https://www.google.com/accounts/ClientLogin";
    private static final String URL_GET_CONTACTS_PREFIX =
      "http://www.google.com/m8/feeds/contacts/";
    private static final String URL_GET_CONTACTS_SUFFIX = "/full";
    private static final String GTOKEN_AUTH_HEADER_NAME = "Authorization";
    private static final String GTOKEN_AUTH_HEADER_VALUE_PREFIX =
      "GoogleLogin auth=";
    private static final String PARAM_ACCOUNT_TYPE = "accountType";
    private static final String PARAM_ACCOUNT_TYPE_VALUE =
      "HOSTED_OR_GOOGLE";
    private static final String PARAM_EMAIL = "Email";
    private static final String PARAM_PASSWD = "Passwd";
    private static final String PARAM_SERVICE = "service";
    private static final String PARAM_SERVICE_VALUE = "cp";
    private static final String PARAM_SOURCE = "source";
    private static final String PARAM_SOURCE_VALUE =
      "manning-unlockingAndroid-1.0";

    private String tokenValue;

    . . . View member declarations omitted for brevity

    private final Handler tokenHandler = new Handler() {
```

**❶ Create Handler
token request**

```
    public void handleMessage(final Message msg) {
        progressDialog.dismiss();
        String bundleResult = msg.getData().getString("RESPONSE");
        String authToken = bundleResult;
        authToken = authToken.substring(authToken.indexOf("Auth=")
            + 5, authToken.length()).trim();
        tokenValue = authToken;                          ◁──── ❷  Set
        GtokenText.setText(authToken);                           tokenValue
    }
};

private final Handler contactsHandler =              ❸  Create Handler for
    new Handler() {                        ◁──────┐     contacts request
      public void handleMessage(final Message msg) {
          progressDialog.dismiss();
          String bundleResult = msg.getData().getString("RESPONSE");
          output.setText(bundleResult);
      }
};

. . . onCreate and onPause omitted for brevity      ❹  Implement
                                                         getToken
private void getToken(String email, String pass) {  ◁────
    final ResponseHandler<String> responseHandler =
      HTTPRequestHelper.getResponseHandlerInstance(
          this.tokenHandler);

    this.progressDialog = ProgressDialog.show(this,
        "working . . .", "getting Google ClientLogin token");

    new Thread() {
       public void run() {
           HashMap<String, String> params =
             new HashMap<String, String>();
           params.put(GoogleClientLogin.PARAM_ACCOUNT_TYPE,
             GoogleClientLogin.PARAM_ACCOUNT_TYPE_VALUE);
           params.put(GoogleClientLogin.PARAM_EMAIL, email);   ❺  Include
           params.put(GoogleClientLogin.PARAM_PASSWD, pass);      necessary
           params.put(GoogleClientLogin.PARAM_SERVICE,            parameters
             GoogleClientLogin.PARAM_SERVICE_VALUE);              for
           params.put(GoogleClientLogin.PARAM_SOURCE,             ClientLogin
            GoogleClientLogin.PARAM_SOURCE_VALUE);

           HTTPRequestHelper helper =
             new HTTPRequestHelper(responseHandler);
           helper.performPost(HTTPRequestHelper.MIME_FORM_ENCODED,
               GoogleClientLogin.URL_GET_GTOKEN,
               null, null, null, params);        ◁──── Perform POST
       }                                         ❻  to get token
    }.start();
}

  private void getContacts(String email, String token) {  ◁────  Implement
      final ResponseHandler<String> responseHandler =         ❼  getContacts
        HTTPRequestHelper.getResponseHandlerInstance(
          this.contactsHandler);

    this.progressDialog = ProgressDialog.show(this,
```

```
        "working . . .", "getting Google Contacts");
    new Thread() {
      public void run() {
        HashMap<String, String> headers =
          new HashMap<String, String>();
        headers.put(GoogleClientLogin.GTOKEN_AUTH_HEADER_NAME,
          GoogleClientLogin.GTOKEN_AUTH_HEADER_VALUE_PREFIX
            + token);
        String encEmail = email;
        try {
          encEmail = URLEncoder.encode(encEmail,
            "UTF-8");
        } catch (UnsupportedEncodingException e) {
          // log and or handle
        }
        String url =
          GoogleClientLogin.URL_GET_CONTACTS_PREFIX + encEmail
            + GoogleClientLogin.URL_GET_CONTACTS_SUFFIX;

        HTTPRequestHelper helper = new
          HTTPRequestHelper(responseHandler);
        helper.performGet(url, null, null, headers);
      }
    }.start();
  }
}
```

8 Add token as header

9 Encode email address in URL

10 Make GET request for Contacts

After a host of constants that represent various `String` values we will use with the GDATA services, we have several `Handler` instances in this class, beginning with a `tokenHandler` **1**. This handler updates a UI `TextView` when it receives a message, like the previous similar examples we have seen, and updates a non–UI member `tokenValue` variable that other portions of our code will use **2**. The next `Handler` we have is the `contactsHandler` that will be used to update the UI after the contacts request **3**.

Beyond the handlers we have the `getToken` method **4**. This method includes all the required parameters for obtaining a `ClientLogin` token from the GDATA servers (http://code.google.com/apis/gdata/auth.html) **5**. After the setup to obtain the token, we make a `POST` request via the request helper **6**.

Once the token details are taken care of, we have the `getContacts` method **7**. This method uses the token obtained via the previous method as a header **8**. After you have the token you can cache it and use it with all subsequent requests (you don't need to re-obtain the token every time). Next we encode the email address portion of the Contacts API URL **9**, and we make a `GET` request for the data—again using the `HttpRequestHelper` **10**.

With this approach we are making several network calls (one as HTTPS to get the token and another as HTTP to get data) using our previously defined helper class. When the results are returned from the GDATA API, we parse the XML block and update the UI.

> **GDATA ClientLogin and CAPTCHA**
>
> While we have included a working `ClientLogin` example here, we have also skipped over an important part—CAPTCHA. Google may optionally require a CAPTCHA with the `ClientLogin` approach. To fully support `ClientLogin` you need to handle that response and display the CAPTCHA to the user, then resend a token request with the user's entered CAPTCHA value. For details see the GDATA documentation.

Now that we have explored some REST-style networking, the last thing we need to discuss with regard to HTTP and Android is SOAP. This topic comes up frequently in discussions of networking mobile devices, but sometimes the forest gets in the way of the trees in terms of framing the real question.

6.5.3 *To SOAP or not to SOAP, that is the question*

SOAP is a powerful protocol that has many uses. We would be remiss if we didn't at least mention that while it's possible, it's not generally recommended on a small, embedded device like a smartphone, regardless of the platform. The question within the limited resources environment Android inhabits is really more one of *should* it be done rather than *can* it be done.

Surely some experienced developers, who may have been using SOAP for years on other devices, are snarling at this sentiment right now. To those of you in that camp we would ask you to bear with us as we try to explain. The things that make SOAP great are its support for strong types (via XML Schema), its support for transactions, its security and encryption, its support for message orchestration and choreography, and all the related WS-* standards. These things are invaluable in many server-oriented computing environments, whether or not they involve the enterprise. And these things add a great deal of overhead, especially on a small, embedded device. In fact, in many situations where people use SOAP on embedded devices, they often don't bother with the advanced features—and they use plain XML with the overhead of an envelope at the end of the day anyway. On an embedded device you will often get better performance, and a simpler design, by using a REST- or POX-style architecture and avoiding the overhead of SOAP.

There are, of course, some situations where it makes sense to investigate using SOAP directly with Android. In the case where you need to talk to existing SOAP services that you have no control over, SOAP might make sense. Also, if you already have J2ME clients for existing SOAP services, you may be able to port those in a limited set of cases. Yet, either of these approaches makes it easier on only you, the developer, and has either no effect or a negative one in terms of performance on the user. Even when you are working with existing SOAP services, remember that you can often write a POX/REST-style proxy for SOAP services on the server side and call that from Android, rather than using SOAP directly from Android.

If you feel like SOAP is still the right choice, you can use one of several ports of the kSOAP toolkit (http://ksoap2.sourceforge.net/), which is specially designed exactly for SOAP on an embedded Java device. Keep in mind, though, even the kSOAP documentation states, "SOAP introduces some significant overhead for web services that may be problematic for mobile devices. If you have full control over the client and the server, a REST-based architecture may be more adequate." In addition, you may be able to write your own parser for simple SOAP services that don't use fancy SOAP features and just use a POX approach that includes the SOAP XML portions you require (you can always roll your own, even with SOAP).

All in all, in our minds the answer to the question is not to use SOAP on Android, even though you can. Our discussion of SOAP, even though we don't advocate it, rounds out our more general web services discussion, and that wraps up our networking coverage.

6.6   *Summary*

In this chapter we started with a brief lesson on the background of basic networking concepts, from nodes and addresses to layers and protocols. With that general background in place, we covered details concerning obtaining network status information and showed several different ways to work with the IP networking capabilities of the platform.

In terms of networking we looked at using basic sockets and the `java.net` package. Then we also examined the included Apache HttpClient API. HTTP is one of the most common, and most important, networking resources available to the Android platform. Using HttpClient we covered a lot of territory in terms of different request types, parameters, headers, authentication, and more. Beyond basic HTTP we also extended into the concepts of POX and REST, and we discussed a bit of SOAP—all of which use HTTP as the transport mechanism.

Now that we have covered a good deal of the networking possibilities, and hopefully given you at least a glint of an idea of what you can do with server-side APIs and integration with Android, we are going to turn to another very important part of the Android world—telephony.

Telephony

With an Android device you can surf the web, store and retrieve data locally, access networks, access location information, use many types of applications, and—get this— actually make phone calls.

After all is said and done, one of the most fundamental components of the platform is the mobile phone. Dialing out, receiving calls, sending and receiving text and multimedia messages, and other related telephony services are all available. The added bonus with Android is that all of these items are accessible to developers through simple-to-use APIs and built-in applications that make use of intents and services. You can use the telephony support Android provides quite easily, and you can combine it and embed it in your own applications (as you have seen in previous examples).

In this chapter we will examine a bit of telephony background and cover terms involved with a mobile device. We will move on to basic Android telephony packages, which will take us through handling calls using built-in `Intent` actions and examining the `TelephonyManager` and `PhoneStateListener` classes. The `Intent` actions are what you will use on a day-to-day basis to initiate phone calls in your applications. `TelephonyManager` is, on the other hand, not related to making calls but rather is used to retrieve all kinds of telephony-related data, such as the state of the voice network, the device's own phone number, and Subscriber Identity Module (SIM) card details. Using `TelephonyManager` is also how you attach a `PhoneStateListener`, which can alert you when call or phone network states change.

Once we have basic telephony APIs in hand, we will move on to working with another very common mobile phone feature—sending and receiving SMS messages. Android provides intents and built-in applications for handling SMS messages as well as APIs that allow you to send SMS messages and be notified when SMS messages are received.

We will also touch on emulator features that allow you to send in test calls and/or messages to exercise your applications.

We are once again going to use a sample application to carry us through the concepts related to the material in this chapter. We will be building a TelephonyExplorer application to demonstrate dialing the phone, obtaining phone and service state information, adding listeners to the phone state, and working with SMS. Our TelephonyExplorer application will have several basic screens, as shown in figure 7.1.

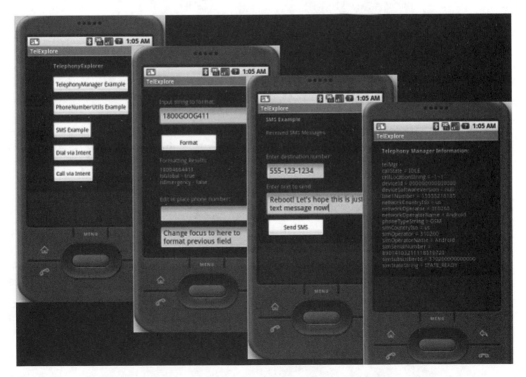

Figure 7.1   TelephonyExplorer main screen, showing all the related activities the sample application performs

TelephonyExplorer, as you can see from the screen shot, is not pretty, nor is it very practical outside of learning the concepts and API details involved. This application is focused on touching the telephony-related APIs while remaining simple and uncluttered.

Before we begin to build TelephonyExplorer, the first thing we first need to clarify what telephony is and learn the terminology.

7.1 *Telephony background and terms*

This basic information about telephony may not be new to experienced mobile developers (if that describes you, feel free to skip to the next section), but it's important to clarify terms and set out some background for those who are new to these concepts.

First, *telephony* is a general term that refers to the details surrounding electronic voice communications over telephone networks. Our scope is, of course, the mobile telephone network that Android devices will participate in, specifically the Global System for Mobile Communications (GSM) network.

NOTE *Telephone* The term *telephone* means "speech over a distance." The Greek roots are tele, which means "distant," and *phone*, which means "speech."

GSM is a cellular telephone network. Devices communicate over radio waves and specified frequencies using the cell towers that are common across the landscape. This means the GSM standard has to define a few important things, such as identities for devices and "cells," along with all of the rules for making communications possible.

We won't delve into the underlying details of GSM, but it's important to know that it's the standard that the Android stack currently uses to support voice calls—and it's the most widely used standard in the world across carriers and devices, Android or otherwise. All GSM devices use a SIM card to store all the important network and user settings.

A SIM card is a small, removable, and secure smart card. Every device that operates on a GSM network has specific unique identifiers, which are stored on the SIM card:

- *Integrated Circuit Card ID (ICCID)*—Identifies a SIM card (also known as a SIM Serial Number, or SSN).
- *International Mobile Equipment Identity (IMEI)*—Identifies a physical device. (The number is usually printed underneath the battery).
- *International Mobile Subscriber Identity (IMSI)*—Identifies a subscriber (and the network that subscriber is on).
- *Location Area Identity (LAI)*—Identifies the region the device is in within a provider network.
- *Authentication Key (Ki)*—A 128-bit key used to authenticate a SIM card on this provider network. A 128-bit key.

These numbers are important for the obvious reasons that they are used to validate and authenticate a SIM card itself, the device it is in, and the subscriber on the network (and across networks if need be).

Along with storing unique identifiers and authentication keys, SIM cards often are capable of storing user contacts and SMS messages. This is convenient for users because they can move their SIM card to a new device and carry along contact and message data easily. At present there are no public APIs for interacting with the SIM card on an Android device directly, though this may become possible in the future. (At present, the platform handles the SIM interaction, and developers can get read-only access via the telephony APIs).

The basic background for working with the Android telephony packages really is that short and simple. You need to know that you are working with a GSM network, and then you need to be aware that you may come across terms like IMSI and IMEI, which are stored on the SIM. Getting at this information, and more, is done with the `TelephonyManager` class.

7.2   *Accessing telephony information*

Android provides a very informative manager class that supplies information about many telephony-related details on the device. Using this class, `TelephonyManager`, you can access many of the GSM/SIM properties we have already discussed, and you can obtain phone network state information and updates.

Attaching an event listener to the phone, in the form of a `PhoneStateListener`, which is done via the manager, is how you can make your applications aware of when phone service is and is not available and when calls are started, in progress, or ending, and more.

Here we are going to examine several parts of the TelephonyExplorer example application to look at both of these classes and concepts, starting with obtaining a `TelephonyManager` instance and using it to query useful telephony information.

7.2.1   *Retrieving telephony properties*

The `android.telephony` package contains the `TelephonyManager` class, and it has details on all of the information you can obtain using it. Here we are going to get and display a small subset of that information to demonstrate the approach. The first `Activity`, beyond the main screen, our TelephonyExplorer application will have is a simple screen that shows some of the information we can obtain via `TelephonyManager`, as shown in figure 7.2.

Figure 7.2   Displaying device and phone network metainformation obtained from the `TelephonyManager` class

The TelephonyManager class is the information hub for telephony-related data in Android. Listing 7.1 demonstrates how you obtain a reference to this class and use it to retrieve data (such as the data shown in figure 7.2).

Listing 7.1 Obtaining a `TelephonyManager` reference and using it to retrieve data

```
// . . . start of class omitted for brevity

final TelephonyManager telMgr =
  (TelephonyManager) this.getSystemService(        ❶ Get TelephonyManager
  Context.TELEPHONY_SERVICE);                          from Context

// . . . onCreate method and others omitted for brevity

public String getTelephonyOverview(       ❷ Implement information
  TelephonyManager telMgr) {                  helper method

  int callState = telMgr.getCallState();          Obtain call state
  String callStateString = "NA";            ❸ information
  switch (callState) {
  case TelephonyManager.CALL_STATE_IDLE:
    callStateString = "IDLE";
    break;
  case TelephonyManager.CALL_STATE_OFFHOOK:
    callStateString = "OFFHOOK";
    break;
  case TelephonyManager.CALL_STATE_RINGING:
    callStateString = "RINGING";
    break;
  }

  GsmCellLocation cellLocation =
    (GsmCellLocation) telMgr.getCellLocation();
  String cellLocationString =
    cellLocation.getLac() + " " + cellLocation.getCid();

  String deviceId = telMgr.getDeviceId();        ❹ Get cell location
  String deviceSoftwareVersion =                    information
    telMgr.getDeviceSoftwareVersion();

  String line1Number = telMgr.getLine1Number();

  String networkCountryIso = telMgr.getNetworkCountryIso();

  String networkOperator = telMgr.getNetworkOperator();
  String networkOperatorName = telMgr.getNetworkOperatorName();

  int phoneType = telMgr.getPhoneType();         Get device
  String phoneTypeString = "NA";                 information ❺
  switch (phoneType) {
  case TelephonyManager.PHONE_TYPE_GSM:
    phoneTypeString = "GSM";
    break;
  case TelephonyManager.PHONE_TYPE_NONE:
    phoneTypeString = "NONE";
    break;
  }
```

```
String simCountryIso = telMgr.getSimCountryIso();
String simOperator = telMgr.getSimOperator();
String simOperatorName = telMgr.getSimOperatorName();
String simSerialNumber = telMgr.getSimSerialNumber();
String simSubscriberId = telMgr.getSubscriberId();
int simState = telMgr.getSimState();
String simStateString = "NA";
switch (simState) {
case TelephonyManager.SIM_STATE_ABSENT:
  simStateString = "ABSENT";
  break;
case TelephonyManager.SIM_STATE_NETWORK_LOCKED:
  simStateString = "NETWORK_LOCKED";
  break;
// . . . other SIM states omitted for brevity
}

StringBuilder sb = new StringBuilder();
sb.append("telMgr - ");
sb.append(" \ncallState = " + callStateString);

// . . . remainder of appends omitted for brevity

return sb.toString();
}
```

6 Get cellGet phone number of device location information

7 Obtain SIM information

The Android Context is used, through the getSystemService method with a constant, to obtain an instance of the TelephonyManager class **1**. Once you have a handle to the manager, you can use it as needed to obtain information. In this case we have created a helper method to get data from the manager and return it as a String we later display on the screen **2**.

The manager allows you to access phone state data, such as whether or not a call is in progress **3**, cell location information **4**, the device ID and software version **5**, the phone number registered to the current user/SIM **6**, and many other SIM details such as the subscriber ID (IMSI) **7**. There are additional properties that we are not using in this example (see the Javadocs for complete details).

Note one more detail here not shown in the listing. In order for this class to work, the READ_PHONE_STATE permission has to be set in the manifest (without it security exceptions will be thrown when you try to read data from the manager). We have consolidated the phone-related permissions into table 7.1, in section 7.3.1.

This handle to the telephony-related information, including metadata about the device, network, and SIM card, is one of the main purposes of the Telephony-Manager class. The other main purpose of TelephonyManager is to allow you to attach a PhoneStateListener.

7.2.2 *Obtaining phone state information*

Obviously a phone has various states that it as a device can be in. The most basic phone states are idle, in a call, or in the process of initiating a call. When building applications on a mobile device, there are times when you not only need to know the current phone state but also want to be alerted anytime the state changes.

In these cases you want to attach a listener to the phone and "subscribe" so that you can be notified of "published" changes. With Android this is done using a PhoneState-Listener, which is attached to the phone through TelephonyManager. Listing 7.2 demonstrates a sample usage of both of these classes.

Listing 7.2 Attaching a PhoneStateListener via the TelephonyManager

```
@Override
public void onStart() {
   super.onStart();

   final TelephonyManager telMgr =
       (TelephonyManager)
         this.getSystemService(                    ❶ Obtain TelephonyManager
           Context.TELEPHONY_SERVICE);    ◁───       from Context

   PhoneStateListener phoneStateListener =     ❷ Create
     new PhoneStateListener() {          ◁───      PhoneStateListener
       public void onCallStateChanged(
         int state, String incomingNumber) {                    ◁──
           telMgrOutput.setText(getTelephonyOverview(telMgr));
       }
   };                                             Implement
   telMgr.listen(phoneStateListener,      onCallStateChanged method ❸
     PhoneStateListener.LISTEN_CALL_STATE);                    ◁──

   String telephonyOverview = this.getTelephonyOverview(telMgr);
   this.telMgrOutput.setText(telephonyOverview);
}                                              Assign listener
                                                 to manager ❹
```

To start working with a PhoneStateListener you need an instance of Telephony-Manager, so you can later assign the listener ❶. PhoneStateListener itself is an interface, so you need to create an implementation ❷, including the onCallStateChanged required method, in order to use it ❸. Once you have a PhoneStateListener instance (your own implementation that implements the interface), you attach it by assigning it to the manager with the listen method ❹.

In the example in listing 7.2 we are listening for any PhoneStateListener. LISTEN_CALL_STATE change in the phone state. This is a constant value from a list of available states that can be seen on the PhoneStateListener class. You can use a single value when assigning a listener with the listen method, as we have done here, or you can combine multiple values.

If a call state change does occur, we reset the details on the screen using the getTelephonyOverview method we used for setting the initial status in listing 7.1. The action you take is defined in the onCallStateChanged method of your PhoneState-Listener. You can filter further in this method too (apart from the types of events you are listening for), based on the passed-in int state, if you need to.

To see the values in this example change while working with the emulator, you can use the SDK tools to send incoming calls or text messages and change the state of the voice connection. The emulator includes a mock GSM modem that you can manipulate using the gsm command from the console. Figure 7.3 shows an example session from the

```
ccollins@crotalus:/opt/android/tools$ telnet localhost 5554
Trying 127.0.0.1...
Connected to localhost.
Escape character is '^]'.
Android Console: type 'help' for a list of commands
OK
gsm
allows you to change GSM-related settings, or to make a new inbound phone call

available sub-commands:
    list            list current phone calls
    call            create inbound phone call
    busy            close waiting outbound call as busy
    hold            change the state of an oubtound call to 'held'
    accept          change the state of an outbound call to 'active'
    cancel          disconnect an inbound or outbound phone call
    data            modify data connection state
    voice           modify voice connection state
    status          display GSM status
```

Figure 7.3   An Android console session demonstrating the `gsm` command and available subcommands

console that demonstrates this. For complete details see the emulator telephony documentation (http://code.google.com/android/reference/emulator.html-telephony).

With many of the larger telephony background details now complete, in the next few sections of this chapter we're going to cover basic uses of the telephony APIs and other related facilities. We will examine intercepting calls, using some of the telephony utility classes, and making calls from your applications.

7.3   *Interacting with the phone*

In your day-to-day development you will often want to interact with the phone. This interaction may be as simple as dialing outbound calls through built-in intents, or it may involve intercepting calls to modify them in some way. In this section we are going to cover these basic tasks, and we will examine some of the phone number utilities Android provides for you out of the box.

One of the more common things you will do with the Android telephony support doesn't involve the telephony APIs directly, and that is making calls using the built-in intents.

7.3.1   *Using intents to make calls*

As we demonstrated in chapter 4, using the `Intent.ACTION_CALL` action and the `tel:` Uri is all you need to invoke the built-in dialer application and make a call. This approach will invoke the dialer application, populate the dialer with the provided telephone number (taken from the Uri), and initiate the call.

Along with this action you can also invoke the dialer application with the `Intent.ACTION_DIAL` action, which will again populate the dialer with the supplied phone number but stop short of initiating the call. Listing 7.3 demonstrates both techniques using the respective actions.

Listing 7.3 Using `Intent` actions to dial and call using the built-in dialer application

```
dialintent = (Button) findViewById(R.id.dialintent_button);
    dialintent.setOnClickListener(new OnClickListener() {
            public void onClick(View v) {
                Intent intent =
                    new Intent(Intent.DIAL_ACTION,
                        Uri.parse("tel:" + NUMBER));
                startActivity(intent);
            }
        });

    callintent = (Button) findViewById(R.id.callintent_button);
    callintent.setOnClickListener(new OnClickListener() {
            public void onClick(View v) {
                Intent intent =
                    new Intent(Intent.CALL_ACTION,
                        Uri.parse("tel:" + NUMBER));
                startActivity(intent);
            }
        });
```

❶ **Usage of DIAL_ACTION**

❷ **Including the tel:number Uri**

❸ **Usage of CALL_ACTION**

At this point we have covered the usage of intents and the Android platform design quite a bit. In listing 7.3 we are once again leveraging this design, to make outgoing calls to specified numbers.

Making calls using the built-in intents through the dialer application is very simple, as we have already shown in previous examples. Basically you need to set the action you want to take place, either populating the dialer with `ACTION_DIAL` ❶ or populating the dialer *and* initiating a call with `ACTION_CALL` ❸. In either case you also need to specify the telephone number you want to use with the `Intent Uri` ❷.

The only other aspect of dialing calls you need to be aware of is permissions. The correct permissions are required in your application manifest in order to be able to access and modify phone state, dial the phone, or intercept phone calls (which we will examine in section 7.3.3). Table 7.1 lists the relevant phone-related permissions and their purposes (for more detailed information see the security section of the Android documentation: http://code.google.com/android/devel/security.html).

Table 7.1 Phone-related manifest permissions and their purpose

Phone-related permission	Purpose
`android.permission.READ_PHONE_STATE`	Allow application to read phone state
`android.permission.MODIFY_PHONE_STATE`	Allow application to modify phone state
`android.permission.CALL_PHONE`	Initiate a phone call without user confirmation in dialer
`android.permission.CALL_PRIVILEGED`	Call any number, including emergency, without confirmation in dialer
`android.permission.PROCESS_OUTGOING_CALLS`	Allow application to receive broadcast for outgoing calls and modify

Dialing from an Android application is very straightforward. The built-in handling via intents and the dialer application make it almost trivial. Helping even more in terms of "making it nice for the people" is the additional `PhoneNumberUtils` class, which you can use to parse and validate phone number strings.

7.3.2   *Helpful phone number–related utilities*

Applications running on mobile devices that support telephony get to experience the joy of dealing with a good deal of `String` formatting for phone numbers. Fortunately, in the Android SDK there is a handy utility class that helps to mitigate the risks associated with this task and standardize the way it's done—`PhoneNumberUtils`.

The `PhoneNumberUtils` class can be used to parse `String` data into phone numbers, parse alphabetical keypad digits into numbers, and determine other properties of phone numbers (such as whether or not they are global or localized). An example usage of this class is shown in listing 7.4.

Listing 7.4   Working with the `PhoneNumberUtils` class

```
. . .

private TextView pnOutput;
private EditText pnInput;
private EditText pnInPlaceInput;
private Button pnFormat;

. . .

this.pnFormat.setOnClickListener(new OnClickListener() {
  public void onClick(View v) {                               ① Format as
    String phoneNumber = PhoneNumberUtils.formatNumber(          phone number
      pnInput.getText().toString());
    phoneNumber = PhoneNumberUtils.convertKeypadLettersToDigits(
      pnInput.getText().toString());
                                                               ② Convert alpha
    StringBuilder result = new StringBuilder();                  characters to digits
    result.append(phoneNumber);
    result.append("\nisGlobal - "
      + PhoneNumberUtils.isGlobalPhoneNumber(phoneNumber));
    result.append("\nisEmergency - "
      + PhoneNumberUtils.isEmergencyNumber(phoneNumber));

    pnOutput.setText(result.toString());                       Use additional phone
    pnInput.setText("");                                       number utilities   ③
  }
});
```

The `PhoneNumberUtils` class has a number of static helper methods for parsing phone numbers, the simplest of which is `formatNumber`. This method takes a single `String` as input and uses the default locale settings to return a formatted phone number ① (there are additional methods to format a number using a locale you specify, to parse different segments of a number, and so on). Parsing a number can be combined with another helpful method, `convertKeypadLettersToDigits`, to further convert any alphabetic keypad letter characters into digits ❷. The conversion method won't work unless it already recognizes the format of a phone number, so in this case it's important to run the format method first.

Along with these basic methods you can also check properties of a number string, such as whether the number is global and whether it represents an emergency call ❸.

An additional way to format a phone number that is useful for any `Editable`, such as the very common `EditText` (or `TextView`), is the `formatNumber` overload that edits these in place. This method updates an `EditText` that is passed in when it is invoked. An example of using this is shown in listing 7.5.

Listing 7.5 Using in-place `Editable View` **formatting via** `PhoneNumberUtils`

```
this.pnInPlaceInput.setOnFocusChangeListener(        ❶ Use OnFocusChangeListener
  new OnFocusChangeListener() {                          for update
    public void onFocusChange(View v, boolean b) {
      if (v.equals(pnInPlaceInput) && (b == false)) {
        PhoneNumberUtils.formatNumber(
          pnInPlaceInput.getText(),            ❷ Call formatNumber
            PhoneNumberUtils.FORMAT_NANP);        method
      }
    }
  }
});
```

The in-place editor can be combined with a dynamic update step using various techniques; one way is to make the update happen automatically when the focus changes away from a phone number field (curiously though, the in-place edit does not also provide the keypad alphabetic character-to-number conversion automatically). To do this we have implemented an `OnFocusChangeListener` ❶. Inside the `onFocusChange` method, which filters for the correct `View` item, we call the `formatNumber` overload, passing in the respective `Editable` and the formatting style we want to use ❷. The `NANP` here stands for North American Numbering Plan, which includes an optional country and area code and a seven-digit phone number.

Apart from using the phone number utilities and making calls, you may also need to intercept calls.

7.3.3 *Intercepting calls*

There are many reasons you may want to intercept calls. For example, you may want to write an application that is aware of incoming phone calls and changes the ringer or uses other different alerts based on the caller. In addition, you may want to write an application that catches outgoing calls and decorates or aborts them, based on certain criteria.

Intercepting outgoing calls is supported in the current Android SDK release, but unfortunately the same is not true of incoming calls. Currently incoming calls cannot be intercepted. Users can still change the ringer and other options for their contacts, but all of that is based on the built-in applications and is not something that's available to you as a developer through the APIs.

Because of the limitations in the API, we will focus on what an intercept for an outgoing call looks like, which is shown in listing 7.6.

Listing 7.6   Catching and aborting an outgoing call

```
public class OutgoingCallReceiver extends BroadcastReceiver {          ← ❶ Create
                                                                            broadcast
    public static final String ABORT_PHONE_NUMBER = "1231231234";           receiver

    private static final String OUTGOING_CALL_ACTION =
        "android.intent.action.NEW_OUTGOING_CALL";            ← ❷ Define constant for
    private static final String INTENT_PHONE_NUMBER =            NEW_OUTGOING_CALL
      "android.intent.extra.PHONE_NUMBER";                   ←

    @Override
    public void onReceive(Context context, Intent intent) {    ← ❹ Override
        if (intent.getAction().equals(                              onReceive
          OutgoingCallReceiver.OUTGOING_CALL_ACTION))        ←

        String phoneNumber =                       Filter Intent for action ❺
          intent.getExtras().getString(INTENT_PHONE_NUMBER);      ←
        if ((phoneNumber != null)                  Get Intent extras data ❺
            && phoneNumber.equals(
            OutgoingCallReceiver.ABORT_PHONE_NUMBER)) {     Define constant for
        Toast.makeText(context,                              PHONE_NUMBER ❸
          "NEW_OUTGOING_CALL intercepted to number "
          + "123-123-1234 - aborting call",

          Toast.LENGTH_LONG).show();             ←        Show
          this.abortBroadcast();              ←          quick
        }                                                message
      }                     Abort Intent ❽           ❼
    }
  }
}
```

The first thing we do to intercept an outgoing call is to extend BroadcastReceiver ❶. Our receiver defines several constants, one for the NEW_OUTGOING_CALL action ❷ and one for the phone number data key, PHONE_NUMBER ❸.

For a BroadcastReceiver we have to implement the onReceive method ❹. Within this method we filter on the Intent action we want, android.intent. action.NEW_OUTGOING_CALL ❺, then we get the Intent data using the phone number key ❻. If the phone number matches, we send a Toast alert to the UI ❼ and abort the outgoing call by calling the abortBroadcast method ❽.

Beyond dialing out, formatting numbers, and intercepting calls, another important area of the telephony support in Android is the support for sending and receiving SMS.

7.4   *Working with messaging: SMS*

SMS is a hugely popular and important means of communication for mobile devices. SMS is used to send simple text messages and small amounts of data. Android includes a built-in SMS application that allows users to view received SMS messages and send messages (including replying to received messages). Along with the built-in user-facing support and the related ContentProvider for interacting with the built-in system, the SDK provides APIs for developers to be able to send and receive messages programmatically.

To explore this support we are going to look at both sides of the coin, sending and receiving. The unadorned screen in figure 7.4 shows the SMS-related `Activity` we will build in the Tele-phonyExplorer application.

To get started working with SMS, we will send SMS messages using the support provided by the `SmsManager`.

7.4.1 Sending SMS messages

The `android.telephony.gsm` subpackage contains the `SmsManager` and `SmsMessage` classes. These are our SMS friends. The `SmsManager` is used to define many important SMS-related constants, and it contains the `sendData-Message`, `sendMultipartTextMessage`, and `sendTextMessage` methods.

In listing 7.7 we have an example from our TelephonyExplorer application of using the SMS manager to send a simple text message.

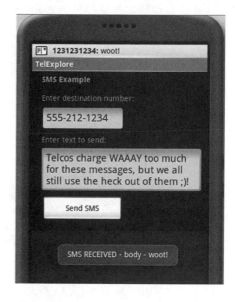

Figure 7.4 An `Activity` that sends SMS messages and an example of an alert based on a received SMS message

Listing 7.7 Using the `SmsManager` to send SMS messages

```
// . . . start of class omitted for brevity
    private Button smsSend;
    private SmsManager smsManager;

    @Override
    public void onCreate(Bundle icicle) {

        super.onCreate(icicle);
        this.setContentView(R.layout.smsexample);

        // . . . other onCreate view item inflation omitted for brevity

        this.smsSend = (Button) findViewById(R.id.smssend_button);

        this.smsManager = SmsManager.getDefault();          Get SmsManager
                                                        ❶ handle
        final PendingIntent sentIntent =
          PendingIntent.getActivity(
            this, 0, new Intent(this,          ❷ Create PendingIntent
            SmsSendCheck.class), 0);              for post action

        this.smsSend.setOnClickListener(new OnClickListener() {
            public void onClick(View v) {
                String dest = smsInputDest.getText().toString();
                if (PhoneNumberUtils.
                    isWellFormedSmsAddress(dest)) {          Check destination
                        smsManager.sendTextMessage(        ❸ is valid
                          smsInputDest.getText().toString, null,
                          smsInputText.getText().toString(),
```

```
                        sentIntent, null);            ⊲——❹ Send message
                Toast.makeText(SmsExample.this,
                  "SMS message sent",
                   Toast.LENGTH_LONG).show();
              } else {
                Toast.makeText(SmsExample.this,
                  "SMS destination invalid - try again",
                   Toast.LENGTH_LONG).show();
              }
            }
          });
      }
```

The first thing we need to do in regard to working with SMS messages is obtain an instance of the SmsManager, which is done with the static getDefault method ❶. The manager will be used later to send the message. Before we can do that, though, we need to create a PendingIntent (which will be used as a parameter in the send method coming up).

What is a PendingIntent?

A PendingIntent is a specification of a future intent. It is basically a way for you to pass a future Intent to another application and allow that application to execute that Intent as if it had the same permissions as your application, whether or not your application is still around when the Intent is eventually invoked. Remember the Activity lifecycle and the separate process logic that the platform uses. A PendingIntent provides a means for applications to, in essence, work "beyond the grave" for a particular Intent. Even after an owning application that creates a PendingIntent has been killed, that Intent can still be run later.

A PendingIntent can specify an Activity, Broadcast, or Service that it requires. In our case we are using the getActivity method, which denotes an Activity, and then we are specifying the context, request code (which is unused), the Intent, and additional flags ❷. The flags indicate whether or not a new instance of the referenced Activity (or Broadcast or Service) should be created if one does not already exist.

Once we have a PendingIntent, we check that the destination address is valid for SMS (using another method from PhoneNumberUtils) ❸, and we send the message using the manager's sendTextMessage method ❹.

This send method takes in several parameters, one of which can be confusing. The signature of this method is as follows:

```
sendDataMessage(String destinationAddress, String scAddress, short
   destinationPort, byte[] data, PendingIntent sentIntent, PendingIntent
   deliveryIntent)
```

The destinationAddress is simple; this is the phone number you want to send the message to. The scAddress is the tricky one. This is not meant to be the source address, but rather it indicates the internal service center address on the network; this should be left null in most cases (which uses the default). The destinationPort is also simple; it's the port. The data is the payload of the message. Finally, the sent-Intent and deliveryIntent are separate PendingIntent instances that are fired when the message is successfully sent and received, respectively.

Much like the permissions we listed in table 7.1 in reference to phone permissions, SMS-related tasks also require manifest permissions. The SMS-related permissions are shown in table 7.2.

Table 7.2 SMS-related manifest permissions and their purpose

Phone-related permission	Purpose
android.permission.RECEIVE_SMS	Allow application to monitor incoming SMS messages
android.permission.READ_SMS	Allow application to read SMS messages
android.permission.SEND_SMS	Allow application to send SMS messages
android.permission.WRITE_SMS	Write SMS messages to the built-in SMS provider (not related to sending messages directly)

Along with sending text and data messages using this basic pattern, you can create an SMS-related BroadcastReceiver to receive incoming SMS messages.

7.4.2 Receiving SMS messages

Receiving an SMS message programmatically is done through receiving a broadcast on the Android platform. To demonstrate this with our TelephonyExplorer application, we are again going to implement a receiver, as shown in listing 7.8.

Listing 7.8 Creating an SMS-related BroadcastReceiver

```
public class SmsReceiver extends BroadcastReceiver {        ◁ ─┐ Extend
   public static final String SMSRECEIVED = "SMSR";           ❶ BroadcastReceiver
   private static final String SMS_REC_ACTION =
    "android.provider.Telephony.SMS_RECEIVED";             ◁ ─┐ Define constant
                                                             SMS_RECEIVED
   @Override                                                ❷ action
   public void onReceive(fContext context, Intent intent) {

       if (intent.getAction().
          equals(SmsReceiver.SMS_REC_ACTION)) {           ◁ ─┐ Filter for action
          StringBuilder sb = new StringBuilder();            ❸ in receiver

          Bundle bundle = intent.getExtras();
          if (bundle != null) {                                ❹ Get pdus from
             Object[] pdus = (Object[]) bundle.get("pdus");  ◁ ─┘ Intent Bundle
             for (Object pdu : pdus) {
                SmsMessage smsMessage =                       ❺ Create SmsMessage
                   SmsMessage.createFromPdu((byte[]) pdu);  ◁ ─┘ from pdus
                sb.append("body - "
                   + smsMessage.getDisplayMessageBody());  ◁ ─┐ Get message
             }                                                ❻ body for display
          }
```

```
            Toast.makeText(context, "SMS RECEIVED - "
                + sb.toString(), Toast.LENGTH_LONG).show();
        }
    }
}
```

To react to an incoming SMS message we once again are creating a BroadcastReceiver by extending that class ❶. Our receiver defines a local constant for the Intent action it wants to catch, in this case android.provider.Telephony.SMS_RECEIVED ❷.

Once the class setup is ready, we filter for the action we want in the onReceive method ❸, and we get the SMS data from the Intent "extras" Bundle using the key pdus ❹. PDU, or Protocol Data Unit, is the term that describes the data packet in SMS messages. In this case the platform is using the String key pdus (we discovered this by trial and error, by getting the key Set from the Bundle and iterating it). For every pdu Object we then construct an SmsMessage by casting the data to a byte array ❺. Once this is in SmsMessage form, we can work with the methods on that class, such as get-DisplayMessageBody ❻.

Sending and receiving messages in SMS form completes our exploration of the telephony APIs.

7.5 *Summary*

In our trip through the Android telephony-related APIs we covered several important topics. We began with a brief overview of some of the telephony terms, and then we moved on to the Android-specific APIs.

With the APIs we looked at accessing telephony information with the Telephony-Manager, including device and SIM card data and phone state. From there we also addressed hooking in a PhoneStateListener to get updates when the phone state changed and reacting to such events.

Beyond retrieving the data we also looked at dialing the phone using built-in intents and actions, intercepting outgoing phone calls, and using the PhoneNumber-Utils class in several ways. After we covered the standard voice usages, we addressed SMS messaging. Here we looked at how to send and receive SMS messages using the SmsManager and SmsMessage classes.

In the next chapter we turn to the specifics of dealing with notifications and alerts on the Android platform.

Notifications and alarms

Today's cell phones are expected to be not only phones but personal assistants, cameras, music and video players, instant-messaging clients, as well as just about everything else a computer might do. With all these applications running on phones, applications need a way to notify users to get their attention or to take some sort of action whether in response to a SMS, to a new voicemail, or to an `Alarm` reminding them of a new appointment.

In this chapter we are going to look at how to use the Android Broadcast-Receiver and the AlarmManager to notify users of just these sorts of events. You will learn what a `Toast` is, what a `Notification` is, how to use the NotificationManager, and how to display a `Notification` to the user or trigger some other action. You will also learn how to create an `Alarm` and use the AlarmManager to schedule your `Alarm` events. Before we go too deeply into how notifications work, let us first create a simple example application.

8.1   *Introducing Toast*

For our example we will create a simple Receiver class that listens for an SMS text message and when a message arrives briefly pops up a message, called a Toast, to the user with the content of the message. A Toast is a simple, nonpersistent message designed to alert the user of some occurring event. Toasts are a great way to let a user know that a call is coming in, an SMS or email has arrived, or some other event has just happened.

To look at how we can use a Toast, let's create a simple example. To build the example, first create a new project called SMSNotifyExample in Eclipse. You can use whatever package name you like, but for this chapter we will use com.msi.manning.chapter8. Now that we have created the project, let's edit AndroidManifest.xml. You will need to add tags so that your AndroidManifest.xml file looks like listing 8.1.

Listing 8.1   AndroidManifest.xml for SMSNotifyExample

```
<?xml version="1.0" encoding="utf-8"?>          Define user permissions to allow SMS messages ❶
<manifest xmlns:android="http://schemas.android.com/apk/res/android"
    package="com.msi.manning.chapter8">
    <uses-permission android:name="android.permission.RECEIVE_SMS" />  ◁─
    <application android:icon="@drawable/chat">                 ◁─
        <activity android:name=".SMSNotifyActivity"
            android:label="@string/app_name">          Define a receiver, SMSNotify,
            <intent-filter>                               with an Intent filter ❷
                <action android:name="android.intent.action.MAIN" />
                <category android:name="android.intent.category.LAUNCHER" />
            </intent-filter>
        </activity>
        <receiver android:name=".SMSNotifyExample">        ◁─
            <intent-filter>
                <action android:name="android.provider.Telephony.SMS_RECEIVED" />
            </intent-filter>
        </receiver>                                      SMSNotifyExample
    </application>                                       acts as receiver ❸
</manifest>
```

The AndroidManifest.xml file needs to have specific user permissions ❶ added to it to allow incoming SMS messages. The Android security model default is to have no permissions associated with applications, meaning applications can essentially do nothing that might harm the device or the data on the device. To provide Android permission you need to use one or more permissions. In chapter 9 we will go into greater detail about Android's security model.

In the next part ❷ of the AndroidManifest.xml file we define SMSNotifyActivity, which is simply our Activity, and the next class is the SMSNotifyExample class ❸, which will act as our receiver. Then we will create a simple Activity class called SMSNotifyActivity, as in listing 8.2.

Listing 8.2   SMS Activity for the SMSNotifyExample class

```
public class SMSNotifyExampleActivity extends Activity {

    @Override
```

```
public void onCreate(Bundle icicle) {
    super.onCreate(icicle);
    setContentView(R.layout.main);
  }
}
```

As you can see there is very little to listing 8.2, in part because for this first example we will be doing little with the `Activity`. Later in this chapter, we will build on this class. Now let us create our `Receiver` class (see chapter 5 for more about `Intent` receivers), which will listen for the SMS message and fire off an action. Listing 8.3 shows the code for our `SMSNotifyExample` class.

Listing 8.3   A sample SMS `IntentReceiver`

```
public class SMSNotifyExample extends BroadcastReceiver {          ◁─┐   Extend the class as a
                                                                     ❶   BroadcastReceiver
    private static final String LOG_TAG = "SMSReceiver";

    public static final int NOTIFICATION_ID_RECEIVED = 0x1221;

    static final String ACTION = "android.provider.Telephony.SMS_RECEIVED";   ◁─┐

    public void onReceiveIntent(Context context, Intent intent) {

        if (intent.getAction().equals(SMSNotifyExample.ACTION)) {
            StringBuilder sb = new StringBuilder();
                                                              Action fired by Android
            Bundle bundle = intent.getExtras();               when a SMS is received  ❷
            if (bundle != null) {

                Object[] pdusObj = (Object[]) bundle.get("pdus");
                SmsMessage[] messages = new SmsMessage[pdusObj.length];

                for (SmsMessage currentMessage : messages) {          ◁─┐
                    sb.append("Received SMS\nFrom: ");
                    sb.append(currentMessage.getDisplayOriginatingAddress());
                    sb.append("\n----Message----\n");
                    sb.append(currentMessage.getDisplayMessageBody());
                }                                             Build message to
            }                                                 share to the user  ❸
            Log.i(SMSNotifyExample.LOG_TAG, "[SMSApp] onReceiveIntent: " + sb);
            Toast.makeText(context, sb.toString(), Toast.LENGTH_LONG).show();   ◁─┐

        }                                                           Create a Toast  ❹
    }

    @Override
    public void onReceive(Context context, Intent intent) {

    }
}
```

Listing 8.3 should be very easy to follow. Extend the `SMSNotifyExample` class using `BroadcastReceiver`, which allows the class to receive `Intent` classes ❶. Then we create a `String` ❷ to hold the action that will be fired by the system when an SMS is received. After that we create a simple method to notify the user that an SMS message has been received, and we parse the SMS message to show who it was from and the content of the message ❸. Finally we use a `Toast` to provide a quick message to the user ❹.

`Toast` classes are transient little messages—they pop up and provide the user with quick information without interrupting what the user is doing. In our code we chain two methods together using the form `makeText(Context context, CharSquence text, int duration ).show()`, where the first method contains a text view for the user and the second method, `show()`, shows the message to the user. `Toast` allows you to set a specific view using `setView`, but for our example we allow it to show the default, which is the Android status bar.

Once you have finished cutting and pasting the code, everything should automatically compile, and you should be able to run the application. The application should come up and look like figure 8.1.

To test our application, select the DDMS option in Eclipse. Now in the Telephony Actions field, type a telephone number, for example, `17035551429`. Select SMS and type a message in the Message field; then click Send. Your message should be sent to the emulator, and you should be able to see the emulator responding in the Eclipse console. A message should appear in the Android status bar on the very top of the Android screen representation, as shown in figure 8.2.

So now that we have created our simple example, know how to display a short message upon receiving an SMS, and know how to use the emulator to create an SMS, let's

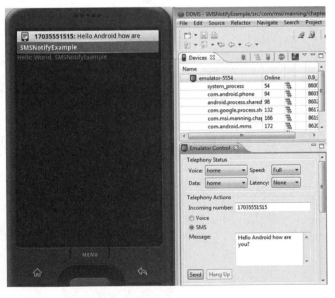

Figure 8.1 A simple `Toast`, the `SMSNotifyExample`, shown running in the emulator

Figure 8.2 Example of a `Toast` message being generated from an SMS message

look at how to create a more persistent message that can also be used to set LEDs, play a sound, or something of that nature, to let the user know an event has occurred.

8.2 Introducing notifications

In the previous section we showed how simple it is to create a quick, unobtrusive message to let the user know an SMS message has arrived. In this next section we are going to look at how to create a persistent notification that not only shows up in the status bar but stays in a notification area until the user deletes it. To do that we need to use the class Notification since we want to do something more complex than Toast can offer us.

A notification on Android can be many things, ranging from a pop-up message, a flashing LED, to a vibration, but all of these actions start with and are represented by the Notification class. The Notification class defines how you want to represent a notification to a user and has three constructors, one public method, and a number of fields. Table 8.1 summarizes the class.

Table 8.1 Notification **fields**

Access	Type	Method	Description
public	int	ledARGB	The color of the LED notification.
public	int	ledOffMS	The number of milliseconds for LED to be off between flashes.
public	int	ledOnMS	The number of milliseconds for LED to be on between flashes.
public	ContentURI	sound	The sound to play.
public	RemoteViews	contentView	View to display when the statusBar-Icon is selected in the status bar.
public	CharSequence	statusBarBalloonText	Text to display when the statusBar-Icon is selected in the status bar.
public	PendingIntent	contentIntent	The Intent to execute when the icon is clicked.
public	int	icon	The resource id of a drawable to use as the icon in the status bar.
public	CharSequence	tickerText	Text to scroll across the screen when this item is added to the status bar.
public	long[]	vibrate	The pattern with which to vibrate.

As you can see, the Notification class has numerous fields since it has to describe every way you can notify a user. Using a Notification is as simple as running this code:

```
Notification notif = new Notification(
    context,        // the application context
    icon,           // the icon for the status bar
    ticketText,      // the text to display in the ticker
    when,           // the timestamp for the notification
    Title,          // the title for the notification
    TextBody,        // the details to display in the notification
    contentIntent,   // the contentIntent
    appIntent);      // the application intent
```

To send the Notification all you have to do is enter the following:

```
nm.notify(String, Notification);
```

where nm is the reference to the NotificationManager. Now let's take our previous example and edit to change it from a Toast notification to a notification in the status bar. Before we do that, we'll make the application more interesting by adding icons to our resources directory. For this example we're going to use the chat.png icon and the incoming.png icon. You can find these files in the downloaded code for this book, or you can get them from http://www.manning.com/ableson/. Simply drop them in the res/drawable directory to have Eclipse automatically register them for you in the R class.

Now let's edit our code. First we'll edit the SMSNotifyActivity class so that when the Activity is called it can find the Notification passed to it from the Notification-Manager. After the Activity has run, SMSNotifyActivity can cancel it. Listing 8.4 provides the code you need for new SMSNotifyActivity class.

Listing 8.4   A sample SMSNotifyActivity

```
public class SMSNotifyActivity extends Activity {

    public void onCreate(Bundle icicle) {
        super.onCreate(icicle);
        setContentView(R.layout.main);

        NotificationManager nm = (NotificationManager)
getSystemService(NOTIFICATION_SERVICE);
            nm.cancel(R.string.app_name);

    }
}
```

❶ Set up the NotificationManager

❷ Cancel the Notification

As you can see, all we did was to use the NotificationManager ❶ to look up the Notification and then used the cancel() ❷ method to cancel it. We could do more here, such as set up a custom view, but for now we will leave it as is.

Next we need to edit the SMSNotifyExample to remove the Toast Notification and support a Notification to the status bar. Listing 8.5 shows the edits we need to make.

Listing 8.5   Updated SMSNotifyExample.java

```
public class SMSNotifyExample extends BroadcastReceiver {

    private static final String LOG_TAG = "SMSReceiver";
```

```
public static final int NOTIFICATION_ID_RECEIVED = 0x1221;
static final String ACTION = "android.provider.Telephony.SMS_RECEIVED";
private CharSequence tickerMessage = null;

public void onReceiveIntent(Context context, Intent intent) {

    NotificationManager nm = (NotificationManager)
    context.getSystemService(Context.NOTIFICATION_SERVICE);
     if (intent.getAction().equals(SMSNotifyExample.ACTION)) {

        StringBuilder sb = new StringBuilder();

        Bundle bundle = intent.getExtras();
        if (bundle != null) {
          Object[] pdusObj = (Object[]) bundle.get("pdus");
          SmsMessage[] messages = new SmsMessage[pdusObj.length];

          for (SmsMessage currentMessage : messages) {
            sb.append("Received compressed SMS\nFrom: ");
            sb.append(currentMessage.getDisplayOriginatingAddress());
            sb.append("\n----Message----\n");
            sb.append(currentMessage.getDisplayMessageBody());
          }
        }

        Log.i(SMSNotifyExample.LOG_TAG, "[SMSApp] onReceiveIntent: " + sb);
        abortBroadcast();

        Intent i = new Intent(context, SMSNotifyActivity.class);
        context.startActivity(i);

        CharSequence appName = "SMSNotifyExample";
        this.tickerMessage = sb.toString();
        Long theWhen = System.currentTimeMillis();

        PendingIntent.getBroadcast((Context) appName, 0, i, 0);
        Notification notif = new Notification(
          R.drawable.incoming,
          this.tickerMessage,
          theWhen);

        notif.vibrate = new long[] { 100, 250, 100, 500};
        nm.notify(R.string.alert_message, notif);
    }
  }

  @Override
  public void onReceive(Context context, Intent intent) {

  }
}
```

Create the Application Intent ❶

Build the Notification ❷

Broadcast the Notification ❸

Notice that the first change we made was to add a called `tickerMessage`. The `ticker-Message` will hold the SMS message that we want to scroll in the notification bar. We add these fields right after our `Action` variable, like this:

```
private CharSequence tickerMessage = null;
```

Next we create an Application Intent ❶. The Application Intent will be the Intent shown when we click on the SMS inbox. For this example it won't do anything, but it is required for building the `Notification`. You could have it pop up in an editor or some other screen with a little more effort.

Once the `Application Intent` is set, we can generate the `Notification` ❷. To make the code easier to understand, we have added some comments next to each attribute of `Notification` from listing 8.5:

```
Notification notif = new Notification(
        R.drawable.incoming, // the icon for the status bar
        tickerMessage,  // the text to display in the ticker
        theWhen
);
```

```
nm.notify(R.string.app_name, notif);
```

On the last line we use the `notify()` method ❸ from the `NotificationManager` to broadcast our `Notification` to the application.

Now if you run the application, then open the DDMS and pass an SMS message as you did earlier, you should see the new `Notification` appear in the status bar. The message displays each line for a short interval until the message is fully displayed. You should also see a new icon pop up in the status bar indicating a new SMS message, as shown in figure 8.3.

When you have sent the message, you can click the New Messages icon, and a bar should drop down from it. Click on the bar and drag it down to the bottom of the screen. This opens the default view of the SMS inbox for Android, as shown in figure 8.4.

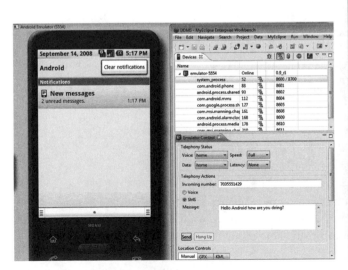

Figure 8.3   Using the Android DDMS to send an SMS message to the application

Figure 8.4   The expanded SMS inbox displaying the `contentIntent` and `appIntent`

There is a lot more you could do with this demo, such as creating a better UI or making the SMS inbox more feature rich. You could even have the application play a sound when a message arrives, but for this example we have looked at everything you need to know to start working with notifications. In the next section we are going to look at Notification's close relative, the Alarm.

8.3 Alarms

In Android, alarms allow you to schedule your application to run at some point in the future. Alarms can be used for a wide range of applications, from notifying a user of an appointment to something more sophisticated, such as having an application start up, check for software updates, and then shut down. An Alarm works by registering an Intent with the Alarm, and then at the time scheduled the Alarm will broadcast the Intent. Android will automatically start the targeted application even if the Android handset is asleep.

Android manages all alarms somewhat like the NotificationManager—via an AlarmManager class. The AlarmManager has four methods: cancel, set, setRepeating, and setTimeZone as shown in table 8.2.

Table 8.2 **AlarmManager public methods**

Returns	Method and description
void	cancel(PendingIntent intent) Remove alarms with matching Intent
void	set(int type, long triggerAtTime, PendingIntent operation) Set an Alarm
void	setRepeating(int type, long triggerAtTime, long interval, PendingIntent operation) Set a repeating Alarm
void	setTimeZone(String TimeZone) Set the time zone for the Alarm

You instantiate the AlarmManager indirectly as you do the NotificationManager by using Context.getSystemService(Context.ALARM_SERVICE).

Setting alarms is very easy, like most things in Android. In the next example we will create a simple application that sets an Alarm when a button is pushed; when the Alarm is triggered, it will pass back a simple Toast to inform us that the Alarm has been fired.

8.3.1 Alarm example

In this next example we are going to create an Android project called SimpleAlarm with the package com.msi.manning.chapter8.simpleAlarm, an application name of SimpleAlarm and an Activity name of GenerateAlarm. In this project we will use another open source icon, which you can find at http://www.manning.com/ableson/ or in the download for this chapter. Change the name of the icon to clock, and add it to the res/drawable directory of the project when you create it.

Next we need to edit the AndroidManifest.xml to have a receiver ❶, which we will create soon, called `AlarmReceiver`, as shown in listing 8.6.

Listing 8.6 AndroidManifest.xml

```xml
<?xml version="1.0" encoding="utf-8"?>
<manifest xmlns:android="http://schemas.android.com/apk/res/android"
  package="com.msi.manning.chapter8.simpleAlarm">
  <application android:icon="@drawable/clock">
    <activity android:name=".GenerateAlarm"
      android:label="@string/app_name">
      <intent-filter>
        <action android:name="android.intent.action.MAIN" />
        <category android:name="android.intent.category.LAUNCHER" />
      </intent-filter>
    </activity>
    <receiver android:name=".AlarmReceiver" android:process=":remote" />  ◁┐
  </application>                                                 **Define the receiver** ❶
</manifest>
```

Now we edit the string.xml file in the values directory and add two new strings:

```xml
<string name="set_alarm_text">Set Alarm</string>
<string name="alarm_message">Alarm Fired</string>
```

We will use this string as the value of the button in our layout. Next we need to add a new button to our layout, so edit the main.xml file to add a new button, like this:

```xml
<Button android:id="@+id/set_alarm_button"
    android:layout_width="wrap_content"
    android:layout_height="wrap_content"
    android:text="@string/set_alarm_text">
        <requestFocus />
</Button>
```

We are ready to create a new class that will act as the `Receiver` for the `Notification` the `Alarm` will generate. In this case we are going to be generating a `Toast`-style `Notification` to let the user know that the `Alarm` has been triggered. Now create a new class as shown in listing 8.7, which waits for the `Alarm` to broadcast to the `AlarmReceiver` and will then generate a `Toast`.

Listing 8.7 AlarmReceiver.java

```java
public class AlarmReceiver extends BroadcastReceiver {
                                                        Create the
                                                        onReceiveIntent method
    public void onReceiveIntent(Context context, Intent intent) {   ◁
        Toast.makeText(context, R.string.app_name, Toast.LENGTH_SHORT).show();  ◁┐
    }
                                                        Broadcast a Toast when
    @Override                                           the Intent is received
```

```
    public void onReceive(Context context, Intent intent) {

    }
}
```

Next we need to edit the `SimpleAlarm` class to create a button widget (as discussed in chapter 3) that calls the inner class `setAlarm`. In `setAlarm` we create an `onClick` method that will schedule our `Alarm`, call our `Intent`, and fire off our `Toast`. Listing 8.8 shows what the finished class should look like.

Listing 8.8   SimpleAlarm.java

```
public class GenerateAlarm extends Activity {

    Toast mToast;

    @Override
    protected void onCreate(Bundle icicle) {          Set up Button to call ❶
        super.onCreate(icicle);                          mOneShotListener
        setContentView(R.layout.main);
        Button button = (Button)findViewById(R.id.set_alarm_button);
        button.setOnClickListener(this.mOneShotListener);      ◄

    private OnClickListener mOneShotListener = new OnClickListener() {

        public void onClick(View v) {            Create Intent to fire when Alarm goes off ❷

            Intent intent = new Intent(GenerateAlarm.this, AlarmReceiver.class);

            PendingIntent appIntent =
            PendingIntent.getBroadcast(GenerateAlarm.this, 0, intent, 0);    ◄

            Calendar calendar = Calendar.getInstance();          ◄        Set the time
            calendar.setTimeInMillis(System.currentTimeMillis());         for Alarm to
            calendar.add(Calendar.SECOND, 30);                    ❸  go off

            AlarmManager am = (AlarmManager)getSystemService(ALARM_SERVICE);  ◄
            am.set(AlarmManager.RTC_WAKEUP, calendar.getTimeInMillis(),
            appIntent);                              ◄
                                                ❺ Set the Alarm
            if (GenerateAlarm.this.mToast != null) {
                GenerateAlarm.this.mToast.cancel();        Create the AlarmManager ❹
            }
            GenerateAlarm.this.mToast = Toast.makeText(GenerateAlarm.this,
            R.string.alarm_message, Toast.LENGTH_LONG);
            GenerateAlarm.this.mToast.show();
        }
    };
}
```

As you can see, this is a pretty simple class. We first create a `Button` to trigger our `Alarm` ❶. Next we create an inner class for our `mOneShotListener`. We then create the `Intent` to be trigged when the `Alarm` actually goes off ❷. In the next section of code we use the `Calendar` class ❸ to help us calculate the number of milliseconds from the time the button is pressed, which we will use to set the `Alarm`.

Now we have done everything necessary beforehand in order to create and set the Alarm. To do this we first create the AlarmManager ❹ and then call its set() method to set the Alarm ❺. To see a little more detail of what's going on in the application, take a look at these lines of code:

```
AlarmManager am = (AlarmManager)getSystemService(ALARM_SERVICE);
    am.set(AlarmManager.RTC_WAKEUP, calendar.getTimeInMillis(), intent);
```

This is where we actually create and set the Alarm by first using getSystemService to create the AlarmManager. The first parameter we pass to the set() method is RTC_WAKEUP, which is an integer representing the Alarm type we want to set. The AlarmManager currently supports four Alarm types, as shown in table 8.3.

Table 8.3 AlarmManager Alarm types

Type	Description
ELAPSED_REALTIME	Alarm time in SystemClock.elapsedRealtime() (time since boot, including sleep)
ELAPSED_REALTIME_WAKEUP	Alarm time in SystemClock.elapsedRealtime() (time since boot, including sleep), which will wake up the device when it goes off
RTC	Alarm time in System.currentTimeMillis() (wall clock time in UTC)
RTC_WAKEUP	Alarm time in System.currentTimeMillis() (wall clock time in UTC), which will wake up the device when it goes off

As you can see, there are multiple types of alarms that you can use depending on your requirements. The RTC_WAKEUP, for example, sets the Alarm time in milliseconds, and when the Alarm goes off it will wake up the device from sleep mode for you, as opposed to RTC, which will not.

The next parameter we pass to the method is the amount of time in milliseconds we want to elapse, after which we want the alarm to be triggered. We set this with:

```
Calendar calendar = Calendar.getInstance();
calendar.setTimeInMillis(System.currentTimeMillis());
calendar.add(Calendar.SECOND, 30);
```

The last parameter is the Intent we want to broadcast to, which is our Intent-Receiver. Now if you build the application and run it in the emulator, you should see something like the screen shown in figure 8.5.

Clicking the Set Alarm button will set the alarm, and after 30 seconds you should see something like figure 8.6, displaying the Toast message.

As you can see, creating an Alarm is pretty easy in Android, but what might make more sense would be for that Alarm to trigger a Notification in the status bar. To do that you would need to add a NotificationManager and generate a Notification. To do this we have created a new method to add to listing 8.8 called showNotification, which takes four parameters and creates our Notification, like this:

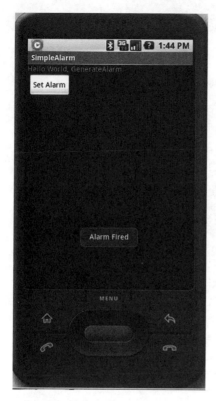 

Figure 8.5   Example of the SimpleAlarm application running in the emulator

Figure 8.6   After the Alarm runs, the application shows a simple Toast message.

```
private void showNotification(int statusBarIconID,
    int statusBarTextID, int detailedTextID, boolean showIconOnly) {

    Intent contentIntent = new Intent(this, SetAlarm.class);
    PendingIntent theappIntent = PendingIntent.getBroadcast(SetAlarm.this,
        0, contentIntent, 0);
    CharSequence from = "Alarm Manager";
    CharSequence message = "The Alarm was fired";

    String tickerText = showIconOnly ? null : this.getString(statusBarTextID);
    Notification notif =  new Notification( statusBarIconID, tickerText,
        System.currentTimeMillis());

    notif.setLatestEventInfo(this, from, message, theappIntent);

    nm.notify(YOURAPP_NOTIFICATION_ID, notif );
}
```

Much of this code is very similar to the SMSNotifyExample code. To add it to your SimpleAlarm, edit listing 8.8 to look like listing 8.9, where the only other things we have done are to import the Notification and NotificationManager to the code, add the private variables nm and ApplicationID, and make a call to showNotification() right after the Toast.

Listing 8.9   SetAlarm.java

```java
public class SetAlarm extends Activity {

    private NotificationManager nm;
       Toast mToast;

    @Override
    protected void onCreate(Bundle icicle) {
       super.onCreate(icicle);
       setContentView(R.layout.main);

       this.nm = (NotificationManager)
       getSystemService(Context.NOTIFICATION_SERVICE);

       Button button = (Button) findViewById(R.id.set_alarm_button);
       button.setOnClickListener(this.mOneShotListener);

    }

    private void showNotification(int statusBarIconID, int statusBarTextID, int
       detailedTextID, boolean showIconOnly) {

       Intent contentIntent = new Intent(this, SetAlarm.class);
       PendingIntent theappIntent = PendingIntent.getBroadcast(SetAlarm.this, 0,
          contentIntent, 0);
       CharSequence from = "Alarm Manager";
       CharSequence message = "The Alarm was fired";

       String tickerText = showIconOnly ? null : this.getString(statusBarTextID);
       Notification notif = new Notification(statusBarIconID, tickerText,
          System.currentTimeMillis());

       notif.setLatestEventInfo(this, from, message, theappIntent);

       this.nm.notify(this.YOURAPP_NOTIFICATION_ID, notif);
    }

    private OnClickListener mOneShotListener = new OnClickListener() {

       public void onClick(View v) {

          Intent intent = new Intent(SetAlarm.this, AlarmReceiver.class);

          PendingIntent appIntent = PendingIntent.getBroadcast(SetAlarm.this, 0,
             intent, 0);

          Calendar calendar = Calendar.getInstance();
          calendar.setTimeInMillis(System.currentTimeMillis());
          calendar.add(Calendar.SECOND, 30);

          AlarmManager am = (AlarmManager)
             getSystemService(Context.ALARM_SERVICE);
          am.set(AlarmManager.RTC_WAKEUP, calendar.getTimeInMillis(),
             appIntent);

          showNotification(R.drawable.alarm, R.string.alarm_message,
             R.string.alarm_message, false);

       }
    };

    }
}
```

If you run the code and click Set Alarm, you should see the Alarm Notification in the status bar, as in figure 8.7. You could easily edit this code to take in parameters for time and date, have it show different Intents when the icons are clicked, and so on.

As you can see from this example, Android alarms and the AlarmManager are very straightforward, and you should be able to easily integrate them into your applications.

8.4 Summary

In this chapter we have looked at two separate but related items: Notification and Alarm. We have looked at how to use the NotificationManager to generate notifications and how the Notification class can be used to present a Notification to the user by building a simple example that displays a Notification when an SMS messages arrives in the inbox.

We have also looked at how to set an Alarm to cause an application to start or take some action in the future, include waking the system from the sleep mode. Finally we looked at how to trigger a Notification from an Alarm. While the code

Figure 8.7 Alarm Notification showing in the status bar

presented in these simple examples gives you a taste of what can be done with notifications and alarms, both have very broad applications limited only by your imagination.

Now that you have an understanding of how to work with the Notification and Alarm classes, we are going to move on a discussion of graphics and animation. In chapter 9 you will learn the basic methods of generating graphics in Android, how to create simple animations, and even how to work with OpenGL to generate stunning 3D graphics.

Graphics and animation

This chapter covers:
- Drawing graphics in Android
- Applying the basics of OpenGL ES
- Animating

One of the main features of Android that you should have picked up on by now is how much easier it is to develop Android applications than mobile application platforms. This really stands out in the creation of visually appealing UIs and metaphors, but there is a limit of what can be done with typical Android UI elements (such as those discussed in chapter 3). In this chapter we are going to look at how to create graphics using Android's Graphic API, develop animations, and look at Android's support for the OpenGL standard (to see examples of what can be done with Android's graphics platform go to http://www.omnigsoft.com/Android/ADC/readme.html).

If you have ever worked with graphics in Java, you will most likely find the Graphics API and how graphics work in Android familiar.

9.1 Drawing graphics in Android

In this section we are going to be looking at Android's graphical capabilities as well as examples of how to make simple 2D shapes. We will be making use of

226

the `android.graphics` package (see http://code.google.com/android/reference/ android/graphics/package-summary.html), which provides all the low-level classes and tooling needed to create graphics. The graphics package supports such things as bitmaps (which hold pixels), canvas (what your draw calls draw on), primitives (such as rectangles or text), and paint (which you use to add color and styling).

To demonstrate the basics of drawing a shape, let's look at a simple example in listing 9.1, where we will draw a rectangle.

Listing 9.1 Shape example

```
package com.msi.manning.chapter9.SimpleShape;

public class SimpleShape extends Activity {

    @Override
    protected void onCreate(Bundle icicle) {
        super.onCreate(icicle);
        setContentView(new SimpleView(this));
    }

    private static class SimpleView extends View {            ❶ Create View
        private ShapeDrawable mDrawable =
            new ShapeDrawable();                              ❷ Create ShapeDrawable
                                                                 to hold Drawable
        public SimpleView(Context context) {
            super(context);
            setFocusable(true);
            this.mDrawable =                                  ❸ Create Rectangle and
                new ShapeDrawable(new RectShape());              assign to mDrawable
            this.mDrawable.getPaint().setColor(0xFFFF0000);
        }

        @Override                                             ❹ The onDraw method
        protected void onDraw(Canvas canvas) {                   draws the graphics

            int x = 10;
            int y = 10;
            int width = 300;
            int height = 50;
            this.mDrawable.setBounds(x, y, x + width, y + height);
            this.mDrawable.draw(canvas);
            y += height + 5;                     Set boundaries and ❺
        }                                        draw on canvas
    }
}
```

Drawing a new shape is simple. First we need to import the necessary packages ❶ including graphics, then `ShapeDrawable`, which will support adding shapes to our drawing, and then shapes, which supports several generic shapes including `RectShape`, which we will use. Next we need to create a view ❷, then a new `ShapeDrawable` to add our `Drawable` to ❸. Once we have a `ShapeDrawable` we can assign shapes to it. In our code we use the `RectShape` ❹, but we could have used `OvalShape`, `PathShape`, `RectShape`, `RoundRectShape`, or `Shape`. We then use the `onDraw()` method to draw the `Drawable` on the `Canvas` ❺. Finally we use the `Drawable`'s `setBounds()` method to set the boundary (a rectangle) in which we will draw our rectangle using the `draw()` method. When you run listing 9.1, you should see a simple red rectangle like the one shown in figure 9.1.

Another way to do the same thing is through the use of XML. Android allows you to define shapes to draw in an XML resource file.

9.1.1   *Drawing with XML*

With Android you can create simple drawings using an XML file approach. To do this, all you need to do is create a `Drawable` object or objects, which are defined as an XML file in your drawable directory, such as res/drawable. The XML to create a simple rectangle would look like listing 9.2.

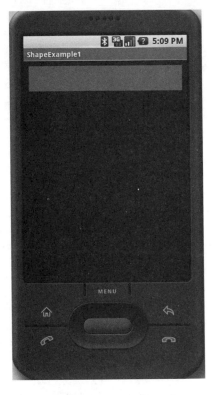

Figure 9.1   A simple red rectangle drawn using Android's Graphics API

Listing 9.2   simplerectangle.xml

```
<?xml version="1.0" encoding="utf-8"?>
<shape xmlns:android="http://schemas.android.com/apk/res/android">
   <solid android:color="#FF0000FF"/>
</shape>
```

With Android XML drawable shapes, the default is a rectangle, but you can change the shape by using the `type` tag and selecting a value of oval, rectangle, line, or arc. To use this XML shape you need to reference it in a layout, as in listing 9.3, where the layout would reside in res/layout.

Listing 9.3   xmllayout.xml

```
<?xml version="1.0" encoding="utf-8"?>
<ScrollView xmlns:android="http://schemas.android.com/apk/res/android"
   android:layout_width="fill_parent"
   android:layout_height="wrap_content">
  <LinearLayout
     android:orientation="vertical"
     android:layout_width="fill_parent"
     android:layout_height="wrap_content">
```

```
<ImageView android:layout_width="fill_parent"
    android:layout_height="50dip"
    android:src="@drawable/simplerectangle" />
```

Then all you need to do is create a simple `Activity`, where you place your UI in a contentView, as in listing 9.4.

Listing 9.4   XMLDraw.java

```java
public class XMLDraw extends Activity {

    @Override
    public void onCreate(Bundle icicle) {
        super.onCreate(icicle);
        setContentView(R.layout.xmldrawable);
    }
}
```

If you run this code, it will draw a simple rectangle. You can make more complex drawings or shapes by stacking or ordering your XML drawables, and you can include as many shapes as you want or need depending on space. You could change your xmldrawable.xml file to look like listing 9.5, which adds a number of shapes and stacks them vertically.

Listing 9.5   xmldrawable.xml

```xml
<?xml version="1.0" encoding="utf-8"?>
<ScrollView xmlns:android="http://schemas.android.com/apk/res/android"
    android:layout_width="fill_parent"
    android:layout_height="wrap_content">

    <LinearLayout
        android:orientation="vertical"
        android:layout_width="fill_parent"
        android:layout_height="wrap_content">
    <ImageView android:layout_width="fill_parent"
        android:layout_height="50dip"
        android:src="@drawable/shape_1" />
    <ImageView android:layout_width="fill_parent"
        android:layout_height="wrap_content"
        android:src="@drawable/line" />
    <ImageView
        android:layout_width="fill_parent"
        android:layout_height="50dip"
        android:src="@drawable/shape_2" />
    <ImageView
        android:layout_width="fill_parent"
        android:layout_height="50dip"
        android:src="@drawable/shape_5" />
    </LinearLayout>
</ScrollView>
```

Finally you need to add the shapes in listings 9.6, 9.7, 9.8, and 9.9 into the res/drawable folder.

Listing 9.6   shape1.xml

```
<?xml version="1.0" encoding="utf-8"?>
<shape xmlns:android="http://schemas.android.com/apk/res/android"
type="oval" >
    <solid android:color="#00000000"/>
    <padding android:left="10sp" android:top="4sp"
    android:right="10sp" android:bottom="4sp" />
    <stroke android:width="1dp" android:color="#FFFFFFFF"/>
</shape>
```

In listing 9.6 we are using an oval. We have added a tag called `padding`, which allows us to define padding or space between the object and other objects in the UI. We are also using the tag called `stroke`, which allows us to define the style of the line that makes up the border of the oval (see listing 9.7).

Listing 9.7   shape2.xml

```
<?xml version="1.0" encoding="utf-8"?>

<shape xmlns:android="http://schemas.android.com/apk/res/android">
    <solid android:color="#FF0000FF"/>
    <stroke android:width="4dp" android:color="#FFFFFFFF"
        android:dashWidth="1dp" android:dashGap="2dp" />
    <padding android:left="7dp" android:top="7dp"
        android:right="7dp" android:bottom="7dp" />
    <corners android:radius="4dp" />
</shape>
```

With this shape we are generating another rectangle, but this time (see listing 9.8) we introduce the tag `corners`, which allows us to make rounded corners with the attribute `android:radius`.

Listing 9.8   shape3.xml

```
<?xml version="1.0" encoding="utf-8"?>
<shape xmlns:android="http://schemas.android.com/apk/res/android"
type="oval">
    <gradient android:startColor="#FFFF0000" android:endColor="#80FF00FF"
        android:angle="270"/>
    <padding android:left="7dp" android:top="7dp"
        android:right="7dp" android:bottom="7dp" />
    <corners android:radius="8dp" />
</shape>
```

In listing 9.9 we create a shape of the type `line` with a `size` tag using the `android:height` attribute, which allows us to describe the number of pixels used on the vertical to size the line.

Listing 9.9   line.xml

```
<?xml version="1.0" encoding="utf-8"?>
<shape xmlns:android=http://schemas.android.com/apk/res/android
type="line" >
    <solid android:color="#FFFFFFFF"/>
```

```
    <stroke android:width="1dp" android:color="#FFFFFFFF"
        android:dashWidth="1dp" android:dashGap="2dp" />
    <padding android:left="1dp" android:top="25dp"
        android:right="1dp" android:bottom="25dp" />

    <size android:height="23dp" />
</shape>
```

If you run this, you should see something like figure 9.2.

As you can see, drawing with Android is straightforward, and Android provides the ability for developers to programmatically draw anything they might need. In the next section we are going to look at what we can draw with Android's animations capabilities.

9.2 Animations

If a picture says a thousand words, then an animation must speak volumes. Android supports multiple methods of animations, including through XML, as you saw in chapter 3, or via Android's XML frame-by-frame animations using the Android Graphics API, or via Android's support for OpenGL ES. In this section we are going to create a very simple animation of a bouncing ball using Android's frame-by-frame animation.

Android allows you to create simple animations by showing a set of images one after another to give the illusion of movement, much like stop-motion film. Android does this by setting each frame image as a drawable resource; the images

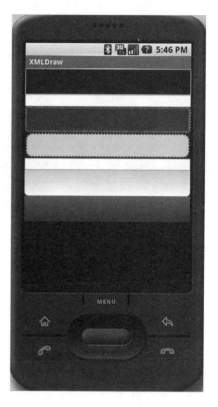

Figure 9.2
Various shapes drawn using XML

are then shown one after the other in the background of a `View`. To use this feature you define a set of resources in a XML file and then call `AnimationDrawable.run()`.

To demonstrate this method for creating an animation, first you need to download the images for this chapter from the book's website at http://www.manning.com/UnlockingAndroid. The images for this exercise are six representations of a ball bouncing. Next, create a project called XMLanimation. Now create a new directory called /anim under the /res resources directory. Place all of the images for this example in the /drawable directory. Now create an XML file called Simple_animation.xml, containing the code shown in listing 9.10.

> **Listing 9.10 Simple_animation.xml**

```
<?xml version="1.0" encoding="utf-8"?>
<animation-list xmlns:android=http://schemas.android.com/apk/res/android
id="selected" android:oneshot="false">
```

```
<item android:drawable="@drawable/ball1" android:duration="50" />
<item android:drawable="@drawable/ball2" android:duration="50" />
<item android:drawable="@drawable/ball3" android:duration="50" />
<item android:drawable="@drawable/ball4" android:duration="50" />
<item android:drawable="@drawable/ball5" android:duration="50" />
<item android:drawable="@drawable/ball6" android:duration="50" />
</animation-list>
```

The XML file defines the list of images to be displayed for the animation. The XML `<animation-list>` tag contains the tags for the two attributes `drawable`, which describes the path to the image, and `duration`, which describes the time to show the image in nanoseconds. Now that you've created the animation XML file, edit the main.xml file to look like listing 9.11.

Listing 9.11   main.xml

```xml
<?xml version="1.0" encoding="utf-8"?>
<LinearLayout xmlns:android="http://schemas.android.com/apk/res/android"
   android:orientation="vertical"
   android:layout_width="fill_parent"
   android:layout_height="fill_parent"
   >
   <ImageView android:id="@+id/simple_anim"
      android:layout_width="wrap_content"
      android:layout_height="wrap_content"
      android:gravity="center"
      android:layout_centerHorizontal="true"
       />
<TextView
   android:layout_width="fill_parent"
   android:layout_height="wrap_content"
   android:text="Hello World, XMLAnimation"
   />
</LinearLayout>
```

All we have done here is to add an `ImageView` tag that sets up the layout for our `ImageView`. Finally, create the code to run the animation, in listing 9.12.

Listing 9.12   xmlanimation.java

```java
public class XMLAnimation extends Activity {

   @Override
   public void onCreate(Bundle icicle) {
      super.onCreate(icicle);
      setContentView(R.layout.main);
      ImageView img =
      (ImageView)findViewById(R.id.simple_anim);        Bind resources
      img.setBackground(R.anim.simple_animation);       to ImageView

      MyAnimationRoutine mar =
      new MyAnimationRoutine();          Call subclasses to start
      MyAnimationRoutine2 mar2 =         and stop Animation
      new MyAnimationRoutine2();
```

```
    Timer t = new Timer(false);
    t.schedule(mar, 100);
    Timer t2 = new Timer(false);
    t2.schedule(mar2, 5000);
}

class MyAnimationRoutine extends TimerTask {

    @Override
    public void run() {
        ImageView img = (ImageView) findViewById(R.id.simple_anim);
        AnimationDrawable frameAnimation = (AnimationDrawable)
        img.getBackground();
        frameAnimation.start();
    }
}

class MyAnimationRoutine2 extends TimerTask {

    @Override
    public void run() {
        ImageView img = (ImageView) findViewById(R.id.simple_anim);
        AnimationDrawable frameAnimation = (AnimationDrawable)
        img.getBackground();
        frameAnimation.stop();
    }
}
}
```

1 Allow wait time before starting Animation

Listing 9.12 might be slightly confusing because of the use of the `TimerTask` classes. Since we cannot control the animation from within the `OnCreate` method, we need to create two subclasses that call `Animation-Drawable`'s start and stop methods. So the first subclass, `MyAnimationRoutine`, extends the `TimerTask` **1** and calls the `frame-Animation.start()` method for the `AnimationDrawable` bound to the `ImageView` background. If you now run the project, you should see something like figure 9.3.

As you can see, creating an `Animation` with XML in Android is pretty simple. You

Figure 9.3 Making a ball bounce using an Android XML `Animation`

can make the animations reasonably complex as you would with any stop-motion-type movie, but to create more sophisticated animations programmatically you need to use Android's 2D and 3D graphics abilities. In this next section we will do just that.

9.2.1 *Programmatically creating an animation*

In the previous section we used Android's frame-by-frame animation capabilities to essentially show a series of images in a loop to give the impression of movement. In this next section we are going to programmatically animate a globe so that it moves around the screen.

To do this we are going to animate a graphics file (a PNG file) with a ball that seems to be bouncing around inside our Android viewing window. We are going to create a `Thread` in which our animation will run and a `Handler` that will help communicate messages back to our program that reflect the changes in state of our animation. We will later use this same approach in the section on OpenGL ES. You will find it the basic way to approach most complex graphics applications and animations.

ANIMATING RESOURCES

In this section we are going to look at a very simple animation technique using an image bound to a sprite and moving that sprite around the screen to give the appearance of a bouncing ball. To get started, create a new project called bouncing ball with a `BounceActivity`. You can copy and paste in the code in listing 9.13 for the Bounce-Activity.java file.

Listing 9.13 BounceActivity.java

```
public class BounceActivity extends Activity {                    ① Create a unique
                                                                      identifier
    protected static final int GUIUPDATEIDENTIFIER = 0x101;

    Thread myRefreshThread = null;
    BounceView myBounceView = null;
                                                    ② Create a
    Handler myGUIUpdateHandler = new Handler() {       handler
        public void handleMessage(Message msg) {
            switch (msg.what) {
                case BounceActivity.GUIUPDATEIDENTIFIER:
                    myBounceView.invalidate();
                    break;
            }
            super.handleMessage(msg);
        }
    };
    @Override
    public void onCreate(Bundle icicle) {
        super.onCreate(icicle);
        this.requestWindowFeature(Window.FEATURE_NO_TITLE);   ③ Create
                                                                  the view
        this.myBounceView = new BounceView(this);
        this.setContentView(this.myBounceView);          ④ Create the
                                                             new thread
        new Thread(new RefreshRunner()).start();

    }

    class RefreshRunner implements Runnable {
                                                        ⑤ Run the
        public void run() {                                animation
            while (!Thread.currentThread().isInterrupted()) {

                Message message = new Message();
                message.what = BounceActivity.GUIUPDATEIDENTIFIER;
                BounceActivity.this.myGUIUpdateHandler
.sendMessage(message);
```

```
        try {
            Thread.sleep(100);
        } catch (InterruptedException e) {
            Thread.currentThread().interrupt();
        }
      }
    }
  }
}
```

In listing 9.13 first we import the `Handler` and `Message` classes, then create a unique identifier to allow us to send a message back to our program to update the view in the main thread. To do this we need to send a message telling the main thread to update the view each time the child thread has finished drawing our ball. Since different messages can be thrown by the system we need to guarantee uniqueness of our message to our handler which we do by creating a unique identifier called GUIUP-DATEIDENTIFIER ❶. Next we create the `Handler` that will process our messages to update the main view ❷. A `Handler` allows us to send and process `Message` classes and `Runnable` objects associated with a thread's message queue. Handlers are associated with a single thread and its message queue. We will use the handler to allow our objects running a thread to communicate changes in state back to the program that spawned them or vice versa.

NOTE For more information on handling long-running requests in your applications see http://developer.android.com/reference/android/app/Activity.html.

We set up a `View` as shown in ❸ and create the new thread ❹. Finally we create a `RefreshRunner` inner class implementing `Runnable`, which will run unless something interrupts the thread, at which point a message is sent to the `Handler` to call its `invalidate()` method ❺. The invalidate method invalidates the `View`, forcing a refresh.

Now we need to create the code that will do our animation and create a `View`. We are going to use an image of a globe, which you can obtain at http://www.manning.com/UnlockingAndroid. Alternatively you could use any other PNG file you'd like. We also want to have the Android logo as our background, which you can find along with the source code downloads. Make sure to drop the images under res/drawable/. Next, create a Java file called BounceView, and copy the code from listing 9.14 and paste it into your editor.

Listing 9.14   BounceView.java

```
public class BounceView extends View {

    protected Drawable mySprite;
    protected Point mySpritePos = new Point(0,0);

    protected enum HorizontalDirection {LEFT, RIGHT}
    protected enum VerticalDirection {UP, DOWN}
    protected HorizontalDirection myXDirection =
```

❶ Create enumerations for directional values

```
HorizontalDirection.RIGHT;

    protected VerticalDirection myYDirection = VerticalDirection.UP;

    public BounceView(Context context) {
        super(context);

this.setBackground(this.getResources().getDrawable(R.drawable.android));
this.mySprite =
        this.getResources().getDrawable(R.drawable.world);
    }

    @Override
    protected void onDraw(Canvas canvas) {

this.mySprite.setBounds(this.mySpritePos.x,
    this.mySpritePos.y,
    this.mySpritePos.x + 50, this.mySpritePos.y + 50);

        if (mySpritePos.x >= this.getWidth() -
mySprite.getBounds().width()) {
            this.myXDirection = HorizontalDirection.LEFT;
        } else if (mySpritePos.x <= 0) {
            this.myXDirection = HorizontalDirection.RIGHT;
        }

        if (mySpritePos.y >= this.getHeight() -
mySprite.getBounds().height()) {
            this.myYDirection = VerticalDirection.UP;
        } else if (mySpritePos.y <= 0) {
            this.myYDirection = VerticalDirection.DOWN;
        }

        if (this.myXDirection ==
HorizontalDirection.RIGHT) {
            this.mySpritePos.x += 10;
        } else {
            this.mySpritePos.x -= 10;
        }

        if (this.myYDirection ==
                        VerticalDirection.DOWN) {
            this.mySpritePos.y += 10;
        } else {
            this.mySpritePos.y -= 10;
        }
        this.mySprite.draw(canvas);
    }
}
```

2 Get image file and map it to the sprite

3 Set the bounds of the globe

4 Move ball left or right, up or down

5 Check if ball is trying to leave screen

6 Draw the globe

In listing 9.14 we do all the real work of animating our image. First we create a Drawable to hold our globe image and a Point, which we will use to position and track our globe as we animate it. Next we create enums to hold directional values for horizontal and vertical directions, which we will use to keep track of the moving globe **1**. Then we map the globe to the mySprite variable and set the Android logo as the background for our animation **2**.

Now that we have done the setup work, we create a new `View` and set all the boundaries for the `Drawable` ❸. After that we create simple conditional logic that detects whether the globe is trying to leave the screen; if it starts to leave the screen, we change its direction ❹. Then we provide simple conditional logic to keep the ball moving in the same direction if it has not encountered the bounds of the `View` ❺. Finally we draw the globe using the `draw` method ❻. Now if you compile and run the project, you should see the globe bouncing around in front of the Android logo, as shown in figure 9.4.

Figure 9.4   A simple animation of a globe bouncing in front of the Android logo

While the simple `Animation` that we created is not too exciting, you could—with very little extra work—leverage the key concepts (dealing with boundaries, moving around drawables, detecting changes, dealing with threads, and so on) to create something like the Google Lunar Lander example game or even a simple version of Asteroids. If you want more graphics power and want to easily work with 3D objects for creating things like games or sophisticated animations, read the next section on OpenGL ES.

9.2.2   *Introducing OpenGL for embedded systems*

One of the most interesting features of Android platform is its support of OpenGL for Embedded Systems, or OpenGL ES. OpenGL ES is the embedded systems version of the very popular OpenGL standard, which defines a cross-platform and cross-language API for computer graphics. The OpenGL ES API does not support the full OpenGL

API, and much of the OpenGL API has been stripped out to allow OpenGL ES to run on a large variety of mobile phones, PDAs, video game consoles, and other embedded systems. OpenGL ES was originally developed by the Kronos Group, an industry consortium, and the most current version of the standard can be found at http://www.khronos.org/opengles/.

OpenGL ES is a fantastic API for 2D and 3D graphics, especially for graphically intensive applications such as games, graphical simulations and visualizations, and all sorts of animations. Since Android also supports 3D hardware acceleration, developers can make graphically intensive applications that target hardware with 3D accelerators.

Because OpenGL and OpenGL ES are such broad topics with whole books dedicated to them, we will cover only the basics of working with OpenGL ES and Android. For a much deeper exploration of OpenGL ES, check out the specification as well as the OpenGL ES tutorial at http://www.zeuscmd.com/tutorials/opengles/index.php. After reading this section on Android support for OpenGL ES, you should have enough information to follow a more in-depth discussion of OpenGL ES as well as to port your code from other languages (such as the tutorial examples) into the Android Framework. If you already know OpenGL or OpenGL ES, then the OpenGL commands will be familiar, and you should concentrate on the specifics of working with OpenGL from Android.

NOTE An excellent book on OpenGL and Java 3D programming is *Java 3D Programming* by Daniel Selman, which is available at http://www.manning.com/selman/.

With that in mind let's apply the basics of OpenGL ES to first create an OpenGL-Context, then a Window that we can draw on. To use OpenGL ES with Android, follow these steps:

1   Create a custom View subclass.
2   Get a handle to an OpenGLContext, which provides access to Android's OpenGL ES functionality.
3   In the View's onDraw() method, use the handle to the GL object and then use its methods to perform any GL functions.

Following these basic steps, first we'll create a class that uses Android to create a blank surface to draw on. In the next section we'll use OpenGL ES commands to draw a square and then an animated cube on the surface. To start, open a new project called OpenGLSquare and create an Activity called OpenGLSquare, as in listing 9.15.

Listing 9.15 OpenGLSquare.java

```
public class SquareActivity extends Activity {

  @Override
  public void onCreate(Bundle icicle) {
    super.onCreate(icicle);
    setContentView(new DrawingSurfaceView(this));
```

```
    }
    class DrawingSurfaceView extends SurfaceView implements
    SurfaceHolder.Callback {
        public SurfaceHolder mHolder;

        public DrawingThread mThread;

        public DrawingSurfaceView(Context c) {
            super(c);
            init();
        }
        public void init() {
            mHolder = getHolder();
            mHolder.addCallback(this);
            mHolder.setType(SurfaceHolder.SURFACE_TYPE_GPU);
        }

        public void surfaceCreated(SurfaceHolder holder) {
            mThread = new DrawingThread();
            mThread.start();
        }

        public void surfaceDestroyed(SurfaceHolder holder) {
            mThread.waitForExit();
            mThread = null;
        }

        public void surfaceChanged(SurfaceHolder holder,
        int format, int w, int h) {
            mThread.onWindowResize(w, h);
        }

        class DrawingThread extends Thread {
            boolean stop;
            int w;
            int h;

            boolean changed = true;

            DrawingThread() {
                super();
                stop = false;
                w = 0;
                h = 0;
            }

            @Override
            public void run() {
EGL10 egl = (EGL10)EGLContext.getEGL();
                EGLDisplay dpy =
                egl.eglGetDisplay(EGL10.EGL_DEFAULT_DISPLAY);
                int[] version = new int[2];
                egl.eglInitialize(dpy, version);
                int[] configSpec = {
                    EGL10.EGL_RED_SIZE,     5,
                    EGL10.EGL_GREEN_SIZE,   6,
                    EGL10.EGL_BLUE_SIZE,    5,
```

1 Handle all creation, destruction, etc.

2 Do the actual drawing

3 Register as a callback

4 Create a new thread

5 Stop thread when surface is destroyed

6 Change size of window

7 Create thread to do drawing

8 Get an EGL Instance

9 Specify a configuration to use

```
                EGL10.EGL_DEPTH_SIZE,   16,
                EGL10.EGL_NONE
           };
           EGLConfig[] configs = new EGLConfig[1];
           int[] num_config = new int[1];
           egl.eglChooseConfig(dpy, configSpec, configs, 1,
num_config);
           EGLConfig config = configs[0];

           EGLContext context = egl.eglCreateContext(dpy,
config, EGL10.EGL_NO_CONTEXT, null);
           EGLSurface surface = null;
           GL10 gl = null;

           while( ! stop ) {
               int W, H;
               boolean updated;
               synchronized(this) {
                   updated = this.changed;
                   W = this.w;
                   H = this.h;
                   this.changed = false;
               }
               if (updated) {

                   if (surface != null) {
                   egl.eglMakeCurrent(dpy,
EGL10.EGL_NO_SURFACE,EGL10.EGL_NO_SURFACE, EGL10.EGL_NO_CONTEXT);
                       egl.eglDestroySurface(dpy,
surface);
                   }

                   surface =
egl.eglCreateWindowSurface(dpy, config, mHolder, null);
                          egl.eglMakeCurrent(dpy, surface,
surface, context);

               gl = (GL10) context.getGL();

               gl.glDisable(GL10.GL_DITHER);

               gl.glHint(GL10.GL_PERSPECTIVE_CORRECTION_HINT,
                   GL10.GL_FASTEST);

               gl.glClearColor(1, 1, 1, 1);
               gl.glEnable(GL10.GL_CULL_FACE);
               gl.glShadeModel(GL10.GL_SMOOTH);
               gl.glEnable(GL10.GL_DEPTH_TEST);
               gl.glViewport(0, 0, W, H);
               float ratio = (float) W / H;
               gl.glMatrixMode(GL10.GL_PROJECTION);
               gl.glLoadIdentity();
               gl.glFrustumf(-ratio, ratio, -1,
1, 1, 10);
               }

           drawFrame(gl);

           egl.eglSwapBuffers(dpy, surface);

           if (egl.eglGetError() ==
```

⑩ Obtain reference to OpenGL ES context

⑪ Do the actual drawing

```
EGL11.EGL_CONTEXT_LOST) {
        Context c = getContext();
        if (c instanceof Activity) {
            ((Activity)c).finish();
        }
      }
    }

    egl.eglMakeCurrent(dpy, EGL10.EGL_NO_SURFACE,
EGL10.EGL_NO_SURFACE,
        EGL10.EGL_NO_CONTEXT);
    egl.eglDestroySurface(dpy, surface);
    egl.eglDestroyContext(dpy, context);
    egl.eglTerminate(dpy);

  }

        public void onWindowResize(int w, int h) {
            synchronized(this) {
                this.w = w;
                this.h = h;
                this.changed = true;
            }
        }

        public void waitForExit() {
            this.stop = true;
            try {
                join();
            } catch (InterruptedException ex) {
            }
        }

        private void drawFrame(GL10 gl) {

            // do whatever drawing here.
            }
    }
  }
}
```

Listing 9.15 will generate an empty white window. Everything in listing 9.15 is essentially code we need to draw and manage any OpenGL ES visualization. First we import all our needed classes. Then we implement an inner class, which will handle everything about managing a surface such as creating it, changing it, or deleting it. We extend the class SurfaceView and implement the SurfaceHolder interface, which allows us to get information back from Android when the surface changes, such as when someone resizes it ❶. With Android all of this has to be done asynchronously; we cannot manage surfaces directly.

Next we create a thread to do the drawing ❷ and create an init method that uses the SurfaceView class's getHolder method to get access to the SurfaceView and add a callback to it via the addCallBack method ❸. Now we can implement surfaceCreated ❹, surfaceChanged ❺, and surfaceDestroyed ❻, which are all methods of the Callback class and are fired on the appropriate condition of change in the Surface's state.

Now that all the `Callback` methods are implemented, we create a thread that will do all our drawing **7**. Before we can draw anything, we need to create an OpenGL ES Context **8** and then create a handler to the surface **9** so that we can use the OpenGL `Context`'s method to act on the surface via the handle **10**. Now we can finally draw something, although in the `drawFrame` method **11** we are not doing anything.

If you were to run the code right now, all you would get would be an empty window, but what we have generated so far will appear in some form or another in any OpenGL ES application you make on Android. Typically you would break up your code to have an `Activity` class to start your code, another class that would implement your custom `View`, another class that might implement your `SurfaceHolder` and `Callback` and provide all the methods for detecting changes to the surface as well as the actual drawing of your graphics in a thread, and finally whatever code represents your graphics. In the next section we will look at how to draw a square on the surface as well as create an animated cube.

DRAWING SHAPES IN OPENGL ES

In our next example we will use OpenGL ES to create a simple drawing, a rectangle, using OpenGL primitives—which are essentially pixels, polygons, and triangles. In drawing our square we will us a primitive called the `GL_Triangle_Strip`, which takes three vertices (the *X, Y, Z* points in an array of vertices) and draws a triangle. The last two vertices become the first two vertices for the next triangle, with the next vertex in the array being the final point. This repeats for as many vertices as there are in the array, and it generates something like figure 9.5, where two triangles are drawn.

OpenGL supports a small set of primitives, shown in table 9.1, from which you can build anything from simple geometric shapes such as a rectangle to 3D models of animated characters .

Table 9.1   OpenGL primitives and their descriptions

Primitive flag	Description
GL_POINTS	Places a point at each vertex.
GL_LINES	Draws a line for every pair of vertices given.
GL_LINE_STRIP	Draws a continuous set of lines. After the first vertex, it draws a line between every successive vertex and the vertex before it.
GL_LINE_LOOP	Same as GL_LINE_STRIP except that it connects the start and end vertices as well.
GL_TRIANGLES	For every triplet of vertices, it draws a triangle with corners specified by the coordinates of the vertices.
GL_TRIANGLE_STRIP	After the first two vertices, every successive vertex uses the previous two vertices to draw a triangle.
GL_TRIANGLE_FAN	After the first two vertices, every successive vertex uses the previous vertex and the first vertex to draw a triangle. This is used to draw cone-like shapes.

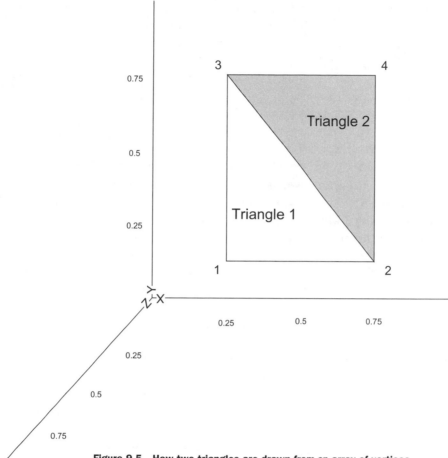

Figure 9.5 How two triangles are drawn from an array of vertices

In listing 9.16 we use an array of vertices to define a square to paint on our surface. To use the code, insert it directly into the code for listing 9.15, right below the commented line // do whatever drawing here.

Listing 9.16   OpenGLSquare.java

```
gl.glClear(GL10.GL_COLOR_BUFFER_BIT |
   GL10.GL_DEPTH_BUFFER_BIT);          ◁──❶ Clear the screen

float[] square = new float[] {        ◁──┐
                                          │  Create array that
   0.25f, 0.25f, 0.0f,              ❷ represents a square
   0.75f, 0.25f, 0.0f,
   0.25f, 0.75f, 0.0f,
   0.75f, 0.75f, 0.0f };

FloatBuffer squareBuff;
                                          │  ❸ Create float buffer
ByteBuffer bb =                           │     to hold square
ByteBuffer.allocateDirect(square.length*4);
   bb.order(ByteOrder.nativeOrder());
```

```
squareBuff = bb.asFloatBuffer();
squareBuff.put(square);
squareBuff.position(0);

gl.glMatrixMode(GL10.GL_PROJECTION);
gl.glLoadIdentity();
GLU.gluOrtho2D(gl, 0.0f,1.2f,0.0f,1.0f);

gl.glVertexPointer(3, GL10.GL_FLOAT, 0, squareBuff);
gl.glEnableClientState(GL10.GL_VERTEX_ARRAY);

gl.glClear(GL10.GL_COLOR_BUFFER_BIT);
gl.glColor4f(0,1,1,1);
gl.glDrawArrays(GL10.GL_TRIANGLE_STRIP, 0, 4);
```

5 Set up 2D orthographic viewing region

4 OpenGL commands to define projection

6 Set current vertices for drawing

Drawing will be done **7** by vertex array

8 Draw the array

This code is dense with OpenGL commands. The first thing we do is clear the screen using `glClear` **1**, which is something you want to do before every drawing. Then we build the array that will represent the set of vertices that will make up our square **2**. As we explained before, we will be using the OpenGL primitive GL_TRANGLE_STRIP to create the rectangle shown in figure 9.5, where the first set of three vertices (points 1, 2, and 3) is the first triangle. The last vertex represents the third vertex (point 4) in the second triangle, which reuses the last two vertices, 2 and 3, from the first triangle as its first two to make the triangle described by points 2, 3 and 4 **2**. To say this more clearly, Open GL takes one triangle and flips it over at the hypotenuse. We then create a buffer to hold that same square data **3**. We also tell the system that we will be using a GL_PROJECTION for our matrix mode, which is simply a type of matrix transformation that is applied to every point in the matrix stack **4**.

The next things we do are more setup related. We load the identity matrix and then use the `gluOrtho2D(GL10 gl, float left, float right, float bottom, float top)` command to set the clipping planes that are mapped to the lower-left and upper-right corners of the window **5**. Now we are ready to start drawing our image. To do this we first use the `glVertexPointer(int size, int type, int stride, pointer to array)` method, which indicates the location of vertices for our triangle strip. The method has four attributes: `size`, `type`, `stride`, and `pointer`. Size specifies the number of coordinates per vertex (for example, a 2D shape might ignore the Z axis and only use two coordinates per vertex), `type` defines the data type to be used (GL_BYTE, GL_SHORT, GL_FLOAT, and so on) **6**, `stride` specifies the offset between consecutive vertices (how many unused values exist between the end of the current vertex and the beginning of the next), and `pointer` is a reference to the array. While most drawing in OpenGL ES is performed by using various forms of arrays such as the vertex array, they are all disabled by default to save on system resources. To enable them we use the OpenGL command `glEnableClientState(array type)`, which accepts a array type, which in our case is the GL_VERTEX_ARRAY **7**.

Finally we use the `glDrawArrays` **8** function to render our arrays into the OpenGL primitives and create our simple drawing. The `glDrawArrays(mode, first, count)` function has three attributes: `mode` indicates which primitive to render, such as GL_TRIANGLE_STRIP; `first` is the starting index of the array, which we set to 0 since we want it to render all the vertices in the array; count specifies the number of indices to be rendered, and in our case that is 4.

Now if you run the code you should see a simple blue rectangle on a white surface, like the one in figure 9.6. It isn't particularly exciting, but most of the code we used you would need for any OpenGL project. In our next example we are going to create a 3D cube with different colors on each side and then rotate it in space.

THREE-DIMENSIONAL SHAPES AND SURFACES WITH OPENGL ES

In this section we are going to use much of the code from the previous example, but we are going to extend it to create a 3D cube that rotates. We will examine how to introduce perspective to our graphics to give the illusion of depth.

Depth works in OpenGL by using a depth buffer, which contains a depth value between 0 and 1 for every pixel. The value represents the perceived distance between objects and your viewpoint, so when two objects' depth values are compared, the value closer to 0 will appear in front on the screen. To

Figure 9.6   A simple square drawn on our surface using OpenGL ES

make use of depth in our program we need to first enable the depth buffer by passing GL_DEPTH_TEST to the glEnable method. Next we need to use glDepthFunc to define how values are compared. For our example we are going to use GL_LEQUAL, defined in table 9.2, which tells the system to show objects in front of other objects if their depth value is lower.

Table 9.2   Flags for determining how values in the depth buffer will be compared

Flag	Description
GL_NEVER	Never passes
GL_LESS	Passes if the incoming depth value is less than the stored value
GL_EQUAL	Passes if the incoming depth value is equal to the stored value
GL_LEQUAL	Passes if the incoming depth value is less than or equal to the stored value
GL_GREATER	Passes if the incoming depth value is greater than the stored value
GL_NOTEQUAL	Passes if the incoming depth value is not equal to the stored value
GL_GEQUAL	Passes if the incoming depth value is greater than or equal to the stored value
GL_ALWAYS	Always passes

When we draw a primitive, the depth test will take place. If the value passes the test, the incoming color value will replace the current one.

The default value is GL_LESS. We want the value to pass the test if the values are equal as well. This will cause objects with the same *z* value to display depending on the order in which they were drawn. We pass GL_LEQUAL to the function.

One very important part of maintaining the illusion of depth is the need for perspective. In OpenGL a typical perspective is represented by a viewpoint with near and far clipping planes and top, bottom, left, and right planes, where objects that are closer to the far plane appear smaller, as in figure 9.7.

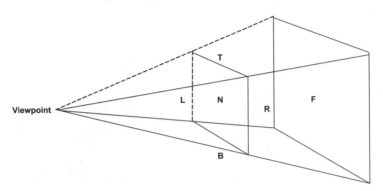

Figure 9.7 **In OpenGL a perspective is made up of a viewpoint and near (N), far (F), left (L), right (R), top (T), and bottom (B) clipping planes.**

OpenGL ES provides a function called gluPerspective(GL10 gl, float fovy, float aspect, float zNear, float zFar) with five parameters (see table 9.3) that allows us to easily create perspective.

To demonstrate depth and perspective we are going to create a project called OpenGLCube and copy and paste the code from listing 9.15 into the OpenGLCube-Activity.

Now add two new variables to your code, as in listing 9.17, right at the beginning of the DrawSurfaceView inner class.

Table 9.3 **Parameters for the gluPerspective function**

Parameter	Description
gl	GL10 interface.
fovy	Field of view angle, in degrees, in the *y* direction.
aspect	The aspect ratio that determines the field of view in the *x* direction. The aspect ratio is the ratio of *x* (width) to *y* (height).
zNear	The distance from the viewer to the near clipping plane, which is always positive.
zFar	The distance from the viewer to the far clipping plane, which is always positive.

Listing 9.17   OpenGLCubeActivity.java

```
class DrawingSurfaceView extends SurfaceView implements
SurfaceHolder.Callback  {
    public SurfaceHolder mHolder;

    float xrot = 0.0f;
    float yrot = 0.0f;
```

We are going to use xrot and yrot variables later in our code to govern the rotation of our cube.

Next, right before the drawFrame method, add a new method called makeFloat-Buffer, as in listing 9.18.

Listing 9.18   OpenGLCubeActivity.java

```
protected FloatBuffer makeFloatBuffer(float[] arr) {
        ByteBuffer bb = ByteBuffer.allocateDirect(arr.length*4);
        bb.order(ByteOrder.nativeOrder());
        FloatBuffer fb = bb.asFloatBuffer();
        fb.put(arr);
        fb.position(0);
        return fb;
}
```

This float buffer is essentially the same as the one in listing 9.16, but we have abstracted it from the drawFrame method so we can focus on the code for rendering and animating our cube.

Next, copy and paste the code in listing 9.19 into the drawFrame method.

Listing 9.19   OpenGLCubeActivity.java

```
    private void drawFrame(GL10 gl, int w1, int h1) {

        float mycube[] = {              ◁────── Create sides
            // FRONT                       ❶  for the cube
            -0.5f, -0.5f,  0.5f,
             0.5f, -0.5f,  0.5f,
            -0.5f,  0.5f,  0.5f,
             0.5f,  0.5f,  0.5f,
            // BACK
            -0.5f, -0.5f, -0.5f,
            -0.5f,  0.5f, -0.5f,
             0.5f, -0.5f, -0.5f,
             0.5f,  0.5f, -0.5f,
            // LEFT
            -0.5f, -0.5f,  0.5f,
            -0.5f,  0.5f,  0.5f,
            -0.5f, -0.5f, -0.5f,
            -0.5f,  0.5f, -0.5f,
            // RIGHT
             0.5f, -0.5f, -0.5f,
```

```
        0.5f,  0.5f, -0.5f,
        0.5f, -0.5f,  0.5f,
        0.5f,  0.5f,  0.5f,
        // TOP
       -0.5f,  0.5f,  0.5f,
        0.5f,  0.5f,  0.5f,
       -0.5f,  0.5f, -0.5f,
        0.5f,  0.5f, -0.5f,
        // BOTTOM
       -0.5f, -0.5f,  0.5f,
       -0.5f, -0.5f, -0.5f,
        0.5f, -0.5f,  0.5f,
        0.5f, -0.5f, -0.5f,
    };

    FloatBuffer cubeBuff;
```
② **Create float buffer for cube vertices**

```
    cubeBuff = makeFloatBuffer(mycube);
    gl.glEnable(GL10.GL_DEPTH_TEST);
    gl.glEnable(GL10.GL_CULL_FACE);
    gl.glDepthFunc(GL10.GL_LEQUAL);
    gl.glClearDepthf(1.0f);
```
③ **Enable the depth test**

```
    gl.glClear(GL10.GL_COLOR_BUFFER_BIT |
GL10.GL_DEPTH_BUFFER_BIT);

    gl.glMatrixMode(GL10.GL_PROJECTION);
    gl.glLoadIdentity();
    gl.glViewport(0,0,w1,h1);
    GLU.gluPerspective(gl, 45.0f,
((float)w1)/h1, 1f, 100f);
```
④ **Define your perspective**

```
    gl.glMatrixMode(GL10.GL_MODELVIEW);
    gl.glLoadIdentity();
    GLU.gluLookAt(gl, 0, 0, 3, 0, 0, 0, 0, 1, 0);
```
⑤ **Define your viewpoint in space**

```
    gl.glShadeModel(GL10.GL_SMOOTH);

    gl.glVertexPointer(3, GL10.GL_FLOAT, 0, cubeBuff);
    gl.glEnableClientState(GL10.GL_VERTEX_ARRAY);
```
⑥ **Select smooth shading for model**

```
    gl.glRotatef(xrot, 1, 0, 0);
    gl.glRotatef(yrot, 0, 1, 0);
```
⑦ **Rotate angle around vector x, y, z**

```
    gl.glColor4f(1.0f, 0, 0, 1.0f);
    gl.glDrawArrays(GL10.GL_TRIANGLE_STRIP, 0, 4);
    gl.glDrawArrays(GL10.GL_TRIANGLE_STRIP, 4, 4);
```
⑧ **Draw the six sides in three colors**

```
    gl.glColor4f(0, 1.0f, 0, 1.0f);
    gl.glDrawArrays(GL10.GL_TRIANGLE_STRIP, 8, 4);
    gl.glDrawArrays(GL10.GL_TRIANGLE_STRIP, 12, 4);

    gl.glColor4f(0, 0, 1.0f, 1.0f);
    gl.glDrawArrays(GL10.GL_TRIANGLE_STRIP, 16, 4);
    gl.glDrawArrays(GL10.GL_TRIANGLE_STRIP, 20, 4);

    xrot += 1.0f;
    yrot += 0.5f;
```
⑨ **Increment the x and y rotations**

There is not much new code in this listing. First we describe the vertices for a cube ❶, which is built in the same way as our simple rectangle in listing 9.16 (using triangles). Next we set up the float buffer for our vertices ❷ and enable the depth function ❸ and perspective function ❹ to provide a sense of depth. Note that with our `gluPerspective` we passed 45.0f (45 degrees) to give a more natural viewpoint.

Next we use the `GLU.gluLookAt(GL10 gl, float eyeX, float eyeY, float eyeZ, float centerX, float centerY, float centerZ, float upX, float upY, float upZ)` ❺ function to move the position of our view without having to modify the projection matrix directly. Once we have established our view position, we turn on smooth shading for the model ❻ and rotate the cube around the *x* and *y* axes ❼. Then we draw the cube sides ❽ and increment the rotation so that on the next iteration of draw, the cube is drawn at a slightly different angle ❾. If you run the code, you should now see a rotating 3D cube like the one shown in figure 9.8.

Figure 9.8   A 3D cube rotating in space

NOTE   You can try experimenting with the `fovy` value to see how changing the angle affects the display of the cube.

9.3   *Summary*

In this chapter we have only lightly touched on a number of topics related to Android's powerful graphics features, including simple drawings, animations, and Android's implementation of the OpenGL ES standard. Graphics and visualizations are a large and complex topic, but because Android uses open and well-defined standards as well as supports an excellent API for graphics, it should be easy for you to use Android's documentation, API, and other resources, such as Manning's *Java 3D Programming* by Daniel Sleman, to develop anything from a new drawing program to complex games.

In the next chapter we are going to move from graphics to working with multiple media. We will explore working with audio and video to lay the groundwork for making rich multimedia applications.

10
Multimedia

This chapter covers:

- Playing audio and video
- Controlling the camera
- Recording audio

Today people use their cell phones for almost everything but phone calls, from chatting, to surfing the web, to listening to music, and even to watching live streaming TV. Nowadays cell phones need to support multimedia to even be considered a usable device. In this chapter we are going to look how you can use Android to play audio files, watch video, take pictures, and even record sound.

Android supports multimedia by making use of the open source multimedia system called OpenCORE from PacketVideo Corporation. OpenCORE provides the foundation for Android's media services, which Android wraps in an easy-to-use API.

In this chapter we will look at OpenCORE's architecture and features and then use it via Android's MediaPlayer API to play audio files, take a picture, play videos, and finally record video and audio from the emulator. To begin let's look at Open-CORE's multimedia architecture.

10.1   *Introduction to multimedia and OpenCORE*

Since the foundation of Android's multimedia platform is PacketVideo's OpenCORE, in this section we will review OpenCORE's architecture and services. OpenCORE is a Java open source multimedia platform supporting the following:

- Interfaces for third-party and hardware media codecs, input and output devices, and content policies
- Media playback, streaming, downloading, and progressive playback, including 3GPP, MPEG-4, AAC, and MP3 containers
- Video and image encoders and decoders, including MPEG-4, H.263, and AVC (H.264), and JPEG
- Speech codecs, including AMR-NB and AMR-WB
- Audio codecs, including MP3, AAC, and AAC+
- Media recording, including 3GPP, MPEG-4, and JPEG
- Video telephony based on the 324-M standard
- PV test framework to ensure robustness and stability; profiling tools for memory and CPU usage

OpenCORE provides all this functionality in a well-laid-out set of services, which are diagrammed in figure 10.1.

NOTE   The current Android SDK does not support video recording via the API. Video recording is still possible but is specific to the phone vendor.

As you can see from figure 10.1, OpenCORE's architecture has excellent support for multimedia and numerous codecs. In the next section we are going to dive right in and use the Android API to play audio files.

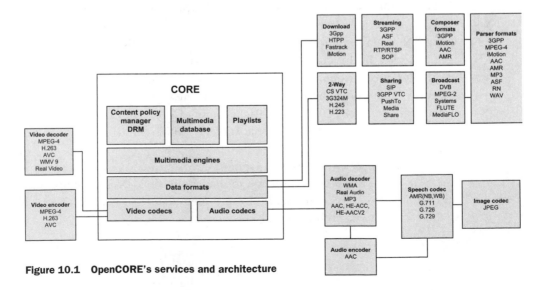

Figure 10.1   OpenCORE's services and architecture

10.2   *Playing audio*

Probably the most basic of needs for multimedia on a cell phone is the ability to play audio files, whether new ringtones, MP3s, or quick audio notes. Android's Media Player is easy to use. At a high level all you need to do to play back an MP3 file is follow these steps:

1   Put the MP3 in the res/raw directory in a project (note that you can also use a URI to access files on the network or via the internet).
2   Create a new instance of the MediaPlayer and reference your MP3 by calling MediaPlayer.create().
3   Call the MediaPlayer methods prepare() and start().

Let's work through a simple example to demonstrate exactly how simple this is. First create a new project called MediaPlayer Example with an Activity called MediaPlayerActivity. Now create a new folder under res/ called raw. This is where we will store our MP3s. For this example we will use a ringtone for the game Halo 3, which you can retrieve from MediaPlayer.create. Download the Halo 3 theme song (and any other MP3s), and put them in the raw directory. Next, create a simple Button for the music player, as in listing 10.1.

> **Listing 10.1   main.xml for MediaPlayer Example**

```xml
<?xml version="1.0" encoding="utf-8"?>
<LinearLayout xmlns:android="http://schemas.android.com/apk/res/android"
   android:orientation="vertical"
   android:layout_width="fill_parent"
   android:layout_height="fill_parent"
   >
<TextView
   android:layout_width="fill_parent"
   android:layout_height="wrap_content"
   android:text="Simple Media Player"
   />

<Button android:id="@+id/playsong"
   android:layout_width="fill_parent"
   android:layout_height="wrap_content"
   android:text="Halo 3 Theme Song"
   />
</LinearLayout>
```

Next we need to fill out our MediaPlayerActivity class, as in listing 10.2.

> **Listing 10.2   MediaPlayerActivity.java**

```java
public class MediaPlayerActivity extends Activity {
   @Override
   public void onCreate(Bundle icicle) {
      super.onCreate(icicle);
      setContentView(R.layout.main);
      Button mybutton = (Button) findViewById(R.id.playsong); 1
```

1 Set the view and a button to play an MP3

```
mybutton.setOnClickListener(new Button.OnClickListener() {
    public void onClick(View v) {
        MediaPlayer mp =
MediaPlayer.create(MediaPlayerActivity.this,
R.raw.halotheme);
        mp.start();
        mp.setOnCompletionListener(new OnCompletionListener(){
            public void onCompletion(MediaPlayer arg0) {

            }
        }
        );
    }
}
);
}
}
```

2 **Get the context and then play the MP3**

As you can see, playing back an MP3 is easy. In listing 10.2 all we did was use a view that we created in listing 10.1 and map the button, `playsong`, to `mybutton`, which we then bound to the `setOn-ClickListener()` **1**. Inside the listener we created the `MediaPlayer` instance **2** using the `create(Context context, int resourceid)` method, which simply takes our context and a resource ID for our MP3. Finally we set the `set-OnCompletionListener`, which will perform some task on completion. For the moment we do nothing, but you might want to change a button's state or provide a notification to a user that the song is over or ask if the user would like to play another song. If so, you would use this method.

Now if you compile the application and run it, you should see something like figure 10.2. Click the button, and you should hear the Halo 3 song played back in the emulator via your speakers. You can also control the volume of the playback with the volume switches on the side of the Android Emulator phone visualization.

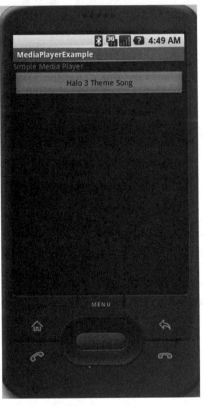

Figure 10.2   Simple media player example

Now that we have looked at how to play an audio file, let's see how we can play a video file.

10.3   *Playing video*

Playing a video is slightly more complicated than playing audio with the MediaPlayer API, in part because you have to provide a view surface for your video to play on. Android has a `VideoView` widget that handles that task for you, and it can be used in any layout manager. Plus it provides a number of display options, including scaling and tinting. So let's get started with playing video by creating a new project called Simple Video Player. Then create a layout as shown in listing 10.3.

NOTE Currently the emulator has some issues playing video content on certain computers and operating systems. Do not be surprised if your audio or video playback is choppy.

Listing 10.3 main.xml—UI for Simple Video Player

```xml
<?xml version="1.0" encoding="utf-8"?>
<LinearLayout xmlns:android="http://schemas.android.com/apk/res/android"
android:orientation="vertical"
android:layout_width="fill_parent"
android:layout_height="fill_parent"
>
   <VideoView android:id="@+id/video"
   android:layout_width="320px"
   android:layout_height="240px"
   />
   <Button android:id="@+id/playvideo"
   android:text="Play Video"
   android:layout_height="fill_parent"
   android:layout_width="fill_parent"
   android:paddingRight="4px"
   android:enabled="false"
   />
</LinearLayout>
```

① Add VideoView widget

② Add a Button to play the video

All we have done in listing 10.3 is to add the VideoView widget ① and a Button to initiate playback of our video ②.

Next we need to write a class to play the video. In addition to the VideoView, we put in a Button that, when pushed, will pop up the VideoView control panel, known as the MediaController. This, by default, overlays the bottom portion of the VideoView and shows your current position in the video clip. Plus it offers pause, rewind, and fast-forward buttons. See listing 10.4.

Listing 10.4 SimpleVideo.java

```java
public class SimpleVideo extends Activity {

   private VideoView myVideo;
   private MediaController mc;

   @Override
   public void onCreate(Bundle icicle) {
      super.onCreate(icicle);
      getWindow().setFormat(PixelFormat.TRANSLUCENT);
      setContentView(R.layout.main);
      Button bPlayVideo=(Button)findViewById(R.id.playvideo);

      bPlayVideo.setOnClickListener(new View.OnClickListener() {
      public void onClick(View view) {
         SimpleVideo.this.mc.show(); }
            });
```

① Create a translucent window

Set the view and button to ② play MP4

Show the MediaController UI widget ③

```
this.myVideo=(VideoView)findViewById(R.id.video);
this.myVideo.setVideoPath("sdcard/test.mp4");
this.mc=new MediaController(this);
this.mc.setMediaPlayer(myVideo);
this.myVideo.setMediaController(mc);
this.myVideo.requestFocus();
    }
}
```

Pass file from sdcard to VideoView ❺

Use VideoView as container for playing video ❹

Callback to VideoView when video is done ❼

Create a ❻ **MediaController**

In listing 10.4 we first created a translucent window which is necessary for our SurfaceView ❶. Then we added a Button to the VideoView widget ❷ and told Android to add a MediaController widget over the VideoView ❸ using the show() method. Next we reference the VideoView ❹ and use its setVideoPath() ❺ to have it look at an SD card (sdcard) for our test MP4. Finally we set up the MediaController ❻ and use the setMediaController() ❼ to perform a callback to the VideoView to notify it when a our video is finished playing.

Before we can run this application, we need to set up an sdcard in the emulator (see chapter 5 for details on the SD card). First, create a new SD card image:

```
mksdcard 512M mysdcard
```

Hit Return. A 512 MB FAT32 image named mysdcard has now been created for you to load into the emulator. Load the SD card into the emulator like this:

```
emulator -sdcard mysdcard
```

Now push the file test.mp4 to the disk image.

Once you have pushed the file to the image, you can launch the SimpleVideo application by going to your IDE and running the project while the emulator is already running. You should now see something like figure 10.3.

As you can see, the VideoView and MediaPlayer classes simplify working with video files. Something you will need to pay attention to when working with video files is that the emulator often has problems with files larger than 1 megabyte, although the current G1 phone does not.

NOTE By default, G1 supports only MP4 and 3GP formats. There are several video converters you can use to convert videos in other formats to these standards. As Android adoption grows, you can expect updates and more players to support a greater number of formats.

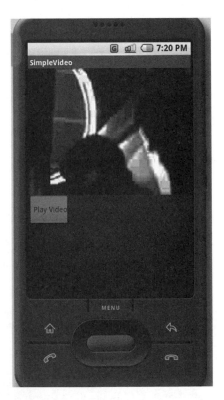

Figure 10.3   Playing an MP4 video in the Android Emulator

Now that you have seen how simple it is to play media using Android's MediaPlayer API, let's look at how we can use a phone's built-in camera or microphone to capture images or audio.

10.4 Capturing media

Using your cell phone to take pictures, record memos, films short videos, and so on are all features now expected of any such device. In this section we are going to not only look at how to capture media from the microphone and camera but also write these files to the simulated SD card image we created previously.

To get started let's examine how to use the Android `Camera` class to capture images and save them to a file.

10.4.1 Understanding the camera

A very important feature of modern cell phones is their ability to take pictures or even video using a built-in camera. Some phones even support using the camera's microphone to capture audio. Android, of course, supports all three features and provides a variety of ways to interact with the camera. In this section we're going to look at how to interact with the camera and take photographs. In the next section we'll use the camera to take video and save it to an SD card.

We will be creating a new project called SimpleCamera to demonstrate how to connect to a phone's camera to capture images. For this project we will be using the `Camera` class (http://code.google.com/android/reference/android/hardware/Camera. html) to tie the emulator's (or phone's) camera to a `View`. Most of the code that we create for this project will be about showing the input from the camera, but the main work for taking a picture is done by a single method called `take-Picture(Camera.ShutterCallback shutter, Camera.PictureCallback raw, Camera.PictureCallback jpeg)`, which has three callbacks that allow you to control how a picture is taken. Before we get any further into the `Camera` class and how to use the camera, let's create a project. We will be creating two classes, and since the main class is long, we will break it into two sections. For the first section look at listing 10.5, CameraExample.java.

NOTE The Android Emulator does not allow you to connect to camera devices on your computer such as a webcam, and thus all your pictures will display a chessboard like the one shown in figure 10.4. It is possible to connect to a web camera and get live images and video, but it requires some hacking. An excellent example on how to do this can be found at Tom Gibara's website, where he has an open source project for obtaining live images from a webcam: http://www.tomgibara.com/android/camera-source. It is possible that in latter versions of the SDK the emulator will support connections to cameras on the hardware the emulator is running on.

Listing 10.5 CameraExample.java

```
public class SimpleCamera extends Activity implements SurfaceHolder.Callback {
    private Camera camera;
```

```
private boolean isPreviewRunning = false;
private SimpleDateFormat timeStampFormat = new
    SimpleDateFormat("yyyyMMddHHmmssSS");

private SurfaceView surfaceView;
private SurfaceHolder surfaceHolder;
private Uri targetResource = Media.EXTERNAL_CONTENT_URI;

public void onCreate(Bundle icicle)    {
    super.onCreate(icicle);
    Log.e(getClass().getSimpleName(), "onCreate");
    getWindow().setFormat(PixelFormat.TRANSLUCENT);
    setContentView(R.layout.main);
    surfaceView = (SurfaceView)findViewById(R.id.surface);
    surfaceHolder = surfaceView.getHolder();
    surfaceHolder.addCallback(this);
    surfaceHolder.setType(SurfaceHolder.SURFACE_TYPE_PUSH_BUFFERS);
}

@Override
public boolean onCreateOptionsMenu(android.view.Menu menu) {

    MenuItem item = menu.add(0, 0, 0, "View Photos?");
    item.setOnMenuItemClickListener(new
      MenuItem.OnMenuItemClickListener() {

        public boolean onMenuItemClick(MenuItem item) {
            Intent intent = new Intent(Intent.ACTION_VIEW,
                SimpleCamera.this.targetResource);
            startActivity(intent);
            return true;
        }
    });
    return true;
}

@Override
protected void onRestoreInstanceState(Bundle savedInstanceState) {
    super.onRestoreInstanceState(savedInstanceState);
}

Camera.PictureCallback mPictureCallbackRaw = new
  Camera.PictureCallback() {
    public void onPictureTaken(byte[] data, Camera c) {
        SimpleCamera.this.camera.startPreview();
    }
};

Camera.ShutterCallback mShutterCallback = new Camera.ShutterCallback() {

    Public void onShutter() {}
    }
};
```

Create menu to Android's Photo Gallery **①**

Create a PictureCallback **②**

Create a ShutterCallback **③**

Listing 10.5 is pretty straightforward. First we set variables for managing a sur-faceView and then set up the View. Next we create a simple menu and menu option that will float over our surface when the user clicks the MENU button on the phone while the application is running ❶. Doing so will open Android's picture browser and let the user view the photos on the camera. Next we create the first PictureCallback, which is called when a picture is first taken ❷. This first callback captures the PictureCallback's only method, onPictureTaken(byte[] data, Camera camera), to grab the raw image data directly from the camera. Next we create a ShutterCallback, which can be used with its method, onShutter(), to play a sound, but here we do not call the method ❸. We will continue with the CameraExample.java in listing 10.6.

Listing 10.6 CameraExample.java continued

```
@Override                                    Create method to detect key events  ❶
  public boolean onKeyDown(int keyCode, KeyEvent event)  {      ◄──────┐
      ImageCaptureCallback camDemo = null;
      if(keyCode == KeyEvent.KEYCODE_DPAD_CENTER) {            ◄────────┤
         try {
             String filename = this.timeStampFormat.format(new Date());
             ContentValues values = new ContentValues();
             values.put(MediaColumns.TITLE, filename);
             values.put(ImageColumns.DESCRIPTION,
                 "Image from Android Emulator");
             Uri uri = getContentResolver().insert(
             Media.EXTERNAL_CONTENT_URI, values);
             camDemo = new ImageCaptureCallback(
                 getContentResolver().openOutputStream(uri));
         } catch(Exception ex ){
         }                                      If center key was depressed,
      }                                            write a file to sdcard  ❷
      if (keyCode == KeyEvent.KEYCODE_BACK) {
         return super.onKeyDown(keyCode, event);
      }

      if (keyCode == KeyEvent.KEYCODE_DPAD_CENTER) {
         this.camera.takePicture(this.mShutterCallback,
             this.mPictureCallbackRaw, this.camDemo);   ◄──┐
         return true;                                     If center key was
      }                                                   depressed, take
                                                       ❸  a picture
      return false;
  }

  @Override
  protected void onResume() {
      Log.e(getClass().getSimpleName(), "onResume");
      super.onResume();
  }

  @Override
  protected void onSaveInstanceState(Bundle outState) {
      super.onSaveInstanceState(outState);
  }

  @Override
  protected void onStop()
  {
```

```
      super.onStop();
   }

   public void surfaceChanged(SurfaceHolder holder, int format, int w, int h) {
      if (this.isPreviewRunning) {
         this.camera.stopPreview();
      }
      Camera.Parameters p = this.camera.getParameters();
      p.setPreviewSize(w, h);
      this.camera.setParameters(p);
      this.camera.setPreviewDisplay(holder);
      this.camera.startPreview();
      this.isPreviewRunning = true;
   }

   public void surfaceCreated(SurfaceHolder holder) {
      this.camera = Camera.open();
   }

   public void surfaceDestroyed(SurfaceHolder holder) {
      this.camera.stopPreview();
      this.isPreviewRunning = false;
      this.camera.release();
   }
}
```

Listing 10.6 is more complicated than listing 10.5 although a large amount of the code in this listing is really about managing the surface for the camera preview. But as you can see, the very first line is the start of an implementation of the method onKey-Down ❶, which checks to see if the center key on the dpad was depressed. If it was, we set up the creation of a file, and by using the ImageCaptureCallback, which we will define in listing 10.7, we create an OutputStream to write our image data to ❷, including not only the image but the filename and other metadata. Next we call the method takePicture() and pass it the three callbacks mShutterCallback, mPictureCall-backRaw, and camDemo, where mPictureCallbackRaw is our raw image and camDemo writes the image to a file on the SD card ❸, as you can see in listing 10.7.

Listing 10.7   ImageCaptureCallback.java

```
public class ImageCaptureCallback implements PictureCallback {

   private OutputStream filoutputStream;                          ❶ Write file to
                                                                     operating
   public ImageCaptureCallback(OutputStream filoutputStream) {      system
      this.filoutputStream = filoutputStream;
   }

   public void onPictureTaken(byte[] data, Camera camera) {
      try {                                                     Capture image
         this.filoutputStream.write(data);                  ❷ from camera
         this.filoutputStream.flush();
         this.filoutputStream.close();
      } catch(Exception ex) {
         ex.printStackTrace();
```

```
        }
    }
}
```

In listing 10.7 the class implements the Picture-Callback interface and provides two methods. The constructor creates a stream to write data to ❶, and the second method, onPictureTaken, takes binary data and writes to the SD card as a JPEG ❷. Now if you build this project and start the emulator running using the SD card image from previously in this chapter, you should see something like figure 10.4 when you start the SimpleCamera application from the Android menu. If you look at figure 10.4 you will notice an odd black-and-white checked background with a bouncing gray box. This is a test pattern that the Android Emulator generates to simulate an image feed since the emulator is not actually pulling a live feed from the camera.

Now if you click the center button on the dpad in the emulator, the application will take a picture. To see the picture click the MENU button, which will cause a menu to appear on the camera view window with a single option, View Pictures. If you select View Pictures, you will be taken to the Android picture

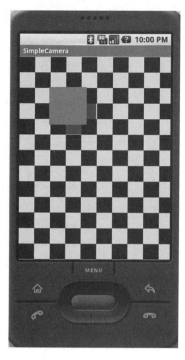

Figure 10.4   Test pattern coming from the emulator camera and displayed in the SimpleCamera application

explorer, and you should see Android's image placeholders representing the number of camera captures. You can also see the JPEG files that were written to the SD card by opening the DDMS in Eclipse and navigating to sdcard > dcim > Camera. You can see an example of what this might look like in figure 10.5.

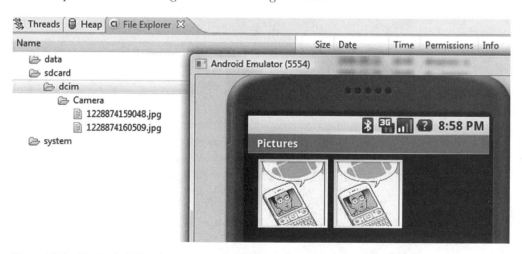

Figure 10.5   The Android Emulator shows placeholder images for each photo taken.

As you can see, working with the camera in Android is not particularly complicated. To see how a real camera will behave, you will have to test on a real handset until the emulator provides a simple way to connect to a camera on your computer. This should not stop you from developing your camera applications, however, and a wealth of Android applications already make sophisticated use of the camera, ranging from games to an application that uses a picture of your face to unlock your phone. Now that you have seen how the Camera class works in Android, let's look at how to capture or record audio from a camera's microphone. In the next section we'll explore the MediaRecorder class and write recordings to an SD card.

10.4.2 *Capturing audio*

Now we'll look at using the onboard microphone to record audio. In this section we're going to use the Android MediaRecorder example from Google Android Developers list, which you can find at http://groups.google.com/group/android-developers/files. The code shown here has been slightly updated.

NOTE   At the time the book was written, Google Android SDK 1 does not allow you to capture audio from the emulator via your computer, but it is likely that later versions of the SDK will.

In general recording audio or video follows the same process in Android:

1 Create an instance of android.media.MediaRecorder.
2 Create an instance of andriod.content.ContentValues, and add properties like TITLE, TIMESTAMP, and the all-important MIME_TYPE.
3 Create a file path for the data to go to using android.content.Content-Resolver.
4 To set a preview display on a view surface, use MediaRecorder.setPreview-Display().
5 Set the source for audio, using MediaRecorder.setAudioSource().
6 Set output file format using MediaRecorder.setOutputFormat().
7 Set your encoding for audio, using MediaRecorder.setAudioEncoder().
8 Use prepare() and start() to prepare and start your recordings.
9 Use stop() and release() to gracefully stop and clean up your recording process.

While recording media is not especially complex, it is, as you can see, more complex than playing it. To really understand how to use the MediaRecorder class, we'll look at an application. Create a new application called SoundRecordingDemo. Next you need to edit the AndroidManifest.xml file and add the following line:

```
<uses-permission android:name="android.permission.RECORD_AUDIO" />
```

This will allow the application to record the audio files and play them. Then create the class shown in listing 10.8.

Listing 10.8 SoundRecordingdemo.java

```java
public class SoundRecordingDemo extends Activity {

    MediaRecorder mRecorder;
    File mSampleFile = null;
    static final String SAMPLE_PREFIX = "recording";
    static final String SAMPLE_EXTENSION = ".mp3";

    private static final String TAG="SoundRecordingDemo";

    @Override
    public void onCreate(Bundle savedInstanceState) {
        super.onCreate(savedInstanceState);
        setContentView(R.layout.main);
        this.mRecorder = new MediaRecorder();

        Button startRecording = (Button)findViewById(R.id.startrecording);
        Button stopRecording = (Button)findViewById(R.id.stoprecording);

        startRecording.setOnClickListener(new View.OnClickListener(){

            public void onClick(View v) {
                startRecording();
            }
        });

        stopRecording.setOnClickListener(new View.OnClickListener(){

            public void onClick(View v) {
                stopRecording();
                addToDB();
            }

        });
    }

    protected void addToDB() {
        ContentValues values = new ContentValues(3);
        long current = System.currentTimeMillis();

        values.put(MediaColumns.TITLE, "test_audio");
        values.put(MediaColumns.DATE_ADDED, (int) (current / 1000));
        values.put(MediaColumns.MIME_TYPE, "audio/mp3");
        values.put(MediaColumns.DATA, mSampleFile.getAbsolutePath());
        ContentResolver contentResolver = getContentResolver();

        Uri base = MediaStore.Audio.Media.EXTERNAL_CONTENT_URI;
        Uri newUri = contentResolver.insert(base, values);

        sendBroadcast(new Intent(Intent.ACTION_MEDIA_SCANNER_SCAN_FILE, newUri));
    }

    protected void startRecording() {
        this.mRecorder = new MediaRecorder();
        this.mRecorder.setAudioSource(MediaRecorder.AudioSource.MIC);
        this.mRecorder.setOutputFormat(MediaRecorder.OutputFormat.THREE_GPP);
        this.mRecorder.setAudioEncoder(MediaRecorder.AudioEncoder.AMR_NB);
        this.mRecorder.setOutputFile(this.mSampleFile.getAbsolutePath());
        this.mRecorder.prepare();
        this.mRecorder.start();
```

① Set the metadata for the audio

② Notify music player new audio file created

③ Start recording the file

```
        if (this.mSampleFile == null) {
            File sampleDir = Environment.getExternalStorageDirectory();

            try {
                this.mSampleFile = File.createTempFile(
                    SoundRecordingDemo.SAMPLE_PREFIX,
                    SoundRecordingDemo.SAMPLE_EXTENSION, sampleDir);
            } catch (IOException e) {
                Log.e(TAG,"sdcard access error");
                return;
            }
        }
    }

    protected void stopRecording() {      ◄───   ❹ Stop recording and
        this.mRecorder.stop();                        release MediaRecorder
        this.mRecorder.release();
    }
}
```

As you can see in listing 10.8, the first part of the code is creating the buttons and button listeners to start and stop the recording. The first part of the listing you need to pay attention to is the addToDB() method. In this method we set all the metadata for the audio file we plan to save, including the title, date, and type of file ❶. Next we call the Intent ACTION_MEDIA_SCANNER_SCAN_FILE to notify applications like Android's Music Player that a new audio file has been created ❷. This will allow us to use the Music Player to look for new files in a playlist and play the file.

Now that we have finished the addToDB method, we create the startRecording method, which creates a new MediaRecorder ❸. As in the steps in the beginning of this section we set a audio source, which is the microphone, set an output format as THREE_GPP, set the audio encoder type to AMR_NB, and then set the output file path to write the file. Next we use the methods prepare() and start() to enable the recording of audio.

Finally we create the stopRecording() method to stop the MediaRecorder from saving audio ❹. We do this by using the methods stop() and release(). Now if you build this application and run the emulator with the SD card image from the previous section, you should be able to launch the application from Eclipse and press the Start Recording button. After a few seconds, press the Stop Recording button and open the DDMS; you should be able to navigate to the sdcard folder and see your recordings, as shown in figure 10.6.

If you have music playing on your computer's audio system, the Android Emulator will pick it up and record it directly from the audio buffer (it is not actually recording from a microphone). You can then easily test this by opening the Android Music Player and selecting Playlists > Recently Added. It should play your recorded file, and you should be able to hear anything that was playing on your computer at the time. While Android currently lets you record only audio, Google plans to soon add support for recording video. This will also use the MediaRecorder class to allow you to record video coming in from the camera much like you would audio.

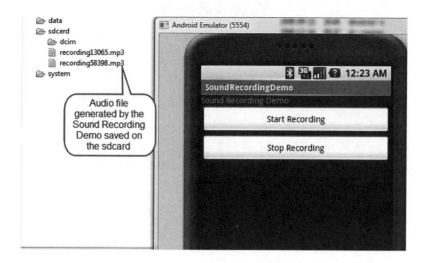

Figure 10.6 An example of audio files being saved to the SD card image in the emulator

10.5 Summary

In this chapter we looked at how the Android SDK makes use of multimedia and how you can play, save, and record video and sound. We also looked at various features the Android MediaPlayer offers the developer, from a built-in video player to wide support for formats, encodings, and standards.

We also looked at how to interact with other hardware devices attached to the phone, such as a microphone and camera. We used the SDK to create an SD card image for the emulator to simulate SD cards, and we used the MediaRecorder application to record audio and save it to the SD card.

While Android's SDK and Emulator, at the time of writing, do not provide a good way to interact with a webcam or microphone on your development platform, you can create real multimedia applications using the SDK now, as some vendors already have done on their phone platforms. Google Android currently offers you everything you need to create rich and compelling media applications, and its focus on supporting industry and open standards guarantees your applications will have wide support on a variety of phones.

In the next chapter you will learn all about how to use Android's location services to interact with GPS and maps. By mixing in what you have learned in this chapter, you could create your own GPS application that not only provides voice direction but could even respond to voice commands.

11

Location,
location, location

This chapter covers:

- Manipulating location properties in the emulator
- Working with `LocationProvider` and `LocationManager`
- Implementing and registering `LocationListener`
- Understanding `MapActivity` and `MapView`
- Using the `Geocoder`

A mobile device with accurate location awareness is very powerful. Combining location awareness with network data access is world changing—and this is where Android shines. Android isn't the only platform to support this capability, of course, but it is set apart somewhat by an easy-to-work-with and popular location API framework (Google Maps) and its open source nature.

From direct network queries to triangulation with cell towers and even GPS, an Android-powered device has access to different types of `LocationProvider` that it can utilize to access location data. Different providers supply a mix of location-related metrics including latitude and longitude, speed, bearing, and altitude.

GPS is the most common location provider you will work with on the Android platform, because it is the most accurate and powerful option. Nevertheless, some devices may either not have a GPS receiver or a GPS signal may not be available. In those instances the Android platform provides the capability for you to fail gracefully—to query other providers when your first choice fails. You can configure which providers are available and hook into one or another through the `LocationManager` class.

Location awareness opens up a new world of possibilities for application development. We are just beginning to see what inventive developers can do with real-time location information and faster and more reliable network data access. In this chapter we are going to follow that nascent path and build an application that combines location awareness with data from the U.S. National Oceanic and Atmospheric Administration (NOAA).

Specifically we will be connecting to the National Data Buoy Center (NDBC) to retrieve data from buoys that are positioned around the coastline in North America (and a few NOAA ships). That's right; we said, "data from buoys." Thanks to the NOAA-NDBC system, which polls sensors on buoys and makes that data available in RSS feeds, we can retrieve data for the vicinity, based on the current location, and display condition information such as wind speed, wave height, and temperature to our users. (Although we won't cover non-location-related details in this chapter, such as using HTTP to pull the RSS feed data, the full source code for the application is available with the code download for this chapter.) This application, which we are calling Wind and Waves, has several main screens, including an Android `MapActivity` with a `MapView`. These components are used for displaying and manipulating map information, as shown in figure 11.1.

We admit that accessing buoy data has a somewhat limited audience—being important mainly for marine use cases (and in this case working only for fixed buoys in North America and several ships that can be used as worldwide data points)—but we wanted to demonstrate the broad scope of possibility here and to come up with something unique. Along with its uniqueness, we hope to make this an interesting application that exercises a great many of the Android location-related capabilities.

In addition to displaying data based on the current location, we will also use this application to create several `LocationListener` instances that we can use to receive updates when the user's location changes. When the location changes and the device lets our application know, we will update our `MapView` using an `Overlay`—an object that allows us to draw on top of the map.

Outside of what our buoy application requires, here we will also pull in a few samples for working with the `Geocoder` class. This class allows you to map between a `GeoPoint` (latitude and longitude) and a place (city or postal code) or address. This is a very helpful utility, so we will cover it even though we won't be using it on the high seas.

Before we begin building any of our example code, we will start with using the built-in mapping application and simulating our position within the Android emulator. This will allow us to mock our location for the emulator. After we have covered all of the emulator location-related options, we will move on to building Wind and Waves.

**Figure 11.1   Screens from the Wind and Waves
location-aware application**

11.1   *Simulating your location within the emulator*

For any location-aware application you will start by working with the provided SDK and
the emulator. The first thing you will want to do within the emulator is set and update
your current location. From there you will want to progress to supplying a range of
locations and times to simulate movement over a geographic area.

There are several ways you can accomplish these tasks for the emulator, either by
using the DDMS tool or by using the command line within the shell. The fastest way to
get started is to send in direct coordinates through the DDMS tool.

11.1.1   *Sending in your coordinates with the DDMS tool*

The DDMS tool is available in two contexts, either launched on its own from the SDK
tools subdirectory or as the Emulator Control view within the Eclipse IDE. (You need
to have Eclipse and the Android Eclipse plug-in to use DDMS within Eclipse; see chapter 2 and appendix A for more details about getting the SDK and plug-in set up.)

The simplest way to set your location with the DDMS tool is to send direct latitude and longitude coordinates manually from the Emulator Control > Location Controls form. This is depicted, using the straightforward manual approach, in figure 11.2. (Note that *Longitude* is the top/first field, which is the standard around the world, but backwards in terms of how latitude and longitude are generally expressed in the United States.)

If you launch the built-in Maps application (which is included with Android on the main menu) and send in a location with the DDMS tool, you should then be able to use the menu to select My Location, and the map will animate to the location you have specified—anywhere on earth.

Try this a few times to make sure you get the hang of it; for example, send the decimal coordinates in table 11.1 one by one, and in between browse around with the built-in map. When you supply coordinates to the emulator, you will need to use the decimal form.

Although the DDMS tool requires the decimal format, latitude and longitude are more commonly expressed on maps and other tools as degrees, minutes, and seconds. Degrees are used because these coordinates represent points on the surface of the globe as measured from either the equator (for latitude) or the prime meridian (for longitude). Each degree is further subdivided into 60 smaller sections, called minutes, and each minute also has 60 seconds (and it goes on from there if need be, tenths of a second, and so on).

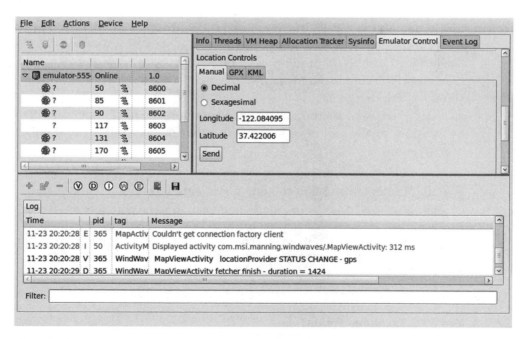

Figure 11.2   Using the DDMS tool to send direct latitude and longitude coordinates to the emulator as a mock location

Table 11.1   Example coordinates for the emulator to set using the DDMS tool

Description	Latitude degrees	Longitude degrees	Latitude decimal	Longitude decimal
Golden Gate Bridge, California	37°49' N	122°29' W	37.49	-122.29
Mount Everest, Nepal	27°59' N	86°56' E	27.59	86.56
Ayer's Rock, Australia	25°23' S	131°05' E	-25.23	131.05
North Pole	90°00' N	-	90.00	-
South Pole	90°00' S	-	-90.00	-

When representing latitude and longitude on a computer, the degrees are usually converted into decimal form with positive representing north and east and negative representing south and west, as shown in figure 11.3.

It's not personal, but if you live in the southern and eastern hemispheres, say in Buenos Aires, Argentina, which is 34°60' S, 58°40' W in the degree form, the decimal form is negative for both latitude and longitude, -34.60, -58.40. If you haven't used latitude and longitude much, the different forms can be confusing at first, but they quickly become second nature after you work with them a bit.

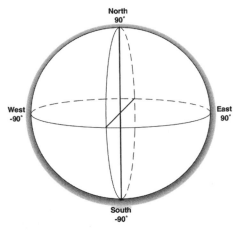

Figure 11.3   Latitude and longitude spherical diagram, showing positive north and east and negative south and west

Once you have mastered setting a fixed position, the next thing you will want to be able to do is supply a set of coordinates that the emulator will use to simulate a range of movement.

Using the command line to send coordinates

You can also send direct coordinates from within the emulator console. If you `telnet localhost 5554`, you will connect to the default emulator's console (adjust the port where necessary). From there you can use the `geo` fix command to send longitude, latitude, and optional altitude, for example, `geo fix -21.55 64.1`. Again keep in mind that the Android tools require that longitude be the first parameter

11.1.2   The GPS Exchange Format

The DDMS tool supports two formats for supplying a range of location data in file form to the emulator. The GPS Exchange Format (GPX) is the first of these and is the more expressive form in terms of working with Android.

GPX is an XML schema (http://www.topografix.com/GPX/1/1/) that allows you to store waypoints, tracks, and routes. Many handheld GPS devices support and/or utilize this format. Listing 11.1 is a portion of an example GPX file that shows the basics of the format.

Listing 11.1　A sample GPX file

```
<?xml version="1.0" encoding="UTF-8" standalone="no" ?>
<gpx xmlns="http://www.topografix.com/GPX/1/1"          ❶ Define root
 version="1.1"                                              gpx element
 creator="Charlie Collins - Hand Rolled"
 xmlns:xsi="http://www.w3.org/2001/XMLSchema-instance"
 xsi:schemaLocation="http://www.topografix.com/GPX/1/1
 http://www.topografix.com/GPX/1/1/gpx.xsd">
                                                         ❷ Include metadata
  <metadata>                                                stanza
     <name>Sample Coastal California Waypoints</name>
       <desc>Test waypoints for use with Android</desc>
     <time>2008-11-25T06:52:56Z</time>
     <bounds minlat="25.00" maxlat="75.00"
      minlon="100.00" maxlon="-150.00" />
  </metadata>

  <wpt lat="41.85" lon="-124.38">          ❸ Supply waypoint
     <ele>0</ele>                             elements
     <name>Station 46027</name>
     <desc>Off the coast of Lake Earl</desc>
  </wpt>
  <wpt lat="41.74" lon="-124.18">
     <ele>0</ele>
     <name>Station CECC1</name>
     <desc>Crescent City</desc>
  </wpt>
  <wpt lat="38.95" lon="-123.74">
     <ele>0</ele>
     <name>Station PTAC1</name>
     <desc>Point Arena Lighthouse</desc>
  </wpt>

  . . . remainder of wpts omitted for brevity
                                                ❹ Supply track
  <trk>                                            element
     <name>Example Track</name>
     <desc>A fine track with trkpt's.</desc>  ❺ Use a track
     <trkseg>                                     segment
        <trkpt lat="41.85" lon="-124.38">     ❻ Provide specific
           <ele>0</ele>                          points
           <time>2008-10-15T06:00:00Z</time>
        </trkpt>
        <trkpt lat="41.74" lon="-124.18">
           <ele>0</ele>
           <time>2008-10-15T06:01:00Z</time>
        </trkpt>
        <trkpt lat="38.95" lon="-123.74">
           <ele>0</ele>
           <time>2008-10-15T06:02:00Z</time>
        </trkpt>
```

```
. . . remainder of trkpts omitted for brevity
        </trkseg>
    </trk>
</gpx>
```

As part of the root `gpx` element, a GPX file requires the correct XML namespace ❶ and then moves on to metadata ❷ and individual waypoints ❸ (waypoints are named locations and are defined using latitude and longitude). Along with individual waypoints, a GPX file also supports related route information in the form of tracks ❹, which can be subdivided further into track segments ❺. Each track segment is made up of track points (which are basically related and ordered waypoints with an additional point-in-time property) ❻.

When working with a GPX file in the DDMS tool you can use two different modes, as the screen shot in figure 11.4 reveals. In the top half of the GPX box individual waypoints are listed; as each is clicked, that individual location is sent to the emulator. In the bottom half of the GPX box all the tracks are displayed. Tracks can be "played" forward and backward to simulate movement. As each track point is reached in the file, based on the time it defines (the times matter with GPX, the file can be run at various speeds using the Speed button), those coordinates are sent to the emulator.

GPX is very simple and extremely useful when working with mock location information for your Android applications, but it's not the only file format supported. The DDMS tool also supports a format called KML.

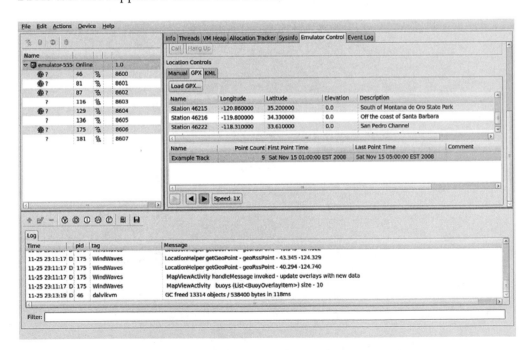

Figure 11.4 Using the DDMS tool with a GPX file to send mock location information

11.1.3 *The Google Earth Keyhole Markup Language*

The second format that the Android DDMS tool supports for sending a range of mock location information to the emulator is the Keyhole Markup Language (KML). KML was originally a proprietary format (created by Keyhole, which was acquired by Google), but it has since been submitted to the Open Geospatial Consortium (OGC) and accepted as an international standard.

The mantra of the OGC KML is stated as:

> *That there be one international standard language for expressing geographic annotation and visualization on existing or future web-based online and mobile maps (2d) and earth browsers (3d).*

A sample KML file for sending location data to the Android Emulator is shown in listing 11.2. This file uses the same coastal location data as we saw with the previous GPX example.

Listing 11.2 A sample KML file

```xml
<?xml version="1.0" encoding="UTF-8"?>          ① Define root
<kml xmlns="http://earth.google.com/kml/2.2">       kml element

   <Placemark>                                               ② Capture
     <name>Station 46027</name>                                 information
     <description>Off the coast of Lake Earl</description>      with Placemark
     <Point>                                              ③ Use a Point
        <coordinates>-124.38,41.85,0</coordinates>
     </Point>
   </Placemark>                        Supply coordinates
                                          for Point ④
   <Placemark>
     <name>Station 46020</name>
     <description>Outside the Golden Gate</description>
     <Point>
        <coordinates>-122.83,37.75,0</coordinates>
     </Point>
   </Placemark>

   <Placemark>
     <name>Station 46222</name>
     <description>San Pedro Channel</description>
     <Point>
        <coordinates>-118.31,33.61,0</coordinates>
      </Point>
   </Placemark>

</kml>
```

KML uses a `kml` root element and, like any self-respecting XML format, requires the correct namespace declaration ①. KML supports many more elements and attributes than the DDMS tool is concerned with parsing. Basically, in DDMS terms, all your KML files need to have are `Placemark` elements ②, which contain `Point` child elements ③, which in turn supply `coordinates` ④.

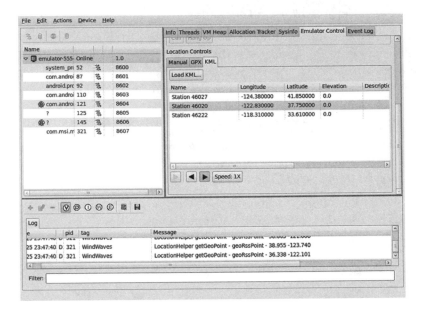

Figure 11.5   Using the DDMS tool with a KML file to send mock location information

Figure 11.5 shows an example of using a KML file with the DDMS tool.

KML is very flexible and expressive, but it has drawbacks when working with it in an Android Emulator context. As we have noted, the DDMS parser basically looks for the `coordinate` elements in the file and sends the latitude, longitude, and elevation for each in a sequence, one per second (the documentation says one `Placemark` per second). Timing and other advanced features of KML are not yet supported by DDMS. Because of this we find it more valuable at present to use GPX as a debugging and testing format (where detailed timing is supported).

KML is still important, though; remember it's the international standard, so it is sure to gain traction. Also, KML is an important format for other Google applications, so you may encounter it more frequently in other contexts than GPX.

Now that we have shown how to send mock location information to the emulator, in various formats, the next thing we need to do is step out of the built-in Maps application and start creating our own programs that rely on location.

11.2   *Using LocationManager and LocationProvider*

When building location-aware applications on the Android platform, there are several key classes you will use very often. A `LocationProvider` provides location data using several metrics, and its data is accessed through a `LocationManager`.

`LocationManager`, along with returning the available providers, also allows you to attach a `LocationListener` to be updated when the device location changes and/or directly fire an `Intent` based on the proximity to a specified latitude and longitude. The last-known `Location` is also available directly from the manager.

The Location class is a bean that represents all the location data available from a particular snapshot in time. Depending on the provider used to populate it, a Location may or may not have all the possible data present (it might not include speed or altitude, for example).

To get our Wind and Waves sample application started and to demonstrate the related concepts, the first thing we need to do is get a handle on the LocationManager.

11.2.1 Accessing location data with LocationManager

The central class that you will use to interact with location-related data on Android is the LocationManager. Before you can check which providers are available or query the last-known Location, you need to get the manager from the system service. The code to do this is shown in listing 11.3, which includes a portion of the MapViewActivity that will drive our Wind and Waves application.

Listing 11.3 Start of MapViewActivity

```
public class MapViewActivity extends MapActivity {          ❶ Extend
                                                              MapActivity
    private static final int MENU_SET_SATELLITE = 1;
    private static final int MENU_SET_MAP = 2;
    private static final int MENU_BUOYS_FROM_MAP_CENTER = 3;
    private static final int MENU_BACK_TO_LAST_LOCATION = 4;

    . . . Handler and LocationListeners omitted here for brevity - shown in
        later listings
                                                   ❷ Define
                                                      LocationManager
    private MapController mapController;
    private LocationManager locationManager;
    private LocationProvider locationProvider;      ❸ Define
    private MapView mapView;                           LocationProvider
    private ViewGroup zoom;
    private Overlay buoyOverlay;
    private ProgressDialog progressDialog;
    private Drawable defaultMarker;
    private ArrayList<BuoyOverlayItem> buoys;

    @Override
    public void onCreate(Bundle icicle) {
        super.onCreate(icicle);
        this.setContentView(R.layout.mapview_activity);

        this.mapView = (MapView) this.findViewById(R.id.map_view);
        this.zoom = (ViewGroup) findViewById(R.id.zoom);
        this.zoom.addView(this.mapView.getZoomControls());

        this.defaultMarker =
          getResources().getDrawable(R.drawable.redpin);
        this.defaultMarker.setBounds(0, 0,
          this.defaultMarker.getIntrinsicWidth(),
          this.defaultMarker.getIntrinsicHeight());

        this.buoys = new ArrayList<BuoyOverlayItem>();
    }

    @Override
```

```
public void onStart() {
  super.onStart();
  this.locationManager =
    (LocationManager)

  this.getSystemService(Context.LOCATION_SERVICE);
  this.locationProvider =
    this.locationManager.getProvider(
    LocationManager.GPS_PROVIDER);
  // LocationListeners omitted here for brevity

  GeoPoint lastKnownPoint = this.getLastKnownPoint();
  this.mapController = this.mapView.getController();
  this.mapController.setZoom(10);
  this.mapController.animateTo(lastKnownPoint);
  this.getBuoyData(lastKnownPoint);
}

. . . onResume and onPause omitted for brevity
. . . other portions of MapViewActivity are included
      in later listings in this chapter

private GeoPoint getLastKnownPoint() {
  GeoPoint lastKnownPoint = null;

  Location lastKnownLocation =
    this.locationManager.getLastKnownLocation(
    LocationManager.GPS_PROVIDER);

  if (lastKnownLocation != null) {
    lastKnownPoint = LocationHelper.getGeoPoint(lastKnownLocation);
  } else {
    lastKnownPoint = LocationHelper.GOLDEN_GATE;
  }
  return lastKnownPoint;
}
```

4 Instantiate LocationManager system service

5 Assign GPS LocationProvider

6 Set up map

7 Get the last known Location

The first thing to note with the MapViewActity is that it extends MapActivity **1**. Although we aren't focusing on the MapActivity details yet (that will be covered in section 11.3), this extension is still important to note. Once we get the class started, we declare member variables for LocationManager **2** and LocationProvider **3**.

In order to instantiate the LocationManager we use the Activity getSystemService(String name) method **4**. LocationManager is a system service, so we don't directly create it; we let the system return it. After we have the LocationManager, we also assign the LocationProvider we want to use with the manager's getProvider method **5**. In this case we are using the GPS provider. We will talk more about the LocationProvider class in the next section.

Once we have the manager and provider in place, we use the onCreate method of our Activity to instantiate a MapController and set initial state for the screen **6**. A MapController and the MapView it manipulates are also items we will cover more in section 11.3.

Along with helping you set up the provider you need, `LocationManager` supplies quick access to the last-known `Location` ❼. This method is very useful if you need a quick fix on the last location, as opposed to the more involved techniques for registering for periodic location updates with a listener (a topic we will cover in section 11.2.3).

Though we don't use it in this listing, or in the Wind and Waves application at all, the `LocationManager` additionally allows you to directly register for proximity alerts. If you need to fire an `Intent` based on proximity to a defined location, you will want to be aware of the `addProximityAlert` method. This method lets you set the location you are concerned about with latitude and longitude, and then it lets you specify a radius and a `PendingIntent`. If the device comes within the range, the `PendingIntent` is fired. (There is a corresponding `removeProximityAlert` method as well.)

Getting back to the main purpose for which we will use the `LocationManager` with Wind and Waves, we next need to look a bit more closely at the GPS `LocationProvider`.

11.2.2 Using a LocationProvider

`LocationProvider` is an abstract class that helps define the capabilities of a given provider implementation. Different provider implementations, which are responsible for returning location information, may be available on different devices and in different circumstances.

So what are the different providers, and why are multiple providers necessary? Those are really context-sensitive questions, meaning the answer is, "it depends." Which provider implementations are available depends on the hardware capabilities of the device—does it have a GPS receiver, for example? It also depends on the situation; even if the device has a GPS receiver, can it currently receive data from satellites, or is the user somewhere that's not possible (an elevator or a tunnel)?

At runtime you will need to query for the list of providers available and use the most suitable one (or ones—it can often be advantageous to fall back to a less-accurate provider if your first choice is not available or enabled). The most common provider, and the only one available in the Android Emulator, is the `LocationManager.GPS_PROVIDER` provider (which uses the GPS receiver). Because it is the most common (and most accurate) and what is available in the emulator, this is the provider we are going to use for Wind and Waves. Keep in mind, though, at runtime in a real device, there will normally be multiple providers, including the `LocationManager.NETWORK_PROVIDER` provider (which uses cell tower and Wi-Fi access points to determine location data).

In listing 11.3 we showed how you can obtain the GPS provider directly using the `getProvider(String name)` method. Some alternatives to this approach of directly accessing a particular provider are shown in table 11.2.

Different providers may support different location-related metrics and have different costs or capabilities. The `Criteria` class helps to define what each provider instance can handle. Among the metrics available are the following: latitude and longitude, speed, bearing, altitude, cost, and power requirements.

Table 11.2   Methods for obtaining a `LocationProvider` reference

`LocationProvider` code snippet	Description
```List<String> providers = locationManager.getAllProviders();```	Get all of the providers registered on the device.
```List<String> enabledProviders = locationManager.getAllProviders(true);```	Get all of the currently enabled providers.
```locationProvider = locationManager.getProviders(true).get(0);```	A shortcut to get the first enabled provider, regardless of type.
```locationProvider = this.locationManager.getBestProvider(myCriteria, true);```	An example of getting a `LocationProvider` using a specified `Criteria`. (You can create a `criteria` instance and specify whether bearing or altitude or cost and other metrics are required or not.)

Another important aspect of working with location data and `LocationProvider` instances is Android permissions. Location-related permissions need to be in your manifest depending on the providers you want to use. Listing 11.4 shows the Wind and Waves manifest XML file, which includes both `COARSE`- and `FINE`-grained location-related permissions.

> **Listing 11.4   A manifest file showing `COARSE` and `FINE` location-related permissions**

```xml
<?xml version="1.0" encoding="utf-8"?>
<manifest xmlns:android="http://schemas.android.com/apk/res/android"
  package="com.msi.manning.windwaves">

  <application android:icon="@drawable/wave_45"
    android:label="@string/app_name"
    android:theme="@android:style/Theme.Black">

    <activity android:name="StartActivity"
     android:label="@string/app_name">
    <intent-filter>
       <action android:name="android.intent.action.MAIN" />
       <category android:name="android.intent.category.LAUNCHER" />
    </intent-filter>
    </activity>

    <activity android:name="MapViewActivity" />
    <activity android:name="BuoyDetailActivity" />

    <uses-library android:name="com.google.android.maps" />

  </application>

  <uses-permission
    android:name=
      "android.permission.ACCESS_COARSE_LOCATION" />
```

❶ Include LocationManager. NETWORK_PROVIDER

```
<uses-permission
  android:name=
    "android.permission.ACCESS_FINE_LOCATION" />
<uses-permission
  android:name="android.permission.INTERNET" />
</manifest>
```

② **Include GPS provider**

In terms of location permissions, we are including both the ACCESS_COARSE_ LOCATION **①**, and ACCESS_FINE_LOCATION **②** permissions in our manifest. The COARSE permission corresponds to the LocationManager.NETWORK_PROVIDER provider (cell and Wi-Fi based data), and the FINE permission corresponds to the LocationManager.GPS_PROVIDER provider. We aren't using the network provider in Wind and Waves, but we have noted that a worthwhile enhancement would be to fall back to the network provider if the GPS provider is unavailable or disabled—this permission would allow that.

Once you understand the basics of LocationManager and LocationProvider, the next step is to unleash the real power and register for periodic location updates in your application with the LocationListener class.

11.2.3 Receiving location updates with LocationListener

One way to keep abreast of the device location from within an Android application is to create a LocationListener implementation and register it to receive updates. LocationListener is a very flexible and powerful interface that lets you filter for many types of location events based on various properties. You have to implement the interface and register your instance to receive location data callbacks.

Listing 11.5 brings all of the pieces we have covered thus far into scope as we create several LocationListener implementations for the Wind and Waves MapViewActivity (the parts we left out of listing 11.3) and then register those listeners using the LocationManager and LocationProvider.

Listing 11.5 Creation of LocationListener implementations in MapViewActivity

```
. . . start of class in Listing 11.3
private final LocationListener locationListenerGetBuoyData =
  new LocationListener() {
    public void onLocationChanged(
      final Location loc) {
        int lat = (int) (loc.getLatitude()
          * LocationHelper.MILLION);
        int lon = (int) (loc.getLongitude()
          * LocationHelper.MILLION);

        GeoPoint geoPoint = new GeoPoint(lat, lon);
        getBuoyData(geoPoint);
    }
    public void onProviderDisabled(String s) {
    }
    public void onProviderEnabled(String s) {
    }
```

① **Create anonymous LocationListener**

② **Implement onLocationChanged**

③ **Get latitude and longitude**

④ **Create GeoPoint**

⑤ **Update map pins (buoy data)**

```
        public void onStatusChanged(String s, int i, Bundle b) {
        }
    };

private final LocationListener locationListenerRecenterMap =
  new LocationListener() {
        public void onLocationChanged(final Location loc) {
            int lat = (int) (loc.getLatitude()
              * LocationHelper.MILLION);
            int lon = (int) (loc.getLongitude()
              * LocationHelper.MILLION);

            GeoPoint geoPoint = new GeoPoint(lat, lon);
            mapController.animateTo(geoPoint);
        }
        public void onProviderDisabled(String s) {
        }
        public void onProviderEnabled(String s) {
        }
        public void onStatusChanged(String s, int i, Bundle b) {
        }
    };

    @Override
    public void onStart() {
        super.onStart();
        this.locationManager -
          (LocationManager)
            this.getSystemService(Context.LOCATION_SERVICE);
        this.locationProvider =
          this.locationManager.getProvider(LocationManager.GPS_PROVIDER);

        if (locationProvider != null) {
            this.locationManager.requestLocationUpdates(
              locationProvider.getName(), 3000, 185000,
                this.locationListenerGetBuoyData);
            this.locationManager.requestLocationUpdates(
              locationProvider.getName(), 3000, 1000,
                this.locationListenerRecenterMap);
        } else {
            Toast.makeText(this, "Wind and Waves cannot continue,"
            + " the GPS location provider is not available"
            + " at this time.", Toast.LENGTH_SHORT).show();
            this.finish();
        }

    . . . remainder of repeated code omitted (see listing 11.3)
    }
```

6 Move map to new location

7 Register locationListener-GetBuoyData

8 Register locationListener-RecenterMap

When implementing the LocationListener interface, it is often practical to use an anonymous inner class **1**. For our MapViewActivity we have created two Location-Listener implementations because we want to register them both using different settings, as we will show momentarily.

Within the first listener, locationListenerGetBuoyData, we see how the onLoca-tionChanged method is implemented **2**. In that method we get the latitude and longitude from the Location sent in the callback **3**. We then use the data to create a

GeoPoint ❹ after multiplying the latitude and longitude by 1 million (1e6). The 1e6 format is necessary because GeoPoint requires microdegrees for coordinates.

After we have the data, we update the map (using a helper method that resets a map Overlay, the details of which we will cover in the next section) ❺. In the second listener, locationListenerRecenterMap, we perform a different task—we center the map ❻.

The reason we are using two listeners becomes crystal clear when you see how listeners are registered with the requestLocationUpdates method of the LocationManager class. Here we are registering the first one, locationListenerGetBuoyData, to fire only when the new device location is a long way off from the previous one (185000 meters; we chose this number to stay just under 100 nautical miles, which is the radius we will use to pull buoy data for our map; we don't need to redraw the buoy data on the map if the user moves less than 100 nautical miles) ❼. We are registering the second one, location-ListenerRecenterMap, to fire more frequently (so the map view recenters if the user stays inside our application but moves more than 1000 meters) ❽. Using separate listeners like this allows us to fine-tune the event processing (rather than having to build in our own logic to do different things based on different values with one listener).

Register location listeners carefully

The time parameter to the requestLocationUpdates method should be used carefully. Getting location updates too frequently (less than 60000 ms per the documentation) can wear down the battery and make the application too noisy. In this sample we have used an extremely low value for the time parameter for debugging purposes (3000 ms). You should never use a value lower than the recommended 60000 ms in production code.

Although our implementation here works, and it is the most straightforward example, keep in mind that our registration of LocationListener instances could be made even more robust by implementing the onProviderEnabled and onProviderDisabled methods. Using those methods and different providers, you can see how you could provide useful messages to the user and also provide a graceful fallback through a set of providers (if GPS becomes disabled, try the network, and so on).

With LocationManager, LocationProvider, and LocationListener instances in place, the next thing we need to address is more detail concerning the MapActivity and MapView we are using.

11.3 *Working with maps*

We have demonstrated the start of the MapViewActivity our Wind and Waves application will use in the previous sections. There we covered the supporting classes and the handling of registering to receive location updates. With that structure in place, we now will focus on the map details themselves.

The `MapViewActivity` screen will look like the screen shot in figure 11.6, where several map `Overlay` classes are used on top of a `MapView` within a `MapActivity`.

In order to use the `com.google.android.maps` package on the Android platform and to support all the concepts related to a `MapView`, we are required to use a `MapActivity`.

11.3.1 *Extending MapActivity*

A `MapActivity` is the gateway to the Android Google Maps-like API package and other useful map-related utilities. There are several details behind creating and using a `MapView` that we as developers are fortunate enough not to have to worry about, because `MapActivity` handles them for us.

You will learn more about `MapView`, which is what we really care about as developers building map applications, in the next section, but it's important to first understand what a `MapActivity` is and why it's necessary. At its core, a `MapActivity` supports a `MapView` (a `MapActivity` is the only place a `MapView` can be used) and manages all the network and file system–intensive setup and teardown tasks needed for supporting the same.

Figure 11.6   The `MapViewActivity` from the Wind and Waves application showing a `MapActivity` with `MapView`

The `MapActivity onResume` method automatically sets up network threads for various map-related tasks and caches map section tile data on the filesystem, for example, and the `onPause` method cleans these up. Without this class, all of these details would be extra housekeeping that any `Activity` wishing to include a `MapView` would have to repeat each time.

There isn't a lot you will need to do with regard to `MapActivity` in code. Extending this class (as we did in listing 11.3), making sure to use only one instance per process (use more than one and unexpected results may occur), and including a special manifest element to enable the `com.google.android.maps` package are all you need. You may have noticed the curious `uses-library` element in the Wind and Waves manifest in listing 11.4.

```
<uses-library android:name="com.google.android.maps" />
```

The `com.google.android.maps` package, where `MapActivity`, `MapView`, `MapCon-troller`, and other related classes such as `GeoPoint` and `Overlay` reside, is "not a standard package in the Android library" per the documentation. This manifest element is required to pull in support for the `maps` package.

Once you have the `uses-library` element and have a basic `Activity` that extends `MapActivity`, the details come inside the `MapView` and related `Overlay` classes.

11.3.2 Using a MapView

A `MapView` is a miniature version of many of the Google Maps API concepts in the form of a `View` for your Android application. A `MapView` displays tiles of a map, which it obtains over the network as the map is moved and zoomed, much like the web version of Google Maps.

Many of the concepts from the standard Google Maps API are also present in Android through the `MapView`. For instance, `MapView` supports a plain map mode, a satellite mode, a street-view mode, and a traffic mode. When you want to write something on top of the map, from a straight line between two points to "pushpin" markers, or full-on images or anything else, you use an `Overlay`.

Examples of several of these concepts can be seen in the `MapViewActivity` screen shots for the Wind and Waves application, such as what is shown in figure 11.6. That same `MapViewActivity` is shown again in figure 11.7, switched into satellite mode and zoomed in several levels.

The `com.google.android.maps` package supports a good many of the Google Maps API concepts but isn't identical. You have already seen the `MapView` we will use for the Wind and Waves application declared and instantiated in listing 11.3. Here we will discuss the use of this class inside our `Activity` to control, position, zoom, populate, and overlay our map.

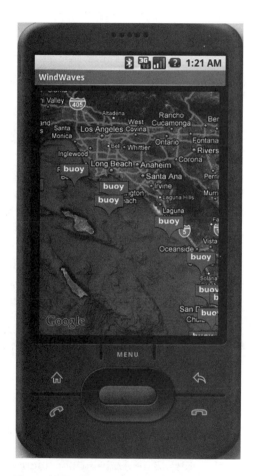

Figure 11.7 The `MapViewActivity` from the Wind and Waves application using satellite mode and zoomed in on a position near Los Angeles

Before we can use a map at all, we have to get a Google Maps API key and declare it in our layout file. Listing 11.6 shows the `MapActivity` layout file we are using with a special `android:apiKey` attribute.

Listing 11.6   A `MapView` layout file including the Google Maps API key

```
<?xml version="1.0" encoding="utf-8"?>
<RelativeLayout xmlns:android="http://schemas.android.com/apk/res/android"
    android:layout_width="fill_parent"
    android:layout_height="fill_parent"
    android:gravity="center_horizontal" android:padding="10px">

    <com.google.android.maps.MapView          ◁──❶ Define MapView element in XML
      android:id="@+id/map_view"
      android:layout_width="fill_parent"
      android:layout_height="fill_parent"
      android:enabled="true"
      android:clickable="true"
      android:apiKey=                                    ❷ Include apiKey
        "05lSygx-ttd-J5GXfsIB-dlpNtggca4I4DMyVqQ" />   ◁──┘    attribute

    <LinearLayout
      android:id="@+id/zoom"
      android:layout_width="wrap_content"
      android:layout_height="wrap_content"
      android:layout_alignParentBottom="true"
      android:layout_centerInParent="true">
    </LinearLayout>

</RelativeLayout>
```

A `MapView` can be declared in XML just like other `View` components ❶. In order to use the Google Maps network resources a `MapView` requires an API key ❷. You can obtain a map key via a special Google Maps Android key registration web page: http://code.google.com/android/maps-api-signup.html.

Before you can register for a key, you need to get the MD5 fingerprint of the certificate that is used to sign your application. This sounds tricky, but it's really very simple. When you are working with the Android Emulator, the SDK has a Debug Certificate that is always in use. To get the MD5 fingerprint for this certificate, you can use the following command (on Mac and Linux; on Windows adjust for the user's home directory and the slashes):

```
cd ~/.android
keytool -list -keystore ./debug.keystore -storepass android -keypass android
```

Getting a key for a production application involves the same process, but you need to use the actual certificate your APK file is signed with (rather than the debug.keystore file). The Android documentation has a good deal of additional information about obtaining a maps key (http://code.google.com/android/toolbox/apis/mapkey.html). For more information about digital signatures, keys, and signing in general, see appendix B.

Once you have a `MapActivity` with a `MapView` and have set up your view in the layout file, complete with map key, you can make full use of the map. Several of the listings we have shown up to this point are using the `MapView` we have declared in the Wind and Waves application. In listing 11.7 we are repeating a few of the map-related lines of code we have already shown, and we are bringing in additional related items to consolidate all the map-related concepts in one listing.

> **The maps key conundrum**
>
> One issue with the maps key process is that you need to declare the key in the layout file. Because there can be only one `MapActivity` and one `MapView` per application/process, it would seem more logical to declare the key in the application manifest or in an environment variable or properties file, but none of those is the case. With the key in the layout file, you have to remember to update the key between debug (emulator) and production modes, *and* if you debug on different development machines, you will also have to remember to switch keys by hand.

Listing 11.7   Portions of code that demonstrate working with maps

```
. . . from onCreate                          Inflate MapView from layout  ❶   ❷  Include View
this.mapView = (MapView) this.findViewById(R.id.map_view);              ◁          for zoom
this.zoom = (ViewGroup) findViewById(R.id.zoom);                       ◁          controls
this.zoom.addView(this.mapView.getZoomControls());                    ◁
                                                                        ❸  Get zoom controls
    . . . from onStart                                                     from MapView
this.mapController = this.mapView.getController();                     ◁
this.mapController.setZoom(10);                                        ◁
this.mapController.animateTo(lastKnownPoint);        ◁                     ❹  Get
                                                                             MapController
    . . . from onMenuItemSelected                Animate to
case MapViewActivity.MENU_SET_MAP:           given GeoPoint  ❻
    this.mapView.setSatellite(false);    ◁                                 ❺  Set initial
    break;                                                                     zoom level
case MapViewActivity.MENU_SET_SATELLITE:           Set map
    this.mapView.setSatellite(true);            ❼ satellite mode
    break;
case MapViewActivity.MENU_BUOYS_FROM_MAP_CENTER:         ❽  Get coordinates
    this.getBuoyData(this.mapView.getMapCenter());   ◁       from map center
    break;
```

`MapView` is a `ViewGroup`, and you can declare it in XML and inflate it just like other view components ❶. Because it is a `ViewGroup` you can also combine and attach other elements to it. Beyond the `MapView` itself, we are using a separate additional `ViewGroup` for the zoom controls ❷ and attaching the controls from the map to it ❸.

Next we get a `MapController` from the `MapView` ❹, and we use the controller to set the initial zoom level ❺ and animate to a specified `GeoPoint` ❻. The controller is what you use to zoom and move the map. Also, when the user chooses to do so via the menu, we set the mode of the map from plain to satellite and vice versa ❼. Along with manipulating the map itself, we can get data back from it, such as the coordinates of the map center ❽.

Above and beyond manipulating the map and getting data from the map, you also have the ability to draw items on top of the map using any number of `Overlay` instances.

11.3.3 *Placing data on a map with an Overlay*

The small buoy icons on the `MapViewActivity` for the Wind and Waves application that we have used in several figures up to this point are drawn on the screen at specified coordinates using an `Overlay`.

Overlay is a generalized base class for different specialized implementations. You can roll your own Overlay by extending the class, or you can use the included MyLocationOverlay. The MyLocationOverlay class lets you display a user's current location with a compass, and it has other useful features like including a Location-Listener for convenient access to position updates.

Another common use case for a map (in addition to showing you where you are) is the need to place multiple marker items on it—the ubiquitous pushpins. We have this exact requirement for the Wind and Waves application. We need to create buoy markers for the location of every buoy using data we get back from the NDBC feeds. Android provides built-in support for this with the ItemizedOverlay base class and the OverlayItem.

An OverlayItem is a simple bean that includes a title, a text snippet, a drawable marker, and coordinates using a GeoPoint (and a few other properties, but you get the idea). Listing 11.8 is the buoy data–related BuoyOverlayItem class that we are using for Wind and Waves.

Listing 11.8   The `OverlayItem` subclass `BuoyOverlayItem`

```
public class BuoyOverlayItem extends OverlayItem {          ①  Extend
                                                               OverlayItem
    public final GeoPoint point;
    public final BuoyData buoyData;

    public BuoyOverlayItem(GeoPoint point, BuoyData buoyData) {
        super(point, buoyData.title, buoyData.dateString);   ②  Call superclass
        this.point = point;                                      constructor
        this.buoyData = buoyData;      ③  Include extra
    }                                      BuoyData property
}
```

We extend OverlayItem to bring in all the necessary properties of an item to be drawn on the map: a location, a title, a snippet, and so on ①. In the constructor we make the call to the superclass with the required properties ②, and we assign additional elements our subclass supports. In this case we are adding a BuoyData member (itself a bean with name, water temperature, wave height, and so on–type properties) ③.

After we have the individual item class prepared, we need a class that extends ItemizedOverlay and uses a Collection of the items to display them on the map one-by-one. Listing 11.9, the BuoyItemizedOverlay class, shows how this works.

Listing 11.9   The `BuoyItemizedOverlay` class

```
public class BuoyItemizedOverlay
    extends ItemizedOverlay<BuoyOverlayItem> {        ①  Extend ItemizedOverlay

    private final List<BuoyOverlayItem> items;        ②  Include Collection
    private final Context context;                        of OverlayItem

    public BuoyItemizedOverlay(List<BuoyOverlayItem> items,
        Drawable defaultMarker, Context context) {   ③  Provide
        super(defaultMarker);                             drawable marker
```

```
      this.items = items;
      this.context = context;
      this.populate();
   }

   @Override
   public BuoyOverlayItem createItem(int i) {
      return this.items.get(i);
   }

   @Override
   protected boolean onTap(int i) {
      final BuoyData bd = this.items.get(i).buoyData;

      LayoutInflater inflater = LayoutInflater.from(this.context);
      View bView = inflater.inflate(R.layout.buoy_selected, null);
      TextView title = (TextView) bView.findViewById(R.id.buoy_title);

   . . . rest of view inflation omitted for brevity

      new AlertDialog.Builder(this.context)
        .setView(bView)
        .setPositiveButton("More Detail",
          new DialogInterface.OnClickListener() {
           public void onClick(DialogInterface di, int what) {
              Intent intent =
                new Intent(context, BuoyDetailActivity.class);
              BuoyDetailActivity.buoyData = bd;
              context.startActivity(intent);
           }
        })
        .setNegativeButton("Cancel",
          new DialogInterface.OnClickListener() {
           public void onClick(DialogInterface di, int what) {
              di.dismiss();
           }
        })
        .show();

      return true;
   }

   @Override
   public int size() {
      return this.items.size();
   }

   @Override
   public void draw(Canvas canvas, MapView mapView, boolean b) {
      super.draw(canvas, mapView, false);
   }
}
```

4 Override createItem

5 Get data and display

6 Override size method

7 Include other methods if needed

The `BuoyItemizedOverlay` class extends `ItemizedOverlay` **1** and includes a `Collection` of `BuoyOverlayItem` elements **2**. In the constructor we pass the `Drawable` marker to the parent class **3**. This marker is what is drawn on the screen in the overlay to represent each point on the map.

`ItemizedOverlay` takes care of many of the details we would have to tackle ourselves if we weren't using it (if we were just making our own `Overlay` with multiple points drawn on it). This includes the drawing of items and focus and event handling. For every element in the `Collection` of items an `ItemizedOverlay` holds, it invokes the `onCreate` method ❹, and it supports facilities like `onTap` ❺, where we can react when a particular overlay item is selected by the user. In our code we inflate some views and display an `AlertDialog` with information about the respective buoy when a `BuoyOverlayItem` is tapped. From the alert, the user can navigate to more detailed information if desired.

The `size` method tells `ItemizedOverlay` how many elements it needs to process ❻, and even though we aren't doing anything special with it in our case, there are also methods like `onDraw` that can be customized if necessary ❼.

When working with a `MapView` you create the `Overlay` instances you need, then add them on top of the map. Wind and Waves uses a separate `Thread` to retrieve the buoy data in the `MapViewActivity` (the data-retrieval code is not shown but is included in the code download for this chapter), and when ready we send a `Message` to a `Handler` to add the `BuoyItemizedOverlay` to the `MapView`. These details are shown in listing 11.10.

Listing 11.10 The `Handler` Wind and Waves uses to add overlays to the `MapView`

```
private final Handler handler = new Handler() {
    public void handleMessage(final Message msg) {

        progressDialog.dismiss();

        if (mapView.getOverlays().contains(buoyOverlay)) {       ❶ Remove Overlay if
          mapView.getOverlays().remove(buoyOverlay);                already present
        }

        buoyOverlay = new BuoyItemizedOverlay(buoys,
          defaultMarker,                                         ❷ Create
        MapViewActivity.this);                                      BuoyItemizedOverlay
        mapView.getOverlays().add(buoyOverlay);                     Add Overlay
    }                                                          ❸ to MapView
};
```

A `MapView` contains a `Collection` of `Overlay` elements, and so you can remove previous elements if you need to. We use the `remove` method to clean up any existing `BuoyOverlayItem` class ❶ before we create ❷ and add a new one ❸. This way we aren't simply adding more items on top of each other; rather we are resetting the data.

The built-in `Overlay` subclasses have handled our requirements here perfectly, which is very helpful. The `ItemizedOverlay` and `OverlayItem` classes have allowed us to complete the Wind and Waves application without having to make our own `Overlay` subclasses directly. Keep in mind, if you need to, you can go to that level and implement your own `draw`, `tap`, `touch`, and so on methods within your custom `Overlay`.

With our sample application now complete and providing us with buoy data using a MapActivity and MapView, we next need to address one additional maps-related concept that we haven't yet encountered but is nonetheless very important—geocoding.

11.4 *Converting places and addresses with Geocoder*

Geocoding is described in the documentation as converting a "street address or other description of a location" into latitude and longitude coordinates. Reverse geocoding is the opposite, converting latitude and longitude into an address. To accomplish this, the Geocoder class makes a network call (automatically) to a web service.

We aren't using geocoding in the Wind and Waves application because it's obviously not as useful in the ocean as it is with landmarks, cities, addresses, and so on. Nevertheless, geocoding is an invaluable tool to have at your disposal when working with coordinates and maps. To demonstrate the concepts surrounding geocoding, listing 11.11 includes a new single Activity application, GeocoderExample.

Listing 11.11   A short Geocoder example

```
@Override
public void onCreate(Bundle savedInstanceState) {
    super.onCreate(savedInstanceState);
    this.setContentView(R.layout.main);
    this.input = (EditText) this.findViewById(R.id.input);
    this.output = (TextView) this.findViewById(R.id.output);
    this.button = (Button) this.findViewById(R.id.geocode_button);
    this.isAddress = (CheckBox)
      this.findViewById(R.id.checkbox_address);

    this.button.setOnClickListener(new OnClickListener() {
      public void onClick(final View v) {
        output.setText(performGeocode(
                input.getText().toString(),
                isAddress.isChecked()));
      }
    });
}

private String performGeocode(String in, boolean isAddr) {
    String result = "Unable to Geocode - " + in;
    if (this.input != null) {
        Geocoder geocoder = new Geocoder(this);        ◁— ❶ Instantiate Geocoder
        if (isAddr) {                                         with Context
            try {
                List<Address> addresses =                  ❷ Get Address from
                  geocoder.getFromLocationName(in, 1);   ◁—  location name
                if (addresses != null) {
                    result = addresses.get(0).toString();
                }
            } catch (IOException e) {
                Log.e("GeocodExample", "Error", e);
            }
        } else {
```

```
    try {
       String[] coords = in.split(",");
       if ((coords != null) && (coords.length == 2)) {
          List<Address> addresses =
            geocoder.getFromLocation(
              Double.parseDouble(coords[0]),
              Double.parseDouble(coords[1]),
              1);
          result = addresses.get(0).toString();
       }
    } catch (IOException e) {
       Log.e("GeocodExample", "Error", e);
    }
  }
}
return result;
  }
}
```

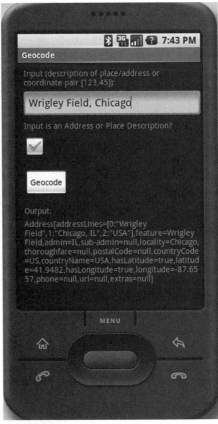

❸ Get Address from coordinates

In Android terms, you create a Geocoder by constructing it with the Context of your application ❶. You then use a Geocoder to covert either String instances that represent place names into Address objects with the get-FromLocationName method ❷ or latitude and longitude coordinates into Address objects with the getFromLocation method ❸.

Figure 11.8 is an example of our simplified GeocoderExample in use. In this case we are converting a String representing a place (Wrigley Field in Chicago) into an Address object that contains latitude and longitude coordinates.

The GeocoderExample application shows how useful the Geocoder is. For instance, if you have data that includes address string portions, or even just place descriptions, it's easy to covert that into latitude and longitude numbers for use with GeoPoint and Overlay, and so on.

Geocoding rounds out our look at the powerful location- and mapping-related components of the Android platform.

Figure 11.8 A Geocoder usage example that demonstrates turning an Address String into an Address object that provides latitude and longitude coordinates

11.5 Summary

"Location, location, location," as they say in real estate, could also be the mantra for the future of mobile computing. One of the most important features of the Android platform is the support for readily available location information and the inclusion of smart-mapping APIs and other location-related utilities.

In this chapter we explored the location and mapping capabilities of the Android platform by building an application that set up a `LocationManager` and `LocationProvider`, to which we attached several `LocationListener` instances. We did this so that we could keep our application informed about the current device location (using updates from the listeners). Along with the `LocationListener`, we also briefly discussed several other ways to get location updates from the Android platform.

After we covered location-awareness basics, we combined that with a somewhat unique data source (the National Data Buoy Center) to provide a draggable, zoomable, interactive map. To build the map we used a `MapActivity`, with `MapView` and `MapController`. These classes make it fairly easy to set up and display maps. Once we had our `MapView` in place, we created an `ItemizedOverlay` to include points of interest on it, using individual `OverlayItem` elements. From the individual points, in our case buoys, we linked into another `Activity` class to display more detailed information—demonstrating how to go from the map to any other kind of `Activity` and back.

One important part of mapping that our water-based sample application did not include was converting from an address into a latitude and longitude and vice versa—geocoding. So we built a separate small sample to demonstrate this process, and there we discussed usage of the `Geocoder` class and how it works.

With our exploration of the mapping capabilities of Android complete, including a fully functional sample application that combines mapping with many other Android tenets we have already explored up to this point, we are going to move into a new stage in the book. In the next few chapters that make up the final section of the book, we will explore complete nontrivial applications that bring together intents, activities, data storage, networking, and more.

Part 3

Android applications

As we have seen in part 2, the Android platform is very capable, enabling rich applications in many genres and vertical industries. The goal of part 3 is to integrate many of the lessons learned in part 2 on a larger scale and to spur you on to explore the platform in greater depth than simply using the Android SDK.

We take a detailed look at the requirements of a Field Service Application. We next map those requirements on a practical application which could be adapted for many industries. The application includes multiple UI elements, server communications, and detecting touch screen events for capturing and uploading a signature (chapter 12).

We wrap up this part and the book with a deeper examination of the Android/Linux relationship by writing native C applications for Android and connecting to Android core libraries such as sqlite and tcp socket communications (chapter 13).

Putting it all together–the Field Service Application

Now that we have introduced and examined Android and its core technologies, it is high time to put together a more comprehensive application. In this chapter we are going to put much of what you have learned into a composite application, leveraging skills gained throughout the book. In addition to an in-depth Android application, this chapter's sample application works with a custom website application that manages data for use by a mobile worker. The aim is to demonstrate a more complex application involving real-world requirements. All of the source code for the server-side application is available for download from the book's companion website.

295

After reading through this chapter and becoming familiar with the sample application, you will be ready to strike out on your own and build useful Android applications. Many of the code samples are explained; however, if you need more background information on a particular topic, please refer to earlier chapters where the Android APIs are more fully presented.

If this example is going to represent a useful real-world application, we need to put some flesh on it. Beyond helping you to understand the application, this definition process will get you thinking about the kinds of impact a mobile application can have on our economy. This chapter's sample application is called Field Service Application. Pretty generic name perhaps, but it will prove to be an ample vehicle for demonstrating key elements required in mobile applications as well as demonstrate the power of the Android platform for building useful applications quickly.

Our application's target user is a fleet technician who works for a national firm that makes its services available to a number of contracted customers. One day our technician, who we will call a *mobile worker,* is replacing a hard drive in the computer at the local fast food restaurant, and the next day he may be installing a memory upgrade in a piece of pick-and-place machinery at a telephone system manufacturer. If you have ever had a piece of equipment serviced at your home or office and thought the technician's uniform did not really match the job he was doing, you have experienced this kind of service arrangement. This kind of technician is often referred to as *hands and feet.* He has basic mechanical or computer skills and is able to follow directions reliably, often guided by the manufacturer of the equipment being serviced at the time. Thanks to workers like this, companies can extend their reach to a much broader geography than the internal staffing levels would ever allow. For example, a small manufacturer of retail music-sampling equipment might contract with such a firm for providing tech support to retail locations across the country.

Because of our mythical technician's varied schedule and lack of experience on a particular piece of equipment, it is important to equip him with as much relevant and timely information as possible. However, he cannot be burdened with thick reference manuals or specialized tools. So, with a toolbox containing a few hand tools and of course an Android-equipped device, our fearless hero is counting on us to provide an application that enables him to do his job. And remember, this is the person who restores the ice cream machine to operation at the local Dairy Barn or perhaps fixes the farm equipment's computer controller so the cows get milked on time. You never know where a computer will be found in today's world!

If built well, this application can enable the efficient delivery of service to customers in many industries, where we live, work, and play. Let's get started and see what this application must be able to accomplish.

12.1   *Field Service Application requirements*

We have established that our mobile worker will be carrying two things: a set of hand tools and an Android device. Fortunately, in this book we are not concerned with the applicability of the hand tools in his toolbox, leaving us free to focus on the capabilities and features of a Field Service Application running on the Android platform. In this section, we're going to define the basic and high-level application requirements.

12.1.1 *Basic requirements*

Before diving into the bits and bytes of data requirements and application features, it is helpful to enumerate some basic requirements and assumptions about our Field Service Application. Here are a few items that come to mind for such an application:

- The mobile worker is dispatched by a home office/dispatching authority, which takes care of prioritizing and distributing job orders to the appropriate technician.

- The mobile worker is carrying an Android device, which has full data service, that is, a device capable of browsing rich web content. The application needs to access the internet for data transfer as well.

- The home office dispatch system and the mobile worker share data via a wireless internet connection on an Android device; a laptop computer is not necessary or even desired.

- A business requirement is the proof of completion of work, most readily accomplished with the capture of a customer's signature. Of course, an electronic signature is preferred.

- The home office desires to receive job completion information as soon as possible, as this accelerates the invoicing process, which improves cash flow.

- The mobile worker is also eager to perform as many jobs as possible since he is paid by the job, not by the hour, so getting access to new job information as quickly as possible is a benefit to the mobile worker.

- The mobile worker needs information resources in the field and can use as much information as possible about the problem he is being asked to resolve. The mobile worker may have to place orders for replacement parts while in the field.

- The mobile worker will require navigation assistance, as he is likely covering a rather large geographic area.

- The mobile worker needs an intuitive application. One that is simple to use with a minimum number of requirements.

There are likely additional requirements for such an application, but this list is adequate for our purposes. One of the most glaring omissions from our list is security.

Security in this kind of an application comes down to two fundamental aspects. The first is physical security of the Android device. Our assumption is that the device itself is locked and only the authorized worker is using it. A bit naïve perhaps, but there are more important topics we need to cover in this chapter. If this bothers you, just assume there is a sign-in screen with a password field that pops up at the most inconvenient times, forcing you to tap in your password on a very small keypad. Feel better now? The second security topic is the secure transmission of data between the

Android device and the dispatcher. This is most readily accomplished through the use of a Secure Sockets Layer (SSL) connection whenever required.

The next step in defining this application is to examine the data flows and discuss the kind of information that must be captured to satisfy the functional requirements.

12.1.2 *Data model*

Throughout this chapter, the term *job* refers to a specific task or event that our mobile worker engages in. For example, a request to replace a hard drive in a computer at the bookstore is a job. A request to upgrade the firmware in the fuel-injection system at the refinery is likewise a job. The home office dispatches one or more jobs to the mobile worker on a regular basis. Certain data elements in the job are helpful to the mobile worker to accomplish his goal of completing the job. This information comes from the home office. Where the home office gets this information is not our concern in this application.

In this chapter's sample application, there are only two pieces of information the mobile worker is responsible for submitting to the dispatcher. The first requirement is that the mobile worker communicates to the home office that a job has been *closed*; that is, completed. The second requirement is the collection of an electronic signature from the customer, acknowledging that the job has, in fact, been completed. Figure 12.1 depicts these data flows.

Of course, there are additional pieces of information that may be helpful here, such as the customer's phone number, anticipated duration of the job, replacement parts required in the repair (including tracking numbers), any observations about the condition of related equipment, and much more. While these are very important to a real-world application, these pieces of information are extraneous to the goals of this chapter and are left as an exercise for you to extend the application for your own learning and use.

The next objective is to determine how data is stored and transported.

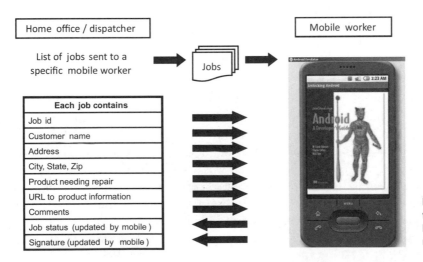

Figure 12.1 Data flows between the home office and a mobile worker

12.1.3 *Application architecture and integration*

Now that we know which entities are responsible for the relevant data elements, and in which direction they flow, let's look at how the data is stored and exchanged. We will be deep into code before too long, but for now we will discuss the available options and continue to examine things from a requirements perspective, building to a proposed architecture.

At the home office, the dispatcher must manage data for multiple mobile workers. The best tool for this purpose is a relational database. The options here are numerous, but we will make the simple decision to use MySQL, a popular open source database. Not only are there multiple mobile workers, but the organization we are building this application for is quite spread out, with employees in multiple markets and time zones. Because of the nature of the dispatching team, it has been decided to host the MySQL database in a data center, where it is accessed via a browser-based application. For this sample application, the dispatcher system is super simple and written in PHP.

Data storage requirements on the mobile device are quite modest. At any point, a given mobile worker may have only a half-dozen or so assigned jobs. Jobs may be assigned at any time, so the mobile worker is encouraged to refresh the list of jobs periodically. Although you learned about how to use SQLite in chapter 5, we have little need for sharing data between multiple applications and don't need to build out a `ContentProvider`, so we've made the decision to use an XML file stored on the filesystem to serve as a persistent store of our assigned job list.

The Field Service Application uses HTTP to exchange data with the home office. Again, we use PHP to build the transactions for exchanging data. While more complex and sophisticated protocols can be employed, such as Simple Object Access Protocol (SOAP), this application simply requests an XML file of assigned jobs and submits an image file representing the captured signature. This architecture is depicted in figure 12.2.

The last item to discuss before diving into the code is configuration. Every mobile worker needs to be identified uniquely. This way, the Field Service Application can retrieve the correct job list, and the dispatchers can assign jobs to workers in the field.

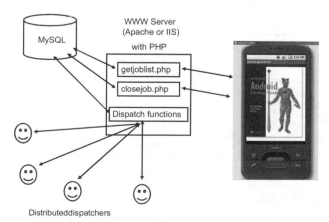

Distributeddispatchers

Figure 12.2 The Field Service Application and dispatchers both leverage PHP transactions.

Similarly, the mobile application may need to communicate with different servers, depending on locale. A mobile worker in the United States might use a server located in Chicago, but a worker in the United Kingdom may need to use a server in Cambridge. Because of these requirements, we have decided that both the mobile worker's identifier and the server address need to be readily accessed within the application. Remember, these fields would likely be secured in a deployed application, but for our purposes they are easy to access and not secured.

We have identified the functional requirements, defined the data elements necessary to satisfy those objectives, and selected the preferred deployment platform. It is time to examine the Android application.

12.2   *Android application tour*

Have you ever downloaded an application's source code, excited to get access to all of that code, but once you did, it was a little overwhelming? You want to make your own changes, to put your own spin on the code, but you unzip the file into all of the various subdirectories, and you just don't know where to start. Before we jump directly into examining the source code, we need to pay a little attention to the architecture, in particular the flow from one screen to the next.

12.2.1   *Application flow*

In this section we will examine the application flow to better understand the relation among the application's functionality, the UI, and the classes used to deliver this functionality. Doing this process up front helps ensure that the application delivers the needed functionality and assists in defining which classes we require when it comes time to start coding, which is soon! Figure 12.3 shows the relation between the high-level

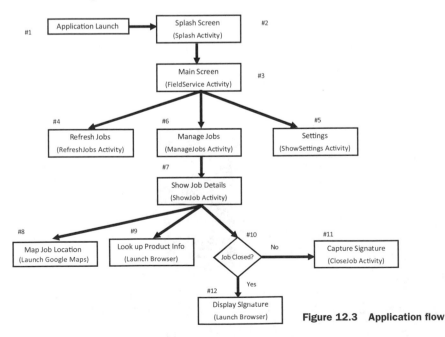

Figure 12.3   Application flow

classes in the application, which are implemented as an Android `Activity` as well as interaction with other services available in Android.

Here is the procession of steps in the application:

1　The application is selected from the application launch screen on the Android device.

2　The application splash screen displays. Why? Some applications require setup time to get data structures initialized. As a practical matter, such time-consuming behavior is discouraged on a mobile device; however, it is an important aspect to application design, so it is included in this sample application.

3　The main screen displays the currently configured user and server settings, along with three easy-to-hit-with-your-finger buttons.

4　The Refresh Jobs button initiates a download procedure to fetch the currently available jobs for this mobile worker from the configured server. The download includes a `ProgressDialog`, which is discussed later in this chapter.

5　The Settings button brings up a screen that allows the configuration of the user and server settings.

6　Selecting Manage Jobs lets our mobile worker review the available jobs assigned to him and proceed with further steps specific to a chosen job.

7　Selecting a job from the list of jobs on the Manage Jobs screen brings up the Show Job Details screen with the specific job information listed. This screen lists the available information about the job and presents three additional buttons.

8　The Map Job Location button initiates a geo query on the device using an `Intent`. The default handler for this `Intent` is the Maps application.

9　Because our mobile worker may not know much about the product he is being asked to service, each job includes a product information URL. Clicking this button brings up the built-in browser and takes the mobile worker to a (hopefully) helpful internet resource. This may be an online manual or an instructional video.

10　The behavior of the third button depends on the current status of the job. If the job is still marked OPEN, this button is used to initiate the closeout or completion of this job.

When the close procedure is selected, the application presents an empty canvas upon which the customer can take the stylus (assuming a touch screen–capable Android device, of course!) and sign that the work is complete. A menu on that screen presents two options: Sign & Close or Cancel. If the Sign & Close option is selected, the application submits the signature as a JPEG image to the server, and the server marks the job as CLOSED. In addition, the local copy of the job is marked as CLOSED. The Cancel button causes the Show Job Details screen to be restored.

11　If the job being viewed has already been closed, the browser window is opened to a page displaying the previously captured signature.

Now that we have a pretty good feel for what our requirements are and how we are going to tackle the problem from a functionality and application-flow perspective, let's examine the code that delivers this functionality.

12.2.2   Code road map

The source code for this application consists of 12 Java source files, one of which is the R.java file, which you will recall is automatically generated based on the resources in the application. This section presents a quick introduction to each of these files. No code is explained yet; we just want to know a little bit about each file, and then it will be time to jump into the application, step-by-step. Table 12.1 lists the source files in the Android Field Service Application.

Table 12.1   The source files used to implement the Field Service Application

Source Filename	Description
Splash.java	`Activity` provides splash screen functionality.
ShowSettings.java	`Activity` provides management of username and server URL address.
FieldService.java	`Activity` provides the main screen of the application.
RefreshJobs.java	`Activity` interacts with server to obtain updated list of jobs.
ManageJobs.java	`Activity` provides access to list of jobs.
ShowJob.java	`Activity` provides detailed information on a specific job, such as an address lookup, or initiates the signature-capture process.
CloseJob.java	`Activity` collects electronic signature and interacts with the server to upload images and mark jobs as CLOSED.
R.java	Automatically generated source file representing identifiers in the resources.
Prefs.java	Helper class encapsulating `SharedPreferences`.
JobEntry.java	Class that represents a job. Includes helpful methods used when passing `JobEntry` objects from one `Activity` to another.
JobList.java	Class representing the complete list of `JobEntry` objects. Includes methods for marshaling and unmarshaling to nonvolatile storage.
JobListHandler.java	Class used for parsing XML document containing job data.

The application also relies on `layout` resources to define the visual aspect of the UI. In addition to the `layout` xml files, an image used by the `Splash Activity` is placed in the drawable subfolder of the res folder along with the stock Android icon image. This icon is used for the home application launch screen. Figure 12.4 depicts the resources used in the application.

In an effort to make navigating the code as easy as possible, the Field Service Application resource files are presented in table 12.2. Note that each of these is clearly seen in figure 12.4, which is a screen shot from our project open in Eclipse.

Figure 12.4   Resources used in the application

Table 12.2 Resource files used in the sample application

Filename	Description
android.jpg	Image used in the `Splash Activity`.
icon.jpg	Image used in the application launcher.
fieldservice.xml	Layout for main application screen, `FieldService Activity`.
managejobs.xml	Layout for the list of jobs, `ManageJobs Activity`.
refreshjobs.xml	Layout for the screen shown when refreshing job list, `RefreshJobs Activity`.
showjob.xml	Layout for job detail screen, `ShowJob Activity`.
showsettings.xml	Layout for configuration/settings screen, `ShowSettings Activity`.
splash.xml	Layout for splash screen, `Splash Activity`.
strings.xml	Strings file containing extracted strings. Ideally all text is contained in a strings file for ease of localization. This application's file contains only the application title.

An examination of the source files in this application tells us that we have more than one `Activity` in use. In order to enable navigation between one `Activity` and the next, our application must inform Android of the existence of these `Activity` classes. If you recall from chapter 1, this registration step is accomplished with the AndroidManifest.xml file.

12.2.3 *AndroidManifest.xml*

Every Android application requires a manifest file to let Android properly "wire things up" when an `Intent` is handled and needs to be dispatched. Let's look at the AndroidManifest.xml file used by our application, which is presented in listing 12.1.

Listing 12.1 The Field Service Application's AndroidManifest.xml file

```
<?xml version="1.0" encoding="utf-8"?>
<manifest xmlns:android="http://schemas.android.com/apk/res/android"
  package="com.msi.manning.UnlockingAndroid">
  <application android:icon="@drawable/icon">
    <activity android:name=".Splash"              Splash Activity is
        android:label="@string/app_name">    ◁┘  the entry point
      <intent-filter>                                      ◁
        <action android:name="android.intent.action.MAIN" />
        <category android:name="android.intent.category.LAUNCHER" />
      </intent-filter>
    </activity>                                    Intent filter for main
    <activity android:name=".FieldService" >    ◁   launcher visibility
    </activity>
    <activity android:name=".RefreshJobs" >     ◁
    </activity>
    <activity android:name=".ManageJobs" >      ◁   Application's
    </activity>                                     defined
    <activity android:name=".ShowJob" >         ◁   Activity list
    </activity>
    <activity android:name=".CloseJob" >        ◁
```

```
        </activity>
        <activity android:name=".ShowSettings" >        ◁          Application's defined
        </activity>                                                Activity list

    </application>
<uses-permission android:name="android.permission.INTERNET">
    </uses-permission>        ◁          Required permission for internet access
</manifest>
```

12.3 *Android code*

After a rather long introduction and stage setting for this chapter, it's time to look at the source code for the Field Service Application. The approach is to largely follow the application flow, step-by-step. Let's start with the splash screen.

12.3.1 *Splash Activity*

We are all very familiar with a splash screen for a software application. It acts like a curtain while important things are taking place behind the scenes. Ordinarily splash screens are visible until the application is ready—this could be a very brief amount of time or much longer in the case where quite a bit of housekeeping is necessary. As a rule, a mobile application should focus on economy and strive to have as little resource consumption as possible. The splash screen in this sample application is meant to demonstrate how such a feature may be constructed—we don't actually need one for housekeeping purposes. But that's okay; you can learn in the process. Two code snippets are of interest to us, the implementation of the Activity as well as the layout file that defines what the UI looks like. First, examine the layout file in listing 12.2.

> **Listing 12.2 splash.xml defines the layout of the application's splash screen.**

```
<?xml version="1.0" encoding="utf-8"?>
<LinearLayout xmlns:android="http://schemas.android.com/apk/res/android"
    android:orientation="vertical"
    android:layout_width="fill_parent"
    android:layout_height="fill_parent"
    >                                              ❶   Full screen
    <ImageView                             ◁           ImageView
    android:layout_width="fill_parent"
    android:layout_height="fill_parent"
    android:scaleType="fitCenter"          ❷   Image
    android:src="@drawable/android"        ◁       reference
    />
</LinearLayout>
```

The splash.xml layout contains a single ImageView ❶, set to fill the entire screen. The source image for this view is defined as the drawable resource ❷, named android. Note that this is simply the name of the file (minus the file extension) in the drawable folder, as shown earlier.

Now we must use this layout in an Activity. Aside from the referencing of an image resource from the layout, this is really not that interesting. Figure 12.5 shows the splash screen running on the Android Emulator.

Figure 12.5 Splash screen

Of interest to us is the code that creates the splash page functionality. This code is shown in listing 12.3.

Listing 12.3   Splash.java implements splash screen functionality.

```
package com.msi.manning.UnlockingAndroid;

// multiple imports omitted for brevity, see full source code

public class Splash extends Activity {
  @Override
  public void onCreate(Bundle icicle) {
    super.onCreate(icicle);

    setContentView(R.layout.splash);            ❶ Set up main View
    Handler x = new Handler();                   ❷ Define and set
    x.postDelayed(new splashhandler(), 2000);       up Handler
  }
  class splashhandler implements Runnable {    ❸ Implement Handler
```

```
public void run() {
    startActivity(
      new Intent(getApplication(),FieldService.class));
    Splash.this.finish();
    }
  }
}
```

4 Start
application's
main Activity

5 Kill the splash screen

Like most `Activity` classes in Android, we want to associate the splash layout with this `Activity`'s `View` **1**. A `Handler` is set up **2**, which is used to close down the splash screen after an elapsed period of time. Note that the arguments to the `postDelayed` method are an instance of a class that implements the `Runnable` interface and the desired elapsed time in milliseconds. In this snippet of code, the screen will be shown for 2000 milliseconds, or 2 seconds. After the indicated amount of time has elapsed, the class `splashhandler` **3** is invoked. The `FieldService Activity` is instantiated with a call to `startActivity` **4**. Note that an `Intent` is not used here—we explicitly specify which class is going to satisfy our request. Once we have started the next `Activity`, it is time to get rid of our splash screen `Activity`, **5**.

The splash screen is happily entertaining our mobile worker each time he starts the application. Let's move on to the main screen of the application.

12.3.2 *FieldService Activity, part 1*

The goal of the `FieldService Activity` is to put the functions the mobile worker requires directly in front of him and make sure they are easy to access. A good mobile application is often one that can be used with one hand, such as the five-way navigation buttons, or in some cases a thumb tapping on a button. In addition, if there is helpful information to display, you should not hide it. It is helpful for our mobile worker to know that he is configured to obtain jobs from a particular server. Figure 12.6 demonstrates the Field Service Application conveying a very simple, yet easy-to-use home screen.

Before reviewing the code in FieldService.java, we need to take a break to discuss how the user and server settings are managed. This is important because these settings are used throughout the application, and as shown in the fieldservice.xml layout file, we need to access those values to display to our mobile worker on the home screen.

Figure 12.6   The home screen. Less is more.

PREFS CLASS

As you learned in chapter 5, there are a number of means for managing data. Because we need to persist this data across multiple invocations of our application, the data must be stored in a nonvolatile fashion. This application employs private `SharedPreferences` to accomplish this. Why? Despite the fact that we are largely ignoring security for this sample application, using private `SharedPreferences` means that other applications cannot casually access this potentially important data. For example, we presently use only an identifier (let's call it an email address for simplicity) and a server URL in this application. However, we might also include a password or a PIN in a production-ready application, so keeping this data private is a good practice.

The Prefs class can be described as a helper or wrapper class. This class wraps the SharedPreferences code and exposes simple getter and setter methods, specific to this application. This implementation knows something about what we are trying to accomplish, so it adds value with some default values as well. Let's look at listing 12.4 to see how our Prefs class is implemented.

Listing 12.4 `Prefs` class provides storage and retrieval for small and useful information.

```
package com.msi.manning.UnlockingAndroid;

// multiple imports omitted for brevity, see full source code

public class Prefs {                                          ❶ SharedPreferences
                                                                  object
    private SharedPreferences _prefs = null;        ◁─┘
    private Editor _editor = null;                  ◁── ❷ Implement Handler
    private String _useremailaddress = "Unknown";
    private String _serverurl =                               ❸ Default
        "http://android12.msi-wireless.com/getjoblist.php"; ◁─┘ values
    public Prefs(Context context) {     ◁─
        _prefs =                        ❹ Initialize SharedPreferences
        context.getSharedPreferences("PREFS_PRIVATE",Context.MODE_PRIVATE);
        _editor = _prefs.edit();
    }
    public String getValue(String key,String defaultvalue){  ◁─┐
        if (_prefs == null) return "Unknown";
        return _prefs.getString(key,defaultvalue);            ❺ Generic
    }                                                            set/get
    public void setValue(String key,String value) {      ◁─   methods
        if (_editor == null) return;
        _editor.putString(key,value);
    }
    public String getEmail(){               ◁── ❻ Extract email value
        if (_prefs == null) return "Unknown";
        _useremailaddress = _prefs.getString("emailaddress","Unknown");
        return _useremailaddress;
    }
    public void setEmail(String newemail) {    ◁── ❼ Set email value
        if (_editor == null) return;
        _editor.putString("emailaddress",newemail);
    }
    ... (abbreviated for brevity)
    public void save() {              ◁── ❽ Save preferences
        if (_editor == null) return;
        _editor.commit();
    }
}
```

To persist the application's settings data, we employ a SharedPreferences object **❶**. To manipulate data within the SharedPreferences object, here named simply _prefs, we use an instance of the Editor class **❷**. This snippet employs some default settings values **❸**, which are appropriate for our application. The Prefs() constructor **❹** does the necessary housekeeping so we can establish our private SharedPreferences object, including using a passed-in Context instance. The Context class is necessary because the SharedPreferences mechanism relies on a Context for segregating data. This snippet shows a pair of set and get methods that are generic in nature **❺**. The getEmail **❻** and setEmail methods **❼** are responsible for manipulating the email setting value. The save() method **❽** invokes a commit() on the Editor, which persists the data to the SharedPreferences store.

Now that you have some feel for how this important preference data is stored, let's return to examine the code of FieldService.java.

12.3.3 FieldService Activity, part 2

Recall that the FieldService.java file implements the FieldService class, which is essentially the home screen of our application. This code does the primary dispatching for the application. Many of the programming techniques in this file have been shown earlier in the book; however, please take note of the use of startActivityForResult and the onActivityResult methods as you read through the code, as shown in listing 12.5.

> **Listing 12.5 FieldService.java implements** FieldService Activity

```
package com.msi.manning.UnlockingAndroid;

// multiple imports trimmed for brevity, see full source code

public class FieldService extends Activity {
   final int ACTIVITY_REFRESHJOBS = 1;
   final int ACTIVITY_LISTJOBS = 2;              Useful constants
   final int ACTIVITY_SETTINGS = 3;
   Prefs myprefs = null;           ◄──❶ Prefs instance
   @Override
   public void onCreate(Bundle icicle) {       Set up UI
      super.onCreate(icicle);
      setContentView(R.layout.fieldservice);  ◄──
      myprefs = new Prefs(this.getApplicationContext());  ◄──
      RefreshUserInfo();
      final Button refreshjobsbutton = (Button) findViewById(R.id.getjobs);  ◄──
      refreshjobsbutton.setOnClickListener(new Button.OnClickListener() {
         public void onClick(View v) {
         try {
            startActivityForResult(new
   Intent(v.getContext(),RefreshJobs.class),ACTIVITY_REFRESHJOBS);
         } catch (Exception e) {
         }
         }
      });
```

Instantiate Prefs instance **❷**

Initiate UI field contents

Connect button to UI **❸**

```
      // see full source comments
    }
    @Override
    protected void onActivityResult(int requestCode, int resultCode, Intent
      data) {                                    ◄─────┐
      switch (requestCode) {
        case ACTIVITY_REFRESHJOBS:
          break;                              ┌──❹ onActivityResult
        case ACTIVITY_LISTJOBS:               │     processing
          break;                              │
        case ACTIVITY_SETTINGS:               │
              RefreshUserInfo();        ◄─────┘
              break;
      }
    }
    private void RefreshUserInfo() {    ◄──❺ RefreshUserInfo
      try {
          final TextView emaillabel = (TextView)
        findViewById(R.id.emailaddresslabel);
          emaillabel.setText("User: " + myprefs.getEmail() + "\nServer: " +
        myprefs.getServer() + "\n");
      } catch (Exception e) {
      }
    }
  }
}
```

This code implements a simple UI that displays three distinct buttons. As each is selected, a particular Activity is started in a synchronous, call/return fashion. The Activity is started with a call to startActivityForResult ❸. When the called Activity is complete, the results are returned to the FieldService Activity via the onActivityResult method ❹. An instance of the Prefs class ❶, ❷ is used to obtain values for displaying in the UI. Updating the UI is accomplished in the method RefreshUserInfo ❺.

Because the settings are so important to this application, the next section covers the management of the user and server values.

12.3.4 Settings

When the user clicks the Settings button from the main application screen, an Activity is started that allows the user to configure his user ID (email address) and the server URL. The screen layout is very basic (listing 12.6). It is shown graphically in figure 12.7.

Listing 12.6   showsettings.xml contains UI elements for the settings screen

```xml
<?xml version="1.0" encoding="utf-8"?>
<LinearLayout xmlns:android="http://schemas.android.com/apk/res/android"
  android:orientation="vertical"
  android:layout_width="fill_parent"
  android:layout_height="fill_parent"
  >                                        ┌─ TextView for
  <TextView                           ◄────┘   display of labels
```

```
android:layout_width="fill_parent"
android:layout_height="wrap_content"
android:text="Email Address"
/>
<EditText
android:id="@+id/emailaddress"
android:layout_width="fill_parent"
android:layout_height="wrap_content"
android:autoText="true"
/>
<TextView
android:layout_width="fill_parent"
android:layout_height="wrap_content"
android:text="Server URL"
/>
<EditText
android:id="@+id/serverurl"
android:layout_width="fill_parent"
android:layout_height="wrap_content"
android:autoText="true"
/>
<Button android:id="@+id/settingssave"
android:text="Save Settings"
android:layout_height="wrap_content"
android:layout_width="wrap_content"
android:enabled="true"
/>
</LinearLayout>
```

TextView for display of labels

EditView for entry of data

Button to initiate saving data

The source code behind the settings screen is also very basic. Note the use of the Populate-Screen() method, which makes sure the EditView controls are populated with the current values stored in the SharedPreferences. Note also the use of the Prefs helper class to retrieve and save the values, as shown in listing 12.7

Figure 12.7   Settings screen in use

Listing 12.7   ShowSettings.java implements the code behind the settings screen

```
package com.msi.manning.UnlockingAndroid;

// multiple imports trimmed for brevity, see full source code

public class ShowSettings extends Activity {
  Prefs myprefs = null;
  @Override
  public void onCreate(Bundle icicle) {
    super.onCreate(icicle);
    setContentView(R.layout.showsettings);
    myprefs = new Prefs(this.getApplicationContext());
    PopulateScreen();
    final Button savebutton = (Button) findViewById(R.id.settingssave);
    savebutton.setOnClickListener(new Button.OnClickListener() {
    public void onClick(View v) {
```

❶ Initialize Prefs instance

❷ Populate UI elements

```
    try {
     final EditText email=
     (EditText)findViewById(R.id.emailaddress);
     if (email.getText().length() == 0) {
     // display dialog, see full source code
      return;
     }
     final EditText serverurl =
         (EditText)findViewById(R.id.serverurl);
      if (serverurl.getText().length() == 0) {
        // display dialog, see full source code
        return;
     }
     myprefs.setEmail(email.getText().toString());
     myprefs.setServer(serverurl.getText().toString());
     myprefs.save();
     finish();
     } catch (Exception e) {
     }
    }
   });
}
  private void PopulateScreen() {
   try {
  final EditText emailfield = (EditText) findViewById(R.id.emailaddress);
  final EditText serverurlfield = (EditText)findViewById(R.id.serverurl);
  emailfield.setText(myprefs.getEmail());
  serverurlfield.setText(myprefs.getServer());
  } catch Exception e) {
  }
 }
}
```

3 Connect EditText to UI

4 Store and save settings

5 Finish this Activity

6 PopulateScreen method sets up UI

This Activity commences by initializing the SharedPreferences instance **1**, which retrieves the settings values and subsequently populates the UI elements **2** by calling the application-defined PopulateScreen method **6**. When the Save Settings button is clicked, the onClick method is invoked, wherein the data is extracted from the UI elements **3** and put back into the Prefs instance **4**. A call to the finish method **5** ends this Activity.

Once the settings are in order, it's time to focus on the core of the application, managing jobs for our mobile worker. In order to get the most out of looking at the higher-level functionality of downloading (refreshing) and managing jobs, we need to look at the core data structures in use in this application.

12.3.5 *Data structures*

Data structures represent a key element of any software project and, in particular, one consisting of multiple tiers, such as this Field Service Application. Job data is exchanged between an Android application and the server, so the elements of the job are central to our application. In Java, we implement these data structures as classes, which include helpful methods in addition to the data elements. XML data shows up in many locations in this application, so we will start there.

JOB XML DESCRIPTION

The same XML format is used as persistent storage by the Android application and for the transmission of job data from the server to Android. There is nothing particularly fancy in the XML document structure, just a collection of jobs.

Perhaps the most straightforward means of describing an XML document is through a Document Type Definition, or DTD. The DTD representing the XML used in this application is shown in listing 12.8.

Listing 12.8   DTD for joblist.xml

```
<?xml version="1.0" encoding="UTF-8"?>     ❶ joblist grouping
<!ELEMENT joblist ((job+))>
<!ELEMENT job ((id, status, customer, address, city, state, zip, product,
    producturl, comments))>              ❷ job element fields
<!ELEMENT zip (#PCDATA)>
<!ELEMENT status (#PCDATA)>
<!ELEMENT state (#PCDATA)>
<!ELEMENT producturl (#PCDATA)>
<!ELEMENT product (#PCDATA)>
<!ELEMENT id (#PCDATA)>
<!ELEMENT customer (#PCDATA)>
<!ELEMENT comments (#PCDATA)>
<!ELEMENT city (#PCDATA)>
<!ELEMENT address (#PCDATA)>
```

The joblist ❶ is the top level of the xml file, containing one or more job elements ❷.

Listing 12.9 shows a sample XML document containing a joblist with a single job entry.

Listing 12.9   XML document containing data for the Field Service Application

```
<?xml version="1.0" encoding="UTF-8" ?>
<joblist>
<job>
<id>22</id>
<status>OPEN</status>
<customer>Big Tristan's Imports</customer>
<address>2200 East Cedar Ave</address>
<city>Flagstaff</city>
<state>AZ</state>
<zip>86004</zip>
<product>UnwiredTools UTCIS-PT</product>
<producturl>http://unwiredtools.com</producturl>
<comments>Requires tuning - too rich in the mid range RPM.
Download software from website before visiting.</comments>
</job>
</joblist>
```

Now that you have a feel for what the job data looks like, you need to see how the data is handled in our Java classes.

JOBENTRY

The individual job is used throughout the application and is therefore essential to understand. In our application, we define the JobEntry class to manage the individual job, shown in listing 12.10. Note that many of the lines are omitted from this listing for brevity; please see the available source code for the complete code listing.

Listing 12.10   JobEntry.java

```
package com.msi.manning.UnlockingAndroid;

import android.os.Bundle;        ◄─── 1  Bundle class import

public class JobEntry {
 private String _jobid="";       ◄───      Each member
 private String _status = "";        2    is a String
 // members omitted for brevity
private String _producturl = "";
 private String _comments = "";

 JobEntry() {
 }
 // get/set methods omitted for brevity      3  toString method
 public String toString() {       ◄───
  return this._jobid + ": " + this._customer + ": " + this._product;
 }
 public String toXMLString() {    ◄───      toXMLString
  StringBuilder sb = new StringBuilder("");     4  method
  sb.append("<job>");
  sb.append("<id>" + this._jobid + "</id>");
  sb.append("<status>" + this._status + "</status>");
  sb.append("<customer>" + this._customer + "</customer>");
  sb.append("<address>" + this._address + "</address>");
  sb.append("<city>" + this._city + "</city>");
  sb.append("<state>" + this._state + "</state>");
  sb.append("<zip>" + this._zip + "</zip>");
  sb.append("<product>" + this._product + "</product>");
  sb.append("<producturl>" + this._producturl + "</producturl>");
  sb.append("<comments>" + this._comments + "</comments>");
  sb.append("</job>");
  return sb.toString() + "\n";
 }                                5  toBundle
 public Bundle toBundle() {    ◄───   method
  Bundle b = new Bundle();
  b.putString("jobid", this._jobid);
  b.putString("status", this._status);
  // assignments omitted for brevity
  b.putString("producturl", this._producturl);
  b.putString("comments", this._comments);
  return b;
 }                                       6  fromBundle
 public static JobEntry fromBundle(Bundle b) {  ◄───  method
  JobEntry je = new JobEntry();
  je.set_jobid(b.getString("jobid"));
  je.set_status(b.getString("status"));
  // assignments omitted for brevity
 je.set_producturl(b.getString("producturl"));
  je.set_comments(b.getString("comments"));
  return je;
 }
}
```

This application relies heavily on the `Bundle` class ❶ for moving data from one `Activity` to another. This will be explained in more detail later in this chapter. A `String` member ❷ exists for each element in the job such as `jobid`, `customer`, and so on. The `toString()` method ❸ is rather important as it is used when displaying jobs in the `ManageJobs  Activity`, discussed later in the chapter. The `toXML-String()` method ❹ generates an XML representation of this `JobEntry`, complying with the `job  element` defined in the previously presented DTD. The `toBundle()` method ❺ takes the data members of the `JobEntry` class and packages them into a `Bundle`. This `Bundle` is then able to be passed between activities, carrying with it the required data elements. The `fromBundle()` static method ❻ returns a `JobEntry` when provided with a `Bundle`. The `toBundle()` and `fromBundle()` work together to assist in the passing of `JobEntry` objects (at least the data portion thereof) between activities. Note that this is one of many ways in which to move data throughout an application. Another method would be to have a globally accessible class instance to store data, for example.

Now that you understand the `JobEntry` class, we need to look at the `JobList` class, which is a class used to manage a collection of `JobEntry` objects.

JOBLIST

When interacting with the server or presenting the available jobs to manage on the Android device, the Field Service Application works with an instance of the `JobList` class. This class, like the `JobEntry` class, has both data members and helpful methods. The `JobList` class contains a typed `List` data member, which is implemented using a `Vector`. This is the only data member of this class, as shown in listing 12.11. The methods of interest are described in the listing.

Listing 12.11   JobList.java code listing

```
package com.msi.manning.UnlockingAndroid;          ❶ List class
                                                      imported
import java.util.List;                                for Vector
import org.xml.sax.InputSource;                    ❷ InputSource
import android.util.Log;                              imported, used
// additional imports omitted for brevity, see source code   by XML parser
                                                      Familiar logging
                                                      mechanism
public class JobList {
    private Context _context = null;
    private List<JobEntry> _joblist;
    JobList(Context context){           ❸ Constructor
      _context = context;
      _joblist = new Vector<JobEntry>(0);
    }
    int addJob(JobEntry job){
      _joblist.add(job);
      return _joblist.size();           ❹ addJob/getJob
    }                                      methods
    JobEntry getJob(int location) {
      return _joblist.get(location);
    }
```

```
        List<JobEntry> getAllJobs() {          ←┐    getAllJobs
          return _joblist;                       ❺   method
        }
        int getJobCount() {
          return _joblist.size();
        }                                        ❻   replace
        void replace(JobEntry newjob){    ←┘         method
          try {
            JobList newlist = new JobList();
            for (int i=0;i<getJobCount();i++) {
              JobEntry je = getJob(i);
              if (je.get_jobid().equals(newjob.get_jobid())) {
                newlist.addJob(newjob);
              } else {
                newlist.addJob(je);
              }
            }
            this._joblist = newlist._joblist;
            persist();
          } catch (Exception e) {
          }
      }                         ❼  persist method writes
      void persist() {    ←┘       data to storage
        try {
          FileOutputStream fos = _context.openFileOutput("chapter12.xml",
          Context.MODE_PRIVATE);
          fos.write("<?xml version=\"1.0\" encoding=\"UTF-8\" ?>\n".getBytes());
          fos.write("<joblist>\n".getBytes());
          for (int i=0;i<getJobCount();i++) {
            JobEntry je = getJob(i);
            fos.write(je.toXMLString().getBytes());
          }
          fos.write("</joblist>\n".getBytes());
          fos.flush();
          fos.close();
        } catch (Exception e) {
          Log.d("CH12",e.getMessage());
        }
      }                                      ❽  parse
      static JobList parse(Context context) {  ←┘  method
        try {
          FileInputStream fis = context.openFileInput("chapter12.xml");
          if (fis == null) {
            return null;
          }
          InputSource is = new InputSource(fis);
          SAXParserFactory factory = SAXParserFactory.newInstance();
          SAXParser parser = factory.newSAXParser();
          XMLReader xmlreader = parser.getXMLReader();
          JobListHandler jlHandler =
  new JobListHandler(null /* no progress updates when reading file */);
          xmlreader.setContentHandler(jlHandler);
          xmlreader.parse(is);
          fis.close();
          return jlHandler.getList();
```

```
    } catch (Exception e) {
      return null;
    }
  }
}
```

The list of jobs is implemented as a `Vector`, which is a type of `List` ❶. The XML structure containing job information is parsed with the SAX parser, so we need to be sure to import those required packages ❷. `JobEntry` objects are stored in the typed `List` object named `_joblist` ❸. Helper methods for managing the list are included as `addJob` and `getJob` ❹. The `getAllJobs()` method ❺ returns the list of `JobEntry` items. Note that generally speaking the application uses the `getJob()` method for individual `JobEntry` management; however, the `getAllJobs()` method is particularly useful when we get to displaying the full list of jobs in the `ManageJobs Activity`, discussed later in this chapter.

The `replace()` method ❻ is used when we have closed a job and need to update our local store of jobs. Note that after it has updated the local list of `JobEntry` items, it calls the `persist()` ❼ method, which is responsible for writing an XML representation of the entire list of `JobEntry` items to storage. This method invokes the `toXML-String()` method on each `JobEntry` in the list. The `openFileOutput` method creates a file within the application's private file area. This is essentially a helper method to ensure we get a file path to which we have full read/write privileges.

Finally, the `parse` method ❽ obtains an instance of a `FileInputStream` to gain access to the file and then creates an instance of an `InputStream` ❷, which is required by the SAX XML parser. In particular, take note of the `JobListHandler`. SAX is a callback parser, meaning that it invokes a user-supplied method to process events in the parsing process. It is up to the `JobListHandler` (in our example) to process the data as appropriate.

We have one more class to go before we can jump back to the higher-level functionality of our application. The next section takes a quick tour of the `JobListHandler`, which is responsible for putting together a `JobList` from an XML data source.

JOBLISTHANDLER

As presented already, our application uses an XML data storage structure. This XML data can come from either the server or from a local file on the filesystem. In either case, the application must parse this data and transform it into a useful form. This is accomplished through the use of the SAX XML parsing engine and the `JobList-Handler`, which is shown in listing 12.12. The `JobListHandler` is used by the SAX parser for our XML data, regardless of the data's source. Where the data comes from dictates how the SAX parser is set up and invoked in this application. The `JobListHandler` behaves slightly differently depending on whether or not the class's constructor includes a `Handler` argument. If the `Handler` is provided, the `JobListHandler` will pass messages back for use in a `ProgressDialog`. If the `Handler` argument is null, this status message passing is bypassed. When parsing data from the server, the `ProgressDialog` is employed; the parsing of a local file is done quickly and without user feedback. The rationale for this is simple—the network connection may be slow and we need to show progress information to the user. An argument could be made for always showing the progress of the parse operation, but this approach gives us opportunity to demonstrate more conditionally operating code.

Listing 12.12 JobListHandler.java

```
package com.msi.manning.UnlockingAndroid;

// multiple imports omitted for brevity, see full source code

public class JobListHandler extends DefaultHandler {
    Handler phandler = null;
    JobList _list;
    JobEntry _job;
    String _lastElementName = "";
    StringBuilder sb = null;
    Context _context;

    JobListHandler(Context c,Handler progresshandler) {          ❶ JobListHandler
        _context = c;                                              constructor
        if (progresshandler != null) {                           ❷ Check for
            phandler = progresshandler;                            progress handler
            Message msg = new Message();
            msg.what = 0;
            msg.obj = (Object)("Processing List");
            phandler.sendMessage(msg);
        }
    }
    public JobList getList() {              ❸ getList
        Message msg = new Message();           method
        msg.what = 0;
        msg.obj = (Object)("Fetching List");
        if (phandler != null) phandler.sendMessage(msg);
        return _list;
    }
    public void startDocument() throws SAXException {   ❹ startDocument
        Message msg = new Message();                        method
        msg.what = 0;
        msg.obj = (Object)("Starting Document");
        if (phandler != null) phandler.sendMessage(msg);
        _list = new JobList(_context);
        _job = new JobEntry();
    }                                                   ❺ endDocument
    public void endDocument() throws SAXException {        method
        Message msg = new Message();
        msg.what = 0;
        msg.obj = (Object)("End of Document");
        if (phandler != null) phandler.sendMessage(msg);
    }
    public void startElement
    ⇒ (String namespaceURI, String localName,String qName,
    ⇒ Attributes atts) throws SAXException {
        try {
            sb = new StringBuilder("");
```

```
            if (localName.equals("job")) {
                Message msg = new Message();
                msg.what = 0;
                msg.obj = (Object)(localName);
                if (phandler != null) phandler.sendMessage(msg);
                _job = new JobEntry();
            }
        } catch (Exception ee) {
        }
    }
    public void endElement
        (String namespaceURI, String localName, String qName)
        throws SAXException {
        if (localName.equals("job")) {          ◁───── Check for end
            // add our job to the list!             6  of job element
            _list.addJob(_job);
            Message msg = new Message();
            msg.what = 0;
            msg.obj = (Object)("Storing Job # " + _job.get_jobid());
            if (phandler != null) phandler.sendMessage(msg);
            return;
        }
    // portions of the code omitted for brevity
    }
    public void characters(char ch[], int start, int length) {
        String theString = new String(ch,start,length);
        Log.d("CH12","characters[" + theString + "]");
        sb.append(theString);     ◁─────── Build up String
    }                                   7  incrementally
}
```

The `JobListHandler` constructor ❶ takes a single argument of `Handler`. This value may be null. If null, `Message` passing is omitted from operation, as we will show. When reading from a local storage file, this `Handler` argument is null. When reading data from the server over the internet, with a potentially slow connection, the `Message`-passing code is utilized to provide feedback for the user in the form of a `Progress-Dialog`. The `ProgressDialog` code is shown later in this chapter in the discussion of the `RefreshJobs Activity`. A local copy of the `Handler` ❷ is set up when using the `ProgressDialog`, as described in ❶.

The `getList()` ❸ method is invoked when parsing is complete. The role of `getList` is to return a copy of the `JobList` that was constructed during the parse process. When the `startDocument()` callback method ❹ is invoked by the SAX parser, the initial class instances are established. The `endDocument()` method ❺ is invoked by the SAX parser when all of the document has been consumed. This is an opportunity for the `Handler` to perform additional cleanup as necessary. In our example, a message is posted to the user by sending a `Message`.

For each element in the XML file, the SAX parser follows the same pattern: `start-Element` is invoked, `characters()` is invoked (one or more times), and `endElement` is invoked. In the `startElement` method, we initialize our `StringBuilder` and evaluate the element name. If the name is "job," we initialize our class-level `JobEntry` instance.

In the endElement() method, the element name is evaluated. If the element name is "job" ❻, the JobListHandler adds this JobEntry to the JobList data member, _joblist with a call to addJob(). Also in the endElement() method, the data members of the JobEntry instance (_job) are updated. Please see the full source code for more details.

The characters() method is invoked by the SAX parser whenever data is available for storage. The JobListHandler simply appends this string data to a StringBuilder instance ❼ each time it is invoked. It is possible that the characters method is invoked more than once for a particular element's data. That is the rationale behind using a StringBuilder instead of a single String variable; StringBuilder is a more efficient class for constructing strings from multiple substrings.

After this lengthy but important look into the data structures and the accompanying explanations, it is time to return to the higher-level functionality of the application.

12.4 Digging deeper into the code

Most of the time our mobile worker is using this application, he will be reading through comments, looking up a job address, getting product information, and performing other aspects of working on a specific job. However, without a list of jobs to work on, our mobile worker will be sitting idle, not earning a dime! Therefore, the first thing to review is the fetching of new jobs. This is also a good time to discuss gathering the list of jobs, coming on the heels of the review of the JobListHandler.

12.4.1 RefreshJobs

The RefreshJobs Activity performs a simple yet vital role in the Field Service Application. Whenever requested, the RefreshJobs Activity attempts to download a list of new jobs from the server. The UI is super simple—just a blank screen with a ProgressDialog informing the user of the application's progress, as shown in figure 12.8.

The code listing for RefreshJobs is shown in listing 12.13. The code is rather straightforward, as most of the heavy lifting is done in the Job-ListHandler. This code's responsibility is to fetch configuration settings, initiate a request to the server, and put a mechanism in place for showing progress to the user.

Figure 12.8 The ProgressDialog in use during RefreshJobs

> **Listing 12.13 RefreshJobs.java**

```
package com.msi.manning.UnlockingAndroid;
// multiple imports omitted for brevity, see full source

public class RefreshJobs extends Activity {
```

```
Prefs myprefs = null;
Boolean bCancel = false;
JobList mList = null;
ProgressDialog progress;              ① Progress
Handler progresshandler;                 indicator
@Override
public void onCreate(Bundle icicle) {
  super.onCreate(icicle);
  setContentView(R.layout.refreshjobs);                    Set up  ②
  myprefs = new Prefs(this.getApplicationContext);      ProgressDialog
  myprogress = ProgressDialog.show(this, "Refreshing Job List",
  ➥ "Please Wait",true,false);
progresshandler = new Handler() {        ◀──③ Define Handler
    @Override
    public void handleMessage(Message msg) {  ④ Update UI with
     switch (msg.what) {                          textual message
       case 0:
         myprogress.setMessage("" + (String) msg.obj);
         break;
       case 1:
         myprogress.cancel();
         finish();                       ⑤ Handle cancel
         break;                             and cancel with
       case 2:    // error occurred   ◀─   error
         myprogress.cancel();
         finish();
         break;
     }                                 ⑥ Use openFileInput
     super.handleMessage(msg);  ◀──       for stream
    }                                         ⑦ Initiate
  };                                             DoReadJobs
  Thread workthread = new Thread(new DoReadJobs());  ◀──  class instance
  workthread.start();
}
class DoReadJobs implements Runnable {
  public void run() {
    InputSource is = null;          ⑧ Create Message
    Message msg = new Message();  ◀──   object
    msg.what = 0;
    try {                            ⑨ Looping      ⑩ Prepare
      //Looper.prepare();               construct        status
      msg.obj = (Object) ("Connecting ...");  ◀──         message
      progresshandler.sendMessage(msg);
      URL url = new URL(myprefs.getServer() +
      ➥ "getjoblist.php?identifier=" + myprefs.getEmail());
      is = new InputSource(url.openStream());
      SAXParserFactory factory = SAXParserFactory.newInstance();
      SAXParser parser = factory.newSAXParser();
      XMLReader xmlreader = parser.getXMLReader();      Prepare to
      JobListHandler jlHandler =                        parse data  ⑪
new JobListHandler(progresshandler);
      xmlreader.setContentHandler(jlHandler);      Instantiate
      msg = new Message();                    ⑫  JobListHandler
      msg.what = 0;
      msg.obj = (Object) ("Parsing ...");
```

```
      progresshandler.sendMessage(msg);
      xmlreader.parse(is);
      msg = new Message();
      msg.what = 0;
      msg.obj = (Object)("Parsing Complete");
      progresshandler.sendMessage(msg);
      msg = new Message();
      msg.what = 0;
      msg.obj = (Object)("Saving Job List");
      progresshandler.sendMessage(msg);
      jlHandler.getList().persist();        ◄──⓭ Persist data
      msg = new Message();
      msg.what = 0;
      msg.obj = (Object)("Job List Saved.");
      progresshandler.sendMessage(msg);
      msg = new Message();              ⓮ Set status flag
      msg.what = 1;                 ◄──┘   for completion
      progresshandler.sendMessage(msg);
      } catch (Exception e) {
        Log.d("CH12","Exception: " + e.getMessage());
        msg = new Message();                    ⓯ Set status
        msg.what = 2;     // error occurred  ◄──┘   flag for error
        msg.obj = (Object)("Caught an error retrieving
        ➥ Job data: " + e.getMessage());
        progresshandler.sendMessage(msg);
      }
    }
  }
}
```

A `ProgressDialog` ❶ is used to display progress information to the user. There are a number of ways to display progress in Android. This is perhaps the most straightforward approach. A `Handler` is employed to process `Message` instances. While the `Handler` itself is defined as an anonymous class, the code requires a reference to it for passing to the `JobListHandler` when parsing, which is shown in ⓬. When instantiating the `ProgressDialog` ❷, the arguments include:

- `Context`
- `Title of Dialog`
- `Initial Textual Message`
- `Indeterminate`
- `Cancelable`

Using `true` for the `Indeterminate` parameter means that we are not providing any clue as to when the operation will complete, such as percentage remaining, just an indicator that something is still happening, which can be a best practice when you don't have a good handle on how long an operation may take. A new `Handler` ❸ is created to process messages sent from the parsing routine, which is introduced momentarily. An important class that has been mentioned but thus far not described is `Message`. This class is used to convey information between different threads of execution. The `Message` class has some generic data members that may be used in a flexible manner. The first of interest is the what member, which acts as a simple identifier, allowing recipients to easily jump to desired code based on the value of the what member. The most typical (and used here) approach is to evaluate the what data member via a switch statement.

In this application, a Message received with its what member equal to 0 represents a textual update message ❹ to be displayed on the ProgressDialog. The textual data itself is passed as a String cast to an Object and stored in the obj data member of the Message. This interpretation of the what member is purely arbitrary. We could have used 999 as the value meaning textual update, for example. A what value of 1 or 2 indicates that the operation is complete ❺, and this Handler can take steps to initiate another thread of execution. For example, a value of 1 indicates successful completion so the ProgressDialog is canceled (dismissed would work here also), and the RefreshJobs Activity is completed with a call to finish(). The value of 2 for the what member has the same effect as a value of 1, but it is provided here as an example of handling different result conditions; for example, a failure response due to an encountered error. In a production-ready application, this step should be fleshed out to perform an additional step of instruction to the user and/or a retry step. Any Message not explicitly handled by the Handler instance should be passed to the super class ❻. In this way system messages may be processed.

When communicating with a remote resource, such as a remote web server in our case, it is a good idea to perform the communications steps in a thread other than the primary GUI thread. A new Thread ❼ is created based on the DoReadJobs class, which implements the Runnable Java interface. A new Message object ❽ is instantiated and initialized. This step takes place over and over throughout the run method of the DoReadJobs class. It is important to not reuse a Message object, as they are literally passed and enqueued. It is possible for them to stack up in the receiver's queue, so reusing a Message object will lead to losing data or corrupting data at best and Thread synchronization issues or beyond at worst!

Why are we talking about a commented-out line of code ❾? Great question—because it caused so much pain in the writing of this application! A somewhat odd and confusing element of Android programming is the Looper class. This class provides static methods to assist Java Threads to interact with Android. Threads by default do not have a message loop, so presumably Messages don't go anywhere when sent. The first call to make is Looper.prepare(), which creates a Looper for a Thread that does not already have one established. Then by placing a call to the loop() method, the flow of Messages takes place. Prior to implementing this class as a Runnable interface, I experimented with performing this step in the same thread and attempted to get the ProgressDialog to work properly. All this said, if you run into funny Thread/Looper messages on the Android Emulator, have a look at adding a call to Looper.prepare() at the beginning of your Thread and then Looper.loop() to help Messages flow.

When we want to send data to the user to inform him of our progress, we update an instance of the Message class ❿ and send it to the assigned Handler.

In order to parse an incoming XML data stream, we create a new `InputSource` from the URL stream ➊➊. This step is required for the SAX parser. This method reads data from the network directly into the parser without a temporary storage file.

Note that the instantiation of the `JobListHandler` ➊➋ takes a reference to the `progresshandler`. This way the `JobListHandler` can (optionally) propagate messages back to the user during the parse process. Once the parse is complete, the `JobListHandler` returns a `JobList` object, which is then persisted ➊➌ to store the data to the local storage. Because this parsing step is complete, we let the `Handler` know by passing a `Message` ➊➍ with the `what` field set to a value of 1. If an exception occurs, we pass a message with `what` set to 2, indicating an error ➊➎.

Congratulations, your Android application has now constructed a `URL` with persistently stored configuration information (user and server) and successfully connected over the internet to fetch XML data. That data has been parsed into a `JobList` containing `JobEntry` objects, while providing our patient mobile worker with feedback, and subsequently storing the `JobList` to the filesystem for later use. Now we want to work with those jobs, because after all, those jobs have to be completed for our mobile worker friend to make a living!

12.4.2 ManageJobs

The `ManageJobs Activity` presents a scrollable list of jobs for review and action. At the top of the screen is a simple summary indicating the number of jobs in the list, and each individual job is enumerated in a `ListView`.

Earlier we mentioned the importance of the `JobEntry`'s `toString()` method:

Figure 12.9 `MangeJobs Activity` lists downloaded jobs.

```
public String toString() {
    return this._jobid + ": " + this._customer +
        ": " + this._product;
}
```

This method generates the `String` that is used to represent the `JobEntry` in the `ListView`, as shown in figure 12.9.

The layout for this `Activity`'s `View` is rather simple, just a `TextView` and a `ListView`, as shown in listing 12.14.

```
<?xml version="1.0" encoding="utf-8"?>
<LinearLayout xmlns:android="http://schemas.android.com/apk/res/android"
    android:id="@+id/joblistview"
    android:orientation="vertical"
    android:layout_width="fill_parent"
```

```
android:layout_height="wrap_content"
android:scrollbars="vertical"
>
<TextView    android:id="@+id/statuslabel"
android:text="list jobs here "
android:layout_height="wrap_content"
android:layout_width="fill_parent"
/>
<ListView   android:id="@+id/joblist"
android:layout_height="fill_parent"
android:layout_width="fill_parent"
/>
</LinearLayout>
```

The code in listing 12.15 for the ManageJobs Activity connects a JobList to the GUI as well as reacts to the selection of a particular job from the ListView. In addition, this class demonstrates taking the result from another, synchronously invoked Activity and processing it according to its specific requirement. For example, when a job is completed and closed, that JobEntry is updated to reflect its new status.

Listing 12.15   ManageJobs.java implements the `ManageJobs Activity`

```
package com.msi.manning.UnlockingAndroid;

// multiple imports omitted for brevity, see full source

public class ManageJobs extends Activity implements OnItemClickListener {
    final int SHOWJOB = 1;
    Prefs myprefs = null;
    JobList _joblist = null;
    ListView jobListView;
    @Override
    public void onCreate(Bundle icicle) {                     Connect
      super.onCreate(icicle);                              TextView to UI           ❶ Parse the
      setContentView(R.layout.managejobs);                                            data in
      myprefs = new Prefs(this.getApplicationContext());                              storage
      TextView tv =
         (TextView) findViewById(R.id.statuslabel);     ◁
      _joblist = JobList.parse(this.getApplicationContext());    ◁              ❷ Handle
      if (_joblist == null) {                                                      a bad
       _joblist = new JobList(this.getApplicationContext());   ◁                   parse
      }
      if (_joblist.getJobCount() == 0){              ◁
        tv.setText("There are No Jobs Available");      Check for an
      } else {                                        empty JobList         ❸ Connect
        tv.setText("There are " + _joblist.getJobCount() + " jobs.");         ListView
      }                                                                       to UI
      jobListView = (ListView) findViewById(R.id.joblist);    ◁
      ArrayAdapter<JobEntry> adapter = new ArrayAdapter<JobEntry>(this,
      android.R.layout.simple_list_item_1, _joblist.getAllJobs());   ◁
      jobListView.setAdapter(adapter);        ◁                             Use a
      jobListView.setOnItemClickListener(this);   ◁      Connect the        built-in
      jobListView.setSelection(0);                       list with the      list
    }                                    Process         dataevents         layout
                                     click events on List  on List
```

```
public void onItemClick(AdapterView parent, View v, int position, long id) {
    JobEntry je = _joblist.getJob(position);
    Log.i("CH12", "job clicked! [" + je.get_jobid() + "]");
    Intent jobintent = new Intent(this, ShowJob.class);
    Bundle b = je.toBundle();
    jobintent.putExtras(b);
    startActivityForResult(jobintent, SHOWJOB);
}
@Override
protected void onActivityResult(int requestCode, int resultCode, Intent
    data) {
    switch (requestCode) {
    case SHOWJOB:
        if (resultCode == 1){
            Log.d("CH12","Good Close, let's update our list");
            JobEntry je = JobEntry.fromBundle(data.getExtras());
            _joblist.replace(je);
        }
        break;
    }
}

}
```

⑤ **Use a Bundle to store Job data**

⑥ **Prepare Intent for showing Job details**

Start ShowJob Activity ⑥

Fetch job from list by ordinal ④

⑦ **Check return code**

Process click events on List

Update the list with via replace method ⑧

Extract returned JobEntry

The objective of this code is to display a list of available jobs to the user in a List-View ❸. In order to display the list of jobs we must first parse the list stored on the device ❶. Note that the Context argument is required to allow the JobList class access to the private file area for this application. If the parse fails, we initialize the JobList instance to a new, empty list. This is a somewhat simplistic way to handle the error without the GUI falling apart ❷.

When a specific job is selected, its details are extracted via a call to the getJob method ❹. The job is stored in a Bundle, put into an Intent ❺, and subsequently sent to the ShowJob Activity for display and/or editing ❻. Note the use of SHOWJOB as the last parameter of the startActivityForResult method. When this called Activity returns, that parameter will help the caller understand the context of the data when the onActivityResult method is invoked ❼ and the return code checked. To obtain the changed JobEntry, we need to extract it from the Intent with a call to getExtras(), which returns a Bundle. This Bundle is turned into a JobEntry instance via the static fromBundle method of the JobEntry class. To update the list of jobs to reflect this changed JobEntry, call the replace method ❽.

Now that we can view and select the job of interest, it is time to look at just what we can do with that job. Before diving in to the next section, be sure to review the ManageJobs code carefully to understand how the JobEntry information is passed between the two activities.

12.4.3 *ShowJob*

The ShowJob Activity is the most interesting element of the entire application, and it is certainly the screen most useful to the mobile worker carrying around his Android-

More on Bundles

We need to pass the selected job to the ShowJob Activity, but we cannot casually pass an object from one Activity to another. We don't want the ShowJob Activity to have to parse the list of jobs again; otherwise we could simply pass back an index to the selected job by using the integer storage methods of a Bundle. Perhaps we could store the currently selected JobEntry (and JobList for that matter) in a global data member of the Application object, should we have chosen to implement one. If you recall in chapter 1 when we discussed the ability of Android to dispatch Intents to any Activity registered on the device, we want to keep the ability open to an application other than our own to perhaps pass a job to us. If that were the case, using a global data member of an Application object would never work! Never mind for the moment the likelihood of such a step being low, particularly considering how the data is stored in this application. This chapter's sample application is an exercise of evaluating some different mechanisms one might employ to solve data movement around Android. The chosen solution is to package the data fields of the JobEntry in a Bundle ❺ (in listing 12.15) to move a JobEntry from one Activity to another. In the strictest sense, we are moving not a real JobEntry object but a representation of a JobEntry's data members. The net of this long discussion is that this method creates a new Bundle by using the toBundle() method of the JobEntry.

capable device and toolbox. To help in the discussion of the different features available to the user on this screen, take a look at figure 12.10.

The layout is very straightforward but this time we have some Buttons and we will be changing the textual description depending on the condition of a particular job's status. A Text-View is used to present job details such as address, product requiring service, and comments. The third Button will have the text property changed, depending on the status of the job. If the job's status is marked as CLOSED, the functionality of the third button will change.

To support the functionality of this Activity, first the code needs to launch a new Activity to show a map of the job's address, as shown in figure 12.11.

The second button, Get Product Info, launches a browser window to assist the user in learning more about the product he is being called upon to work with. Figure 12.12 shows this in action.

Figure 12.10   An example of a job shown in the ShowJob **Activity**

The third requirement is to allow the user to close the job or to view the signature if it is already closed, the details of which are covered in the next section on the CloseJob Activity.

Figure 12.11 Viewing a job address in the Maps application

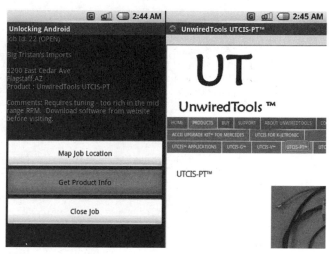

Figure 12.12 Get Product Info takes the user to a web page specific to this job.

Fortunately, the steps required for the first two operations are quite simple with Android—thanks to the Intent. Listing 12.16 and the accompanying descriptions show you how.

Listing 12.16 ShowJob.java

```java
package com.msi.manning.UnlockingAndroid;

// multiple imports omitted for brevity, see full source

public class ShowJob extends Activity {
    Prefs myprefs = null;
    JobEntry je = null;
    final int CLOSEJOBTASK = 1;
    public void onCreate(Bundle icicle) {
        super.onCreate(icicle);
        setContentView(R.layout.showjob);
        myprefs = new Prefs(this.getApplicationContext());
        StringBuilder sb = new StringBuilder();
        String details = null;
        Intent startingIntent = getIntent();              ⟵ Get Intent
        if (startingIntent != null) {
            Bundle b = startingIntent.getExtas();          ⟵┐ Extract the Bundle
            if (b == null) {                                │ from the Intent
                details = "bad bundle?";
            } else {
            je = JobEntry.fromBundle(b);
            sb.append("Job Id: " + je.get_jobid() + " (" + je.get_status()+
            ➥ ")\n\n");
            sb.append(je.get_customer() + "\n\n");
            sb.append(je.get_address() + "\n" + je.get_city() + "," +
            ➥ je.get_state() + "\n" );
            sb.append("Product : "+ je.get_product() + "\n\n");
```

```
        sb.append("Comments: " + je.get_comments() + "\n\n");
        details = sb.toString();
      }
} else {
  details = "Job Information Not Found.";
  TextView tv = (TextView) findViewById(R.id.details);
  tv.setText(details);
  return;
}
TextView tv = (TextView) findViewById(R.id.details);
tv.setText(details);
Button bmap = (Button) findViewById(R.id.mapjob);
bmap.setOnClickListener(new Button.OnClickListener() {
    public void onClick(View v) {
        // clean up data for use in GEO query
        String address = je.get_address() + " " + je.get_city() + " " +
        je.get_zip();
        String cleanAddress = address.replace(",", "");
        cleanAddress = cleanAddress.replace(' ','+');
        try {
          Intent geoIntent = new
Intent("android.intent.action.VIEW",android.net.Uri.parse("geo:0,0?q=" +
cleanAddress));
          startActivity(geoIntent);
        } catch (Exception ee) {
        }
    }
});
Button bproductinfo = (Button) findViewById(R.id.productinfo);
bproductinfo.setOnClickListener(new Button.OnClickListener() {
    public void onClick(View v) {
      try {
        Intent productInfoIntent = new Intent("android.intent.action.VIEW",
        android.net.Uri.parse(je.get_producturl()));
        startActivity(productInfoIntent);
      } catch (Exception ee) {
      }
    }
});
Button bclose = (Button) findViewById(R.id.closejob);
if (je.get_status().equals("CLOSED")) {
  bclose.setText("Job is Closed. View Signature");
}
bclose.setOnClickListener(new Button.OnClickListener() {
    public void onClick(View v) {
      if (je.get_status().equals("CLOSED")) {
        Intent signatureIntent = new Intent("android.intent.action.VIEW",
        android.net.Uri.parse(myprefs.getServer() + "sigs/" +
          je.get_jobid() + ".jpg"));
        startActivity(signatureIntent);
      } else {
      Intent closeJobIntent = new Intent(ShowJob.this,CloseJob.class);
      Bundle b = je.toBundle();
      closeJobIntent.putExtras(b);
      startActivityForResult(closeJobIntent,CLOSEJOBTASK);
```

Update UI upon error and return

Build and launch a geo query

Obtain product information via URL

Selectively update Button label

Show Signature for CLOSED JobEntrys

Initiate CloseJob Activity

```
            }
          }
        });
        Log.d("CH12","Job status is :" + je.get_status());
      }
      @Override
      protected void onActivityResult(int requestCode, int resultCode, Intent
        data) {
        switch (requestCode) {
          case CLOSEJOBTASK:
            if (resultCode == 1) {                        ❶ Handle newly
              this.setResult(1, "", data.getExtras());  ◁──┘ closed JobEntry
              finish();
            }
            break;
        }
      }
    }
```

Upon completion of the `CloseJob` Activity, the `onActivityResult` callback is invoked. When this situation occurs, this method receives a `Bundle` containing the data elements for the recently closed `JobEntry` ❶. If you recall, the `ShowJob` Activity was launched "for result." The requirement is to propagate this `JobEntry` data back up to the calling Activity, `ManageJobs`. Calling `setResult()` and passing the `Bundle` (obtained with `getExtras()`) fulfills this requirement.

Despite the simple appearance of some text and a few easy-to-hit buttons, the `ShowJob` Activity provides a significant amount of functionality to the user. All that remains is to capture the signature to close out the job. To do this requires an examination of the `CloseJob` Activity.

12.4.4 CloseJob

Our faithful mobile technician has just completed the maintenance operation on the part and is ready to head off to lunch before stopping for another job on the way home, but first he must close out this job with a signature from the customer. To accomplish this, the Field Service Application presents a blank screen, and the customer uses a stylus (or a mouse in the case of the Android Emulator) to sign the device, acknowledging that the work has been completed. Once the signature has been captured, the data is submitted to the server. The proof of job completion has been captured, and the job can now be billed. Figure 12.13 demonstrates this sequence of events.

This `Activity` can be broken down into two basic functions. The first is the capture of a signature. The second is transmittal of job data to the server. Of interest is that this `Activity`'s UI has no layout resource. All of the UI elements in this `Activity` are generated dynamically, as shown in listing 12.17. In addition, the `ProgressDialog` introduced in the `RefreshJobs` Activity is brought back for an encore, to let our mobile technician know that the captured signature is being sent when the Sign & Close menu

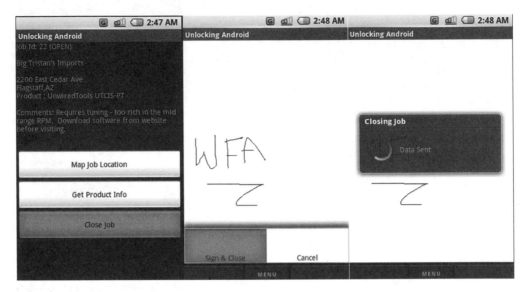

Figure 12.13   The `CloseJob Activity` **capturing a signature and sending data to the server**

option is selected. If the user selects Cancel, the ShowJob Activity resumes control. Note that the signature should be made prior to selecting the menu option.

> **Local queuing**
>
> One element not found in this sample application is the local queuing of the signature. Ideally this would be done in the event that data coverage is not available. The storage of the image is actually quite simple; the perhaps more challenging piece is the logic on when to attempt to send the data again. Considering all of the development of this sample application is done on the Android Emulator with near-perfect connectivity, it is of little concern here. However, in the interest of best preparing you to write real-world applications, it is worth the reminder of local queuing in the event of communications trouble in the field.

Listing 12.17   CloseJob.java—GUI setup

```
package com.msi.manning.UnlockingAndroid;

// multiple imports omitted for brevity, see full source

public class CloseJob extends Activity {
    ProgressDialog myprogress;
    Handler progresshandler;
    Message msg;
    JobEntry je = null;
    private closejobView sc = null;
    @Override
    public void onCreate(Bundle icicle)  {
```

```
     super.onCreate(icicle);
     Intent startingIntent = getIntent();
     if (startingIntent != null) {
       Bundle b = startingIntent.getExtras()
       if (b != null) {
         je = JobEntry.fromBundle(b);
       }
     }
     sc = new closejobView(this);                    ① Instantiate instance
     setContentView(sc);                                 of closejobView
     if (je == null) {
       finish();
     }
   }
   @Override
   public boolean onCreateOptionsMenu(Menu menu) {    ② Define available
     super.onCreateOptionsMenu(menu);                     menus
     menu.add(0,0,"Sign & Close");
     menu.add(0,1,"Cancel");
     return true;                                       ③ Handle selected
   }                                                        menu
   public boolean onOptionsItemSelected(Menu.Item item) {
     Prefs myprefs = new Prefs(CloseJob.this.getApplicationContext());
     switch (item.getId()) {
       case 0:
       try {
         myprogress = ProgressDialog.show(this, "Closing Job ",
         ➡ "Saving Signature to Network",true,false);
         progresshandler = new Handler() {
         @Override
         public void handleMessage(Message msg) {
           switch (msg.what) {
             case 0:
               myprogress.setMessage("" + (String) msg.obj);
               break;
             case 1:
               myprogress.cancel();
               finish();
               break;
         }
       super.handleMessage(msg);
       }
     };                                                ④ Start Thread
     Thread workthread = new Thread(new DoCloseJob(myprefs));    to CloseJob
         workthread.start();
   } catch (Exception e) {
     Log.d("closejob",e.getMessage());
     msg = new Message();
     msg.what = 1;
     progresshandler.sendMessage(msg);
   }
   return true;
 case 1:
   finish();
   return true;
```

```
    }
    return false;
}
```

Unlike previous activities in this chapter, the UI does not come from a design time–defined layout, but rather an instance of a `closejobView` ❶ is the primary UI. The `closejobView` is defined in listing 12.18.

The `onCreateOptionsMenu` method ❷ is an override of the base `View`'s method, allowing a convenient way to add menus to this screen. Note that two menus are added, one for Sign & Close and one for Cancel. The `onOptionsItemSelected` method ❸ is invoked when the user selects a menu item. A `ProgressDialog` and accompanying `Handler` are instantiated when the menu to close a job is selected. Once the progress-reporting mechanism is in place, a new `Thread` is created and started in order to process the steps required to actually close the job ❹. Note that an instance of `Prefs` is passed in as an argument to the constructor, as that will be needed to store a signature, as we'll show in listing 12.19.

The UI at this point is only partially set up; we need a means to capture a signature on the screen of our Android device. Listing 12.18 implements the class `closejob-View`, which is an extension of the `View` class.

Listing 12.18 CloseJob.java—`closejobView` class

```
public class closejobView extends View {          ◁──  ❶ closejobView extends
    Bitmap _bitmap;                                        the base class View
    Canvas _canvas;          ❷ Required classes
    final Paint _paint;          for drawing
    int lastX;
    int lastY;
    public closejobView(Context c) {       ┐ Initialize drawing
      super(c);                            │ classes
      _paint = new Paint();        ◁───────┘
      _paint.setColor(Color.BLACK);
      lastX = -1;                           ❸ Save method
    }                                          persists
    public boolean Save(OutputStream os){   ◁─┘ signature        ❹ Add
      try {                                                         contextual
        _canvas.drawText("Unlocking Android", 10, 10, _paint);  ◁─  data to image
        _canvas.drawText("http://manning.com/ableson", 10, 25, _paint);
        _canvas.drawText("http://android12.msi-wireless.com", 10, 40, _paint);
        _bitmap.compress(Bitmap.CompressFormat.JPEG, 100, os);  ◁── Convert
        invalidate();                                               image to
        return true;                                                JPEG
      } catch (Exception e) {
        return false;
      }
    }                                              Bitmap initialization code
    @Override
    protected void onSizeChanged(int w, int h, int oldw, int oldh) {
      Bitmap img =
        Bitmap.createBitmap(w, h,Bitmap.Config.ARGB_8888);   ◁──
      Canvas canvas = new Canvas();
```

```
      canvas.setBitmap(img);
      if (_bitmap != null) {
        canvas.drawBitmap(img, 0, 0, null);
      }
      _bitmap = img;
      _canvas = canvas;
      _canvas.drawColor(Color.WHITE);
    }
    @Override
    protected void onDraw(Canvas canvas) {
      if (_bitmap != null) {                            ❺ Draw image
        canvas.drawBitmap(_bitmap, 0, 0, null);    ◁──┘   on screen
      }
    }
    @Override
    public boolean onTouchEvent(MotionEvent event) {     ❻ Handle Touch Events
      int action = event.getAction();           ◁──┘      (i.e., capture signature!)
      int X = (int)event.getX();
      int Y = (int)event.getY();
      switch (action ) {
        case MotionEvent.ACTION_UP:
          // reset location
          lastX = -1;
          break;
        case MotionEvent.ACTION_DOWN:
          if (lastX != -1){
           if ((int) event.getX() != lastX) {
            _canvas.drawLine(lastX, lastY, X, Y, _paint);
           }
          }
          lastX = (int)event.getX();
          lastY = (int)event.getY();
          break;
        case MotionEvent.ACTION_MOVE:
          if (lastX != -1){
            _canvas.drawLine(lastX, lastY, X, Y, _paint);
          }
          lastX = (int)event.getX();
          lastY = (int)event.getY();
          break;
      }
      invalidate();
      return true;
    }
  }
}
```

The closejobView extends the base View class ❶. The Bitmap and Canvas classes ❷ work together to form the drawing surface for this Activity. Note the call to the Canvas.drawColor method, which sets the background color to WHITE. When the onDraw() method is invoked, the canvas draws its associated bitmap with a call to drawBitmap() ❺.

The logic for where to draw relies on the onTouchEvent method ❻, which receives an instance of the MotionEvent class. The MotionEvent class tells what happened and where. `ACTION_UP`, `ACTION_DOWN`, and `ACTION_MOVE` are the events captured, with some logic to guide when and where to draw. Once the signature is complete, the `Save` method ❸ is responsible for converting the contents of the image to a form usable for submission to the server. Note that additional text is drawn on the signature ❹. In this case, it is little more than a shameless plug for this book's webpage; however, this could also be location-based data. Why is this important? Imagine someone forging a signature. Could happen, but it would be more challenging and of less value to a rogue mobile technician if the GPS/location data were actually stamped on the job, along with the date and time. When converting the image to our desired JPEG format, there is an additional input argument to this method—an `OutputStream`, used to store the image data. This `OutputStream` reference was actually an input argument to the `Save` method.

Now that the UI has been created and a signature drawn on the screen, let's look at the code used to close the job. Closing the job involves capturing the signature and sending it to the server via an HTTP POST. The class `DoCloseJob` is shown in listing 12.19.

Listing 12.19   CloseJob.java—`DoCloseJob` class

```java
class DoCloseJob implements Runnable {
Prefs _myprefs;
DoCloseJob(Prefs p) {                      // Constructor uses
  _myprefs = p;                            // Prefs instance
}
public void run() {
  try {
    FileOutputStream os =                                    // ❶ Open a file for
    getApplication().openFileOutput("sig.jpg", 0);           //    storing signature
     sc.Save(os);
    os.flush();
    os.close();
    // reopen to so we can send this data to server
    File f = new
File(getApplication().getFileStreamPath("sig.jpg").toString());
        long flength = f.length();
        FileInputStream is = getApplication().openFileInput("sig.jpg");
        byte data[] = new byte[(int) flength];
     int count = is.read(data);
     if (count != (int) flength) {
         // bad read?
     }
    msg = new Message();
    msg.what = 0;
    msg.obj = (Object)("Connecting to Server");
    progresshandler.sendMessage(msg);
    URL url = new URL(_myprefs.getServer() +                 // ❷ Construct
        "/closejob.php?jobid=" + je.get_jobid());            //    storage URL
    URLConnection conn = url.openConnection();
    conn.setDoOutput(true);
    BufferedOutputStream wr = new                            // ❸ Write data
BufferedOutputStream(conn.getOutputStream());               //    to server
```

```
      wr.write(data);
      wr.flush();
      wr.close();
      msg = new Message();
      msg.what = 0;
      msg.obj = (Object)("Data Sent");
      progresshandler.sendMessage(msg);
      BufferedReader rd = new BufferedReader(new          ❹ Read server
    ➡ InputStreamReader(conn.getInputStream()));   ◄─┘   response
      String line = "";
      Boolean bSuccess = false;
      while ((line = rd.readLine()) != null) {       ❺ Check for successful
        if (line.indexOf("SUCCESS") != -1) {    ◄─┘    processing
          bSuccess = true;
        }
      }
      wr.close();
      rd.close();
      if (bSuccess) {
        msg = new Message();
        msg.what = 0;
        msg.obj = (Object)("Job Closed Successfully");
        progresshandler.sendMessage(msg);                 ❻ Update local
        je.set_status("CLOSED");                    ◄─┘    JobEntry status
        CloseJob.this.setResult(1,"",je.toBundle());  ◄─┐
      } else {                                             Set result and
        msg = new Message();                               store updated
        msg.what = 0;                               ❼      JobEntry
        msg.obj = (Object)("Failed to Close Job");
        progresshandler.sendMessage(msg);
        CloseJob.this.setResult(0);
      }
    } catch (Exception e) {
      Log.d("CH12","Failed to submit job close signature: " + e.getMessage());
    }
    msg = new Message();
    msg.what = 1;
    progresshandler.sendMessage(msg);
  }
}
```

At this point, we have a signature on the screen and need to capture it. A new File-
OutputStream ❶ is obtained for a file on the local filesystem, and the signature is written to this file. We are now ready to transmit this file to the server—remember, we
want to bill the client as soon as possible for work completed!

In preparation for sending the signature to the server, the signature file contents
are read into a byte array via an instance of a FileInputStream. Using the Prefs
instance to get specific configuration information, a URL ❷ is constructed in order to
POST data to the server. The query String of the URL contains the jobid and the POST
data contains the image itself. A BufferedOutputStream ❸ is employed to POST data,
which consists of the captured signature in JPEG format.

Once the job data and signature have been sent to the server, the response data is read back from the server ❹. A specific string indicates a successful transmission ❺.

Upon successful closing, the JobEntry status member is marked as CLOSED ❻, and this JobEntry is converted to a Bundle so that it may be communicated to the caller by invoking the setResult() method ❼. Once the Handler receives the "I'm done" message and the Activity finishes, this data is propagated back to the ShowJob and all the way back to the ManageJob Activity.

And that thankfully wraps up the source code review for the Android side of things! There were some methods omitted from this text to limit this already very long chapter, so please be sure to examine the full source code. Now it's time to look at the server application.

12.5   *Server code*

A mobile application often relies on server-side resources, and our Field Service Application is no exception. Since this is not a book on server-side development techniques, server-related code, and discussion, things will be presented briefly and matter of factly. We will introduce the UI and the accompanying database structure that makes up our list of job entries, and then we'll review the two server-side transactions that concern the Android application.

12.5.1 *Dispatcher user interface*

Before jumping into any server code–specific items, it is important to understand how the application is organized. All jobs entered by a dispatcher are assigned to a particular mobile technician. That identifier is interpreted as an email address, as seen in the Android example where the user ID was used throughout the application. Once the user ID is specified, all of the records revolve around that data element. For example, figure 12.14 demonstrates this by showing the jobs assigned to the author, fableson@msiservices.com.

Unlocking Android, Chapter 12 Sample Application

For assistance with this application, please contact Frank Ableson of MSI Services, Inc.

Job List for [fableson@msiservices.com].

Job Id#	Customer	Address	City	State	Zip	Product	Product URL	Comments	Status
18	Path of Growth, LLC.	123 Main Street	Chester	NJ	07930	Wireless Router	http://cisco.com	SID broadcast not working	CLOSED
19	Indy Products	49 Route 206	Stanhope	NJ	07874	Water Cooler	http://whirlpool.com	Water is not cold enough!	CLOSED
21	Slim's Boats, Inc	1 Orchard Lane	Chester	NJ	07930	Cigarette Boat	http://chriscraft.com/	needs a light	CLOSED
22	Big Tristan	2200 East Cedar Ave	Flagstaff	AZ	86004	UnwiredTools UTCIS-PT	http://unwiredtools.com	Requires tuning - too rich in the mid range RPM. Download software from website before visiting.	CLOSED
23	JJ's Ices	17 Route 206	Stanhope	NJ	07874	Gelato Machine	http://ge.com	Ice pops	CLOSED
24	Matyas Grocer	144 Whitehall Road	Andover	NJ	07821	Rototiller	http://johndeere.com	Required firmware upgrade.	CLOSED
27	Google	123 Main Street	Somewhere	CA	12345	Android	http://google.com	test	CLOSED

Export Your Job List

Add a Job

Home

MSI Wireless is a division of MSI Services.
Check out Unlocking Android

Figure 12.14   The server-side dispatcher screen

NOTE This application is available for testing the sample application yourself. It is located at http://android12.msi-wireless.com. Simply sign on and add jobs for your email address.

Let's now turn our attention to the underlying data structure, which contains the list of jobs.

12.5.2 Database

As mentioned earlier in the architecture section, the database in use in this application is MySQL, with a single database table called tbl_jobs. The SQL to create this table is provided in listing 12.20.

Listing 12.20   Data definition for tbl_jobs

```
CREATE TABLE IF NOT EXISTS 'tbl_jobs' (
  'jobid' int(11) NOT NULL auto_increment,        ◄──❶ Unique record id
  'status' varchar(10) NOT NULL default 'OPEN',
  'identifier' varchar(50) NOT NULL,              ◄──❷ User identification
  'address' varchar(50) NOT NULL,
  'city' varchar(30) NOT NULL,
  'state' varchar(2) NOT NULL,
  'zip' varchar(10) NOT NULL,
  'customer' varchar(50) NOT NULL,
  'product' varchar(50) NOT NULL,
  'producturl' varchar(100) NOT NULL,             ◄──❸ Product URL
  'comments' varchar(100) NOT NULL,
  UNIQUE KEY 'jobid' ('jobid')
) ENGINE=MyISAM DEFAULT CHARSET=ascii AUTO_INCREMENT=25 ;
```

Each row in this table is uniquely identified by the jobid ❶, which is an auto-incrementing integer field. The identifier field ❷ corresponds to the user ID/email of the assigned mobile technician. The producturl field ❸ is designed to be a specific URL to assist the mobile technician in the field to quickly gain access to helpful information to assist in completing the assigned job.

The next section provides a road map to the server code.

12.5.3 PHP dispatcher code

The server-side dispatcher system is written in PHP and contains a number of files working together to create the application. Table 12.3 presents a brief synopsis of each source file to help you navigate the application should you choose to host a version of this application yourself.

Table 12.3   Server-side source code

Source File	Description
addjob.php	Form for entering new job information
closejob.php	Used by Android application to submit signature
db.php	Database connection info

Table 12.3   Server-side source code *(continued)*

Source File	Description
export.php	Used to export list of jobs to a csv file
footer.php	Used to create a consistent look and feel for the footer of each page
getjoblist.php	Used by Android application to request job XML stream
header.php	Used to create a consistent look and feel for the header of each page
index.php	Home page, including search form
manage.php	Used to delete jobs on the web application
savejob.php	Used to save a new job (called from addjob.php)
showjob.php	Used to display job details and load into a form for updating
showjobs.php	Displays all jobs for a particular user
updatejob.php	Used to save updates to a job
utils.php	Contains various routines for interacting with the database

Of all of these files, only two actually concern the Android application. These are discussed in the next section.

12.5.4 *PHP mobile integration code*

When the Android application runs the `RefreshJobs Activity`, the server side generates an XML stream. Without going into excessive detail on the server-side code, the getjoblist.php file is explained in listing 12.21.

Listing 12.21   getjoblist.php

```
<?
require('db.php');              ◁——  Database routines
require('utils.php');           ◁——  Helper routines
$theuser = $_GET['identifier'];        Extract the
                                       user identifier
print (getJobsXML($theuser));   ◁——  Build list of jobs
?>                               ❶   for this user
```

The getJobsXML ❶ function retrieves data from the database and formats each row into an XML representation. It wraps the list of XML-wrapped job records in the `<job-list>` tags along with the `<?xml ...>` header declaration to generate the expected XML structure used by the Android application. Remember, this is the data ultimately parsed by the SAX-based `JobListHandler` class, as shown in listing 12.12.

The other transaction that is important to our Android Field Service Application is the closejob.php file, examined in listing 12.22.

Listing 12.22   closejob.php

```
<?
require('db.php');
```

```
require('utils.php');                              ❶ Read in image data
$data = file_get_contents('php://input');    ←┘
$jobid = $_GET['jobid'];                          ←──❷ Get the job ID
$f = fopen("~/pathtofiles/sigs/".$jobid.".jpg","w");
fwrite($f,$data);                                        Write out the
fclose($f);                                        ❸ image data
print(closeJob($_GET['jobid']));   ←──❹ Close the job
?>
```

The POST-ed image data is read via the file_get_contents() function ❶. The secret
is the special identifier of php://input. This is the equivalent of a binary read. This
data is read into a variable named $data. The jobid is extracted from the query
String ❷. The image file is written out to a directory that contains signatures as JPEG
files, keyed by the jobid as part of the filename ❸. When a job has been closed and
the signature is requested by the Android application, it is this file that is requested in
the Android browser. The closeJob function ❹ (implemented in utils.php) updates
the database to mark the selected job as CLOSED.

That wraps up the review of the source code for this chapter's sample application.

12.6   *Summary*

This chapter certainly was not short, but hopefully it was worth the read. The intent of
the sample application was to tie together many things learned in previous chapters
into a composite application that has real-world applicability to the kind of uses an
Android device is capable of bringing to fruition. Is this sample application production ready? Of course not, but almost! That is, as they say, an exercise for the reader.

Starting with a simple splash screen, this application demonstrated the use of Handlers and displaying images stored in the resources section of an Android project.
Moving along to the main screen, a simple UI led to different activities useful for
launching various aspects of the realistic application.

Communications with the server downloaded XML data, while showing the user a
ProgressDialog along the way. Once the data stream commenced, the data was parsed
by the SAX XML parser, using a custom Handler to navigate the XML document.

Managing jobs in a ListView was demonstrated to be as easy as tapping on the
desired job in the list. The next screen, the ShowJobs Activity, allowed even more
functionality with the ability to jump to a Map showing the location of the job and even
a specific product information page customized to this job. Both of those functions
were as simple as preparing an Intent and a call to startActivity().

Once the mobile technician completed the job in the field, the CloseJob Activity brought the touch-screen elements into play by allowing the user to capture a signature from his customer. That digital signature was then stamped with additional,
contextual information and transmitted over the internet to prove the job was done!
Jumping back to what you learned earlier, it would be straightforward to add location-
based data to further authenticate the captured signature.

The chapter wrapped up with a quick survey of the server-side components to
demonstrate some of the steps necessary to tie the mobile and the server sides
together.

The sample application is hosted on the internet and is free for you to test out with your own Android application, and of course the full source code is provided for the Android and server applications discussed in this chapter.

Now that we have shown what can be accomplished when exercising a broad range of the Android SDK, the next chapter takes a decidedly different turn as we explore the underpinnings of Android a little deeper and look at building native C applications for the Android platform.

Hacking Android

13

This chapter covers:

- Android's Linux foundation
- Building a C application
- Using the SQLite database from C
- Bridging the gap with a Java client application

This book has presented a cross section of development topics in an effort to unlock the potential of the Android platform for the purpose of delivering useful, and perhaps even fun, mobile applications. In chapter 12 we built a more comprehensive application, building on what was introduced in the prior chapters. As we embark on this final chapter, we are leaving behind the comforts of working strictly in the Android SDK, Java, and Eclipse.

The Android SDK is quite comprehensive and capable, as this book has attempted to convey, but there may be times when your application requires something more. This chapter explores the steps required to build applications that run in the Linux foundation layer of Android. To accomplish this, we are going to use the C programming language. In this chapter we use the term *Android/Linux* to refer to the Linux underpinnings of the Android platform. We also use the term *Android/Java* to refer to a Java application built using the Android SDK and Eclipse.

We demonstrate the steps of building an Android/Linux application commencing with a description of the environment and the required tool chain. After an obligatory Hello World–caliber application, we construct a more sophisticated application that implements a daytime server. Ultimately any application built for Android/Linux needs to bring value to the user in some form. In an effort to meet this objective, it is desirable that Android/Java be able to interact in a meaningful manner with our Android/Linux application. To that end we will build a traditional Android application using Java in Eclipse to interact with the Android/Linux server application.

Let's get started with an examination of the requirements of building our first C application for Android.

13.1   The Android/Linux:junction

Applications for Android/Linux are markedly different from applications constructed with the Android SDK. Applications built with Eclipse and the context-sensitive Java syntax tools make for a comfortable learning environment. In line with the spirit of Linux development, from here on out all development takes place with command-line tools and nothing more sophisticated than a text editor. While the Eclipse environment could certainly be leveraged for non-Java development, the focus of this chapter is on core C language coding for Android/Linux. The first place to start is with the cross-compiling tool chain required to build Android/Linux applications.

13.1.1   Tool chain

Building applications for Android/Linux requires the use of a cross-compiler tool chain from CodeSourcery. The specific version required is the Sourcery G++ Lite Edition for ARM, found at http://www.codesourcery.com/gnu_toolchains/arm/portal/package2548?@template=release. Once installed, the Sourcery G++ tool chain contributes a number of useful tools to assist in the creation of applications targeting Linux on ARM, which is the architecture of the Android platform. The ARM platform is a 32-bit reduced instruction set computer (RISC) processor, used in numerous devices including smartphones, PDAs, and technology appliances such as low-end routers and disk drive controllers. The CodeSourcery installation comes with a fairly comprehensive set of PDF documents describing the main components of the tool chain, including the C compiler, the assembler, the linker, and many more tools. A full discussion of these versatile tools is well beyond the scope of this chapter; however, three tools in particular are demonstrated in the construction of this chapter's sample applications. We will be using these tools right away, so we briefly introduce them in this section.

The first and most important tool introduced is gcc. This tool is the compiler responsible for turning C source files into object files and optionally initiating the link process to build an executable suitable for the Android/Linux target platform. The full name of the gcc compiler for our cross-compilation environment is arm-none-linux-gnueabi-gcc. This tool is invoked from the command line of the development machine. The tool takes command-line arguments of one or more source files along with zero or more of the numerous available switches.

The linker, arm-none-linux-gnueabi-ld, is responsible for producing an executable application for our target platform. When performing the link step, object code along with routines from one or more library files are combined into a relocatable, executable binary file, compatible with the Android Emulator's Linux environment. While a simple application may be compiled and linked directly with gcc, the linker is used when creating applications with more than one source file and/or more complex application requirements.

If the linker is responsible for constructing applications from more than one contributing component, the object dump utility is useful for dissecting, or disassembling, an application. We introduce the objdump, or arm-none-linux-gnueabi-objdump, tool presently; its usefulness becomes more apparent later in the chapter. This utility examines an executable application—a binary file—and turns the machine instructions found there into an assembly language listing file, suitable for analysis.

NOTE: All of the examples in this chapter take place on a Windows XP workstation. It is also possible to use this tool chain on a Linux development machine.

With this brief introduction behind us, let's build the obligatory Hello Android application to run in the Linux foundation of the Android Emulator.

13.1.2 *Building an application*

The first thing we want to accomplish with our journey into Android/Linux development is to print something to the screen of the emulator to demonstrate that we are running something on the platform outside the Android SDK and its Java application environment. There is no better way to accomplish this feat than by writing a variant of the Hello World application. At this point, there will be little talk of Android activities, views, or resource layouts. Most code samples in this chapter are in the C language. Listing 13.1 shows the code listing for our first Hello Android application.

Listing 13.1 Hello.c

```
#include <stdio.h>        ◁━━❶ Standard include file

int main(int argc,char * argv[])    ◁━━❷ Application entry point
{
    printf("Hello, Android!\n");   ◁━━❸ Display a string
    return 0;
}
```

Virtually all C language applications require a #include header file containing function definitions, commonly referred to as *prototypes*. In this case, the application includes the header file ❶ for the standard input and output routines, stdio.h. The standard C language entry point for user code ❷ is the function named main. The function returns an integer return code (a value of zero is returned in this simple example) and takes two arguments. The first, `argc`, is an integer indicating the number of command-line arguments passed in to the program when invoked. The second, `argv`, is an array of pointers to null-terminated strings representing each of the command-line arguments. The first argument, `argv[0]`, is always the name of the program executing. This application has but a single useful instruction, `printf`, which is to write to standard output (the screen) a textual string ❸. The `printf` function is declared in the header file, stdio.h.

To build this application, we employ the gcc tool:

```
arm-none-linux-gnueabi-gcc hello.c -static -o hellostatic
```

There are a few items to note about this command-line instruction:

- The compiler is invoked with the full name arm-none-linux-gnueabi-gcc.
- The source file is named hello.c.
- The `-static` command-line switch is used to instruct gcc to fully link all required routines and data into the resulting binary application file. In essence, the application is fully standalone and ready to be run on the target Android Emulator without any additional components. An application that's statically linked tends to be rather large because so much code and data are included in the executable file. For example, this statically linked application with basically a single line of code weighs in at 568,231 bytes. Ouch! If this `-static` switch is omitted, the application is built without any extra routines linked in. In this case the application will be much smaller; however, it will rely on finding compatible routines on the target system in order to run. For now, we are keeping things simple and building our sample application in such a manner that all support routines are linked statically.
- The output switch, `-o`, is used to request the name of the executable application to be hellostatic. If this switch is not provided, the default application name is a.out.

Now that the application is built, it's time to try it out on the Android Emulator. In order to do this we will rely on the adb tool introduced in chapter 2.

13.1.3 *Installing and running the application*

In preparation to install and run the Hello Android application, let's take a tour of our build and testing environment. We need to identify four distinct environments/tools and clearly understand them when building applications for Android/Linux. The first environment to grasp is the big-picture architecture of the Android Emulator running essentially on top of Linux, as shown in figure 13.1.

Android GUI running within a Linux executable environment

Figure 13.1   Android runs atop a Linux kernel.

As presented in the early chapters of this book, there is a Linux kernel running underneath the pretty, graphical face of Android. There exist device drivers, process lists, and memory management, among other elements of a sophisticated operating system.

As shown in the previous section, we need an environment in which to compile our C code. This is most likely to be a command-prompt window on a Windows machine, or a shell window on a Linux desktop machine, exercising the CodeSourcery tool chain. This is the second environment to be comfortable operating within.

NOTE The CodeSourcery tool chain is not designed to run on the Android/Linux environment itself, so the development work being done here is considered to be cross compiling. The figures and example code presented in this chapter were taken from a Windows development environment used by the author. There are a number of long path and directory structures in the Android SDK and the CodeSourcery tools. In order to help simplify some of the examples and keep certain command line entries from running over multiple lines some drive mappings were set up. For example a drive letter of "m:" seen in scripts and figures corresponds to the root location of source code examples on the author's development machine. Likewise the "g:" drive points to the currently installed Android SDK on the author's development machine. Note that this technique may also be used in Linux of Mac OSX environments with a "soft link" (ln) command.

The next requirement is to copy our newly constructed binary executable application to the Android Emulator. This can be done with a call to the adb utility or by using the DDMS view in Eclipse. Both of these tools were demonstrated in chapter 2. Here is the syntax for copying the executable file to the Android Emulator:

```
adb push hellostatic /data/ch13
```

Note a few items about this command:

- The command name is `adb`. This command takes a number of arguments that guide its behavior. In this case, the subcommand is `push`, which means to copy a file to the Android Emulator. There is also a `pull` option for moving files from the Android Emulator file system to the local development machine's hard drive.
- After the `push` option, the next argument, `hellostatic` in this case, represents the local file, stored on the development machine's hard drive.
- The last argument is the destination directory (and/or filename) for the transferred file. In this sample, we are copying the hellostatic file from the current working directory to the /data/ch13 directory on the Android Emulator.

Be sure that the desired target directory exists first! You can accomplish this with a `mkdir` command on the adb shell, described next.

The final tool to become familiar with is the `shell` option of the adb shell. Using this command, we can interact directly on the Android Emulator's file system with a limited shell environment. To enter this environment (and assuming the Android Emulator is already running), execute adb shell from the command line. When invoked, the shell displays the # prompt, just as if you had made a secure shell (ssh) or telnet connection to a remote Unix-based machine. Figure 13.2 shows these steps in action.

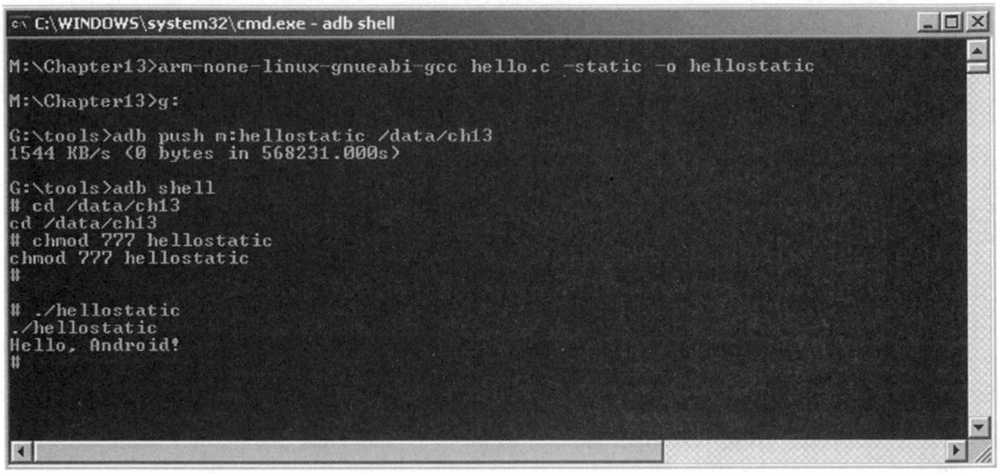

Figure 13.2   The build, copy, run cycle

Note the sequence shown in figure 13.2. First the application is built with a call to gcc. Next we push the file over to the Android Emulator. We then connect to the Android emulator via the adb shell command, which gives us the # prompt, indicating that we are now on the shell. Next we change directory (cd) to /data/ch13. Remember that this is Linux, so the application by default may not be executable. A call to chmod sets the file's attributes, turning on the executable bits and allowing the application to be invoked. Lastly, we invoke the application with a call to ./hellostatic. The search path for executable applications does not by default include the current directory on a Linux system, so we must provide a more properly qualified path, which explains the ./ prefix. Of course, we can see that our application has run successfully because we see the "Hello, Android!" text displayed on the screen.

Congratulations! We have a successful, albeit simple, Android/Linux application running on the Android Emulator. In the next section, we take a quick look at streamlining this build process.

13.1.4 *Build script*

In the last section we reviewed each step in building and preparing to test our application. Due to the rather tedious nature of executing each of these steps, we have a strong desire to utilize command-line tools when building C applications, as it greatly speeds up the edit, compile, copy, debug cycle. This example with only a single C source file is rather simplistic; however, when multiple source files must be linked together, the thought of having a build script is very appealing. The need for a build script is particularly evident where there are numerous source files to compile and link, as we will encounter later in this chapter.

Listing 13.2 shows the build script for our Hello Android application.

Listing 13.2   Build script for Hello Android, buildhello.bat

```
arm-none-linux-gnueabi-gcc hello.c -static -o hellostatic    ←—❶ Compile and link
g:\tools\adb push hellostatic /data/ch13                     ←—❷ Copy file
g:\tools\adb shell "chmod 777 /data/ch13/hellostatic"        ←—❸ Change permissions
```

A call to arm-none-linux-gnueabi-gcc ❶ compiles the source file, hello.c. The file is statically linked against the standard C libraries, and the resulting binary executable file is written out as hellostatic. The file hellostatic is copied to the Android Emulator ❷ and placed in the directory /data/ch13. The permissions for this file are changed ❸, permitting execution. Note the use of the adb shell with a quote-delimited command. Once this command executes, the adb application exits and returns to the Windows command prompt.

This example can be extended to perform other build steps or cleanup procedures such as removing temporary test data files on the Android Emulator or any similarly helpful tasks. As you progress, it will become clear what commands to put into your build script to make the testing process more efficient.

Now that the pressure is off—we have successfully written, built, and executed an application in the Android/Linux environment—it is time to deal with the problematic issue of a simple application requiring a file size of half a megabyte.

13.2   A better way

That was fun, but who wants a 500+ KB file that only displays something to the screen? Recall that the -static flag links in the essentials for running the application, including the input/output routines required for actually printing a message to the screen. If you are thinking there must be a better way, you are correct; we need to link our application to existing system libraries rather than including all of that code in our application's executable file.

13.2.1   The static flag, revisited

When an application is built with the -static flag, it is entirely self-contained, meaning that all of the routines it requires are linked directly into the application. This is not new information; we have already discussed this. It has another important implication beyond just the size of the code: it also means that using Android resident code libraries is a bigger challenge. Let's dig deeper to understand why. In order to do this, we have to look at the filesystem of Android/Linux.

System libraries in Android/Linux are stored in the directory /system/lib. This directory contains important functionality, such as OpenGL, SQLite, C standard routines, Android runtime, UI routines, and much more. Figure 13.3 shows a list of the available libraries in the Android Emulator. In short, everything that is specific to the

Android platform is found in /system/lib, so if we are going to build an application that has any significant functionality, we cannot rely on the libraries that ship with CodeSourcery alone. We have to write an application that can interact with the Android system libraries. This calls for a side trip to discuss the functionality of the linker application.

When building an application that requires the use of the linker, a few things change. First, the gcc command is no longer responsible for invoking the linker. Instead, the -c option is used to inform the tool to simply compile the application and leave the link step to a subsequent build step. Here is an example:

```
arm-none-linux-gnueabi-gcc -c hello.c -o hello.o
```

This command tells the compiler to compile the file hello.c and place the resulting object code into the file hello.o.

This process is repeated for as many source files as necessary for a particular application. For our sample application, we have only this single source file. However, in order to get an executable application, we must employ the services of the linker.

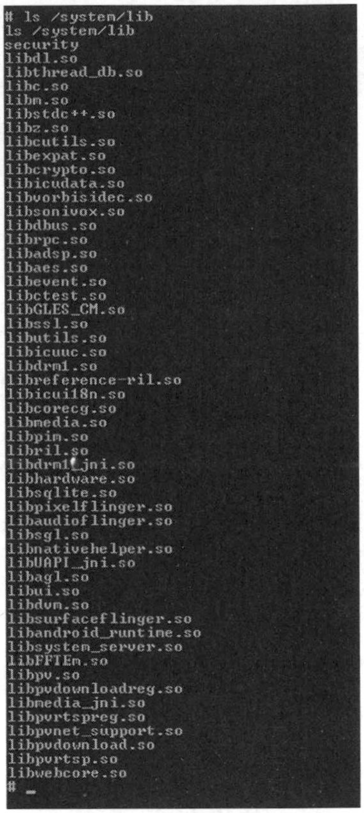

Another important change in the build environment is that we need to get a copy of the Android/

Figure 13.3   Available libraries in /system/lib

Linux libraries. We are compiling on the Windows platform (or Linux if you prefer), so we need to get access to the Android Emulator's /system/lib contents in order to properly link against the library files. Just how do we go about this? We use the adb utility, of course! Listing 13.3 shows a Windows batch file used to extract the system libraries from a running instance of the Android Emulator. A few of the libraries are pointed out.

Listing 13.3   pullandroid.bat

```
adb pull /system/lib/libdl.so    m:\android\system\lib      <--- libdl.so, dynamic loading
adb pull /system/lib/libthread_db.so    m:\android\system\lib
adb pull /system/lib/libc.so    m:\android\system\lib       <--- libc.so, C runtime
adb pull /system/lib/libm.so    m:\android\system\lib       <--- libm.so, math library
adb pull /system/lib/libGLES_CM.so    m:\android\system\lib    <--- libGLES_CM.so,
adb pull /system/lib/libssl.so    m:\android\system\lib              OpenGL
...
adb pull /system/lib/libhardware.so    m:\android\system\lib
adb pull /system/lib/libsqlite.so    m:\android\system\lib    <--- libsqlite.so,
many entries omitted for brevity                                    SQLite database
```

Figure 13.4 shows these files now copied over to the development machine.

```
M:\android\system\lib>dir
 Volume in drive M has no label.
 Volume Serial Number is 48F6-A2D6

 Directory of M:\android\system\lib

07/29/2008  12:22 AM    <DIR>          .
07/29/2008  12:22 AM    <DIR>          ..
07/29/2008  12:04 AM            13,836 libadsp.so
07/29/2008  12:04 AM            34,100 libaes.so
07/29/2008  12:05 AM            96,032 libagl.so
07/29/2008  12:05 AM           366,756 libandroid_runtime.so
07/29/2008  12:05 AM           100,332 libaudioflinger.so
07/29/2008  12:04 AM           241,868 libc.so
07/29/2008  12:05 AM            48,324 libcorecg.so
07/29/2008  12:04 AM           893,856 libcrypto.so
07/29/2008  12:05 AM             3,916 libctest.so
07/29/2008  12:04 AM            57,584 libcutils.so
07/29/2008  12:04 AM           321,560 libdbus.so
07/29/2008  12:04 AM             7,036 libdl.so
07/29/2008  12:05 AM            46,280 libdrm1.so
07/29/2008  12:05 AM            11,236 libdrm1_jni.so
07/29/2008  12:05 AM           451,900 libdvm.so
07/29/2008  12:05 AM            19,992 libevent.so
07/29/2008  12:04 AM           122,480 libexpat.so
07/29/2008  12:05 AM           402,404 libFFTEm.so
07/29/2008  12:05 AM            30,004 libGLES_CM.so
07/29/2008  12:05 AM            22,328 libhardware.so
07/29/2008  12:04 AM         1,041,236 libicudata.so
07/29/2008  12:05 AM           754,916 libicui18n.so
07/29/2008  12:05 AM           806,380 libicuuc.so
07/29/2008  12:04 AM           133,192 libm.so
07/29/2008  12:05 AM            84,344 libmedia.so
07/29/2008  12:05 AM            16,944 libmedia_jni.so
07/29/2008  12:05 AM           317,528 libnativehelper.so
07/29/2008  12:05 AM             6,452 libpim.so
07/29/2008  12:05 AM           114,400 libpixelflinger.so
07/29/2008  12:05 AM         4,737,012 libpv.so
07/29/2008  12:05 AM           139,296 libpvdownload.so
07/29/2008  12:05 AM            13,068 libpvdownloadreg.so
07/29/2008  12:05 AM           589,180 libpvnet_support.so
07/29/2008  12:05 AM           705,712 libpvrtsp.so
07/29/2008  12:05 AM            13,188 libpvrtspreg.so
07/29/2008  12:05 AM            18,844 libreference-ril.so
07/29/2008  12:05 AM            31,100 libril.so
07/29/2008  12:04 AM            20,752 librpc.so
07/29/2008  12:05 AM         1,078,252 libsgl.so
07/29/2008  12:04 AM           280,844 libsonivox.so
07/29/2008  12:05 AM           444,324 libsqlite.so
07/29/2008  12:05 AM           158,608 libssl.so
07/29/2008  12:04 AM             4,152 libstdc++.so
07/29/2008  12:05 AM           147,716 libsurfaceflinger.so
07/29/2008  12:05 AM             6,936 libsystem_server.so
07/29/2008  12:04 AM             9,952 libthread_db.so
07/29/2008  12:05 AM           771,672 libUAPI_jni.so
07/29/2008  12:05 AM           109,504 libui.so
07/29/2008  12:05 AM           379,744 libutils.so
07/29/2008  12:04 AM           122,032 libvorbisidec.so
07/29/2008  12:05 AM         3,908,228 libwebcore.so
07/29/2008  12:04 AM            78,452 libz.so
              52 File(s)     20,335,784 bytes
               2 Dir(s)     441,020,416 bytes free

M:\android\system\lib>_
```

Figure 13.4   Android libraries pulled to the development machine

Once these files are available on the development machine, we can proceed with the build step using the linker.

13.2.2 *Linking*

The name for the linker is arm-none-linux-gnueabi-ld. In most Linux environments the linker is named simply ld. When using the linker, many command-line options are available for controlling the output. There are so many options that an entire book could be written covering no other topic. Our interest in this chapter is writing applications, and we are taking as streamlined an approach as possible. So while there may be other options available to get the job done, the aim here is to learn how to build an application that enables us as much flexibility as possible to employ the Android system libraries. To that end, listing 13.4 shows the build script for building a dynamic version of Hello Android.

Listing 13.4   Build script for dynamically linked Android application

```
arm-none-linux-gnueabi-gcc -c hello.c -o hello.o

arm-none-linux-gnueabi-ld -entry=main -dynamic-linker /system/bin/linker
  -nostdlib -rpath /system/lib -rpath-link /android/system/lib -L
  /android/system/lib -l android_runtime -l c -o
  hellodynamic hello.o

g:\tools\adb push hellodynamic /data/ch13
g:\tools\adb shell "chmod 777 /data/ch13/hellodynamic"
```

❷ **Link**   **Compile only** ❶

❸ **Copy and change permissions**

This build script passes the –c compiler option ❶ when compiling the source file, hello.c. This way gcc does not attempt to link the application. The link command, arm-none-linux-gnueeabi-ld, has a number of options ❷. These options are more fully described in table 13.1. As in the previous example, adb is used to push the executable file ❸ over to the Android Emulator. The permissions are also modified to mark the application as executable.

Table 13.1   Linker options

Linker option	Description
-entry=main	Indicates the entry point for the application, in this case, the function named main.
-dynamic-linker /system/bin/linker	Tells the application where the dynamic linker application may be found at runtime. The /system/bin/ linker path is found on the Android Emulator, not the development environment.
-nostdlib	Tells linker to not include standard C libraries when attempting to resolve code during the link process.
-rpath /system/lib	Tells the executable where libraries can be found at runtime. This works in a manner similar to the environment variable LD_LIBRARY_PATH.
-rpath-link /android/system/lib	Tells the linker where libraries can be found when linking.
-L /android/system/lib	Tells the linker where libraries can be found. This is the linker import directory.
-l android_runtime	Tells the linker that this application requires routines found in the library file libandroid_runtime.so.
-l c	Tells the linker that this application requires routines found in the library file libc.so.
-o hellodynamic	Requests an output filename of hellodynamic.
hello.o	Includes hello.o as an input to the link process.

If our application required routines from the Open GL or SQLite library, the link command would have additional parameters of -l GLES_CM or -l sqlite, respectively. Leaving those library options off the link command prevents the application from linking properly because certain symbols (functions, data) cannot be found.

So, did it work? The hellodynamic binary is now only 2504 bytes. That's a great improvement. Figure 13.5 shows a listing of the two Hello Android files for a remarkable comparison. Each program is run, first the static version, then the dynamic version.

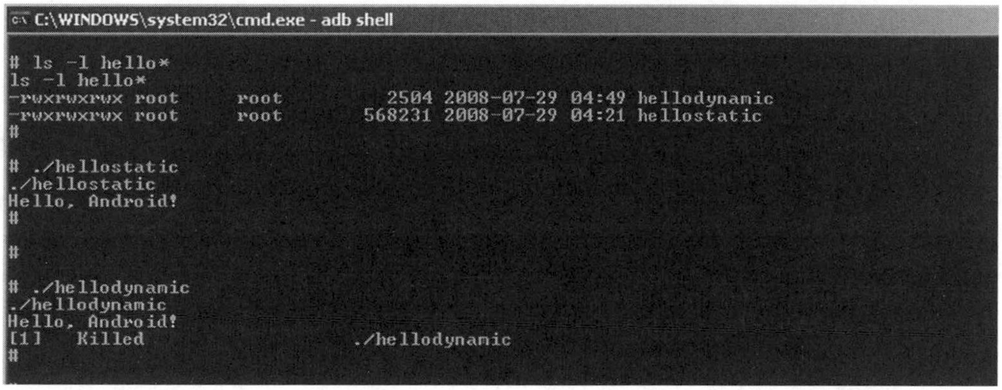

```
C:\WINDOWS\system32\cmd.exe - adb shell

# ls -l hello*
ls -l hello*
-rwxrwxrwx root        root          2504 2008-07-29 04:49 hellodynamic
-rwxrwxrwx root        root        568231 2008-07-29 04:21 hellostatic
#

# ./hellostatic
./hellostatic
Hello, Android!
#

#

# ./hellodynamic
./hellodynamic
Hello, Android!
[1]   Killed                       ./hellodynamic
#
```

Figure 13.5 Hello Android, static and dynamically linked

This looks great, except for one little problem. Note the last line in figure 13.5, which says, "Killed." Is there a problem with our dynamic version? Let's look closer.

13.2.3 *Exit, not return*

While our application has successfully linked with the Android system libraries of libc.so and libandroid_runtime.so and can actually run, there are missing pieces that cause the application to not properly execute. When we build an application in this manner, without letting the linker do all of its magic of knitting the entire application together, we have to do some housekeeping ourselves. Looks like there was something to that 500 KB application after all!

For one thing, if our application's entry point is the main function, and the main function executes a return statement, just where does it return to? Let's replace the return statement with an exit() call, as shown in listing 13.5.

Listing 13.5 Add an exit() call

```c
#include <stdio.h>

int main(int argc, char * argv[])
{
    printf("Hello, Android!\n");

    exit(0);    ⟵──❶ Add exit
```

```
    //return 0;     ←—② Remove return call
}
```

Add a call ❶ to the function exit(). This should return execution to the operating system. Comment out the call to return() ❷. A return call in this location causes a stack underflow because there is nowhere within this application to return to!

This fixed the problem—no more killed messages! Look at figure 13.6, where we see that the dynamic version of Hello, Android! now runs just fine.

Figure 13.6   A better-behaving dynamic version of Hello Android

Unfortunately we are not finished. It turns out that our application does not properly interact with other libraries, nor does it properly handle the argc and argv[] arguments to the main function. The C library (remember, we are linking against libc.so) has certain expectations for application structure and stack location. We're closer but still not quite ready for prime time.

What our application requires is a start routine, which is called by the operating system when our application is invoked. This function in turn calls our application's main function. This start routine must set up the necessary structures to allow the application to properly interact with the operating system and the core C libraries.

13.2.4   *Startup code*

We have surmised that our application is missing the proper startup code, but just what does startup code for an Android/Linux application on ARM look like? Where do we turn to get this kind of information? Let's look deeper into the bag of Code-Sourcery tricks for a clue.

A number of executable applications ship with Android. Let's pull one of those over to the desktop and see what we can learn. Perhaps we can extract information from that file that can assist in solving this puzzle.

The tool we are going to use to assist us in this effort is the object dump command, arm-none-linux-gnueabi-objdump. This utility has a number of options for tearing apart an ELF (Executable and Linkable Format) file for examination. This is the kind of file structure used by applications in the Android/Linux environment. Using the -d option of the objdump command results in a disassembly of the executable file, showing the assembly language equivalent of the code in each executable section. Our interest is in the first .text section of the disassembly, as this ought to be the entry point of the application. Listing 13.6 shows the .text section from the ping program taken from the Android Emulator (via adb pull).

Listing 13.6   Disassembly of ping

```
000096d0 <dlopen-0x60>:
   96d0:    e1a0000d    mov  r0, sp          ←──❶ Stack pointer
   96d4:    e3a01000    mov  r1, #0; 0x0     ←──❷ mov instruction
   96d8:    e28f2004    add  r2, pc, #4; 0x4
   96dc:    e28f3004    add  r3, pc, #4; 0x4    ❸ add instruction
   96e0:    eaffff8b    b    9514 <dlopen-0x21c>    ←──❹ Branch instruction
   96e4:    ea000e03    b    cef8 <dlclose+0x37bc>   ←──❺ Branch instruction
   96e8:    0000e408    andeq lr, r0, r8, lsl #8    ←──❻ Conditional expressions
   96ec:    0000e410    andeq lr, r0, r0, lsl r4
   96f0:    0000e418    andeq lr, r0, r8, lsl r4
   96f4:    0000e420    andeq lr, r0, r0, lsr #8
   96f8:    e1a00000    nop (mov r0,r0)      ←──❼ nop instruction
   96fc:    e1a00000    nop (mov r0,r0)
```

The first instruction assigns the value of the stack pointer (sp) to register 0 (r0) ❶. Next the literal value of zero is assigned to register r1 ❷. The address counter plus four memory location spaces is stored in registers r2 and r3 ❸. The b instruction tells the code to branch to a specific address ❹. In this case, the address is 0x21c bytes prior to the address of the dlopen function. This value is 9514 in decimal. The next branch is to an address that is 0x37bc bytes beyond the dlclose label ❺. The next few instructions ❻ are conditional operations. The code snippet finishes up with a pair of nop instructions ❼. Note that the address of each instruction is shown to the very left of each line. Each instruction occurs at a 4-byte offset from its predecessor. Four bytes times eight bits per byte equals a 32-bit address bus, which makes sense because the ARM processor family is 32-bit.

Okay, so that looks a little different from the rest of the code in this chapter—and just what does it do? Unfortunately, other than some basic interpretation of the op codes used, there is little to tell us why those instructions are there. After doing some research on the internet, we found a better example of this code, shown in listing 13.7.

Listing 13.7   crt.S

```
        .text              ←──❶ .text directive
        .global _start     ←──❷ global directive
_start:                    ←──❸ start label
        mov  r0, sp         ←──❹ Set up stack pointer
        mov  r1, #0
        add  r2, pc, #4
        add  r3, pc, #4        ❺ Branch to initialization
        b    __libc_init    ←──┘
        b    main           ←──❻ Branch to main
        .word  __preinit_array_start    ←──┐
        .word  __init_array_start        ❼ Jump table
        .word  __fini_array_start
```

```
        .word   __ctors_start
        .word   0
        .word   0
        .section .preinit_array
__preinit_array_start:
        .word   0xffffffff
        .word   0x00000000

        .section .init_array
__init_array_start:
        .word   0xffffffff
        .word   0x00000000

        .section .fini_array
__fini_array_start:
        .word   0xffffffff
        .word   0x00000000

        .section .ctors
__ctors_start:
        .word   0xffffffff
        .word   0x00000000
```

The .text directive indicates that this code should be placed in the .text section of the resulting executable ❶. The global start directive ❷ makes the start routine visible to the rest of the application and the linker. The start: ❸ label indicates the first location of the start routine. The mov and add instructions perform some housekeeping ❹ with the stack pointer, sp, just as seen in the extracted code from the ping program. Initialization takes place via a branch instruction to call the __libc_init routine ❺. This routine is found in the library libc.so. When this routine is complete, execution returns to the next instruction, another branch of the main routine ❻. This is the main() routine implemented by our C application. The next instructions ❼ set up a jump table to the sections required by a C language executable application. A pair of nop instructions round out the table. The sections preinit_array, init_array, fini_array, and .ctors are defined ❽. Note that it appears that these sections are required and that the values provided are an allowable address range for these sections. The linker takes care of putting these sections into the resulting executable file. Attempting to run the application without these sections results in code that crashes. I know—I tried!

NOTE   All credit for this crt.S file belongs to the author of a blog found at http://honeypod.blogspot.com/2007/12/initialize-libc-for-android.html. Additional reference material for low-level Android programming information can be found at http://benno.id.au.

Now that we have found an adequate startup routine, let's take a quick look at how to add this routine to our application. The assembly file is handled just like a C language file by the compiler:

```
arm-none-linux-gnueabi-gcc -c -o crt0.o crt.S
```

The resulting object file, crt0.o, is passed to the linker as an input file, just as any other object file would be. Also, the `entry` switch to the linker must now specify `_start` rather than `main`:

```
arm-none-linux-gnueabi-ld --entry=_start --dynamic-linker /system/bin/linker -
    nostdlib -rpath /system/lib -rpath-link \android\system\lib -L
    \android\system\lib -l c -l android_runtime -l sqlite -o executablefile
    csourcefile.o crt0.o
```

At this point, we are comfortable that we can build applications for Android/Linux, so it's time to build something useful. The next section walks through the construction of a daytime server.

13.3 What time is it?

Although we do not talk about it much today, Linux systems (and more generically, Unix systems) have a service running that provides the server's current date and time. This application, known as a daytime server, typically runs as a daemon, meaning in the background and not connected to a particular shell. For our purposes, we will implement a basic daytime server for Android/Linux, but we won't worry about turning it into a background service.

This application helps exercise our interest in developing Android/Linux applications. First and most important, this is an application of some significance beyond a simple `printf` statement. Second, once this application is built we write an Android/Java application to interact with the daytime server.

13.3.1 Daytime Server application

Our Daytime Server application has a very basic function. The application listens on a TCP port for incoming socket connections. When a connection is made, the application writes a short textual string representation of the date and time via the socket, closes the socket, and then returns to listening for a new connection.

In addition to the TCP socket interactions, our application logs requests to a SQLite database. Why? Because we can! The purpose of this application is to demonstrate nontrivial activities in the Android/Linux environment, including the use of the SQLite system library. Let's get started with examining the Daytime Server application.

13.3.2 daytime.c

The Daytime Server application can be broken into two basic functional parts. The first is the TCP socket server.

Our Daytime Server application binds to TCP port 1024 when looking for new connections. Ordinarily a daytime service binds to TCP port 13; however, Linux has a security feature where only trusted users can bind to any port below 1023. The second feature is the insertion of data into a SQLite database. Listing 13.8 shows the code for the Daytime Server application.

Listing 13.8 daytime.c

```
#include <time.h>
#include <stdio.h>
#include <string.h>
#include <errno.h>
#include <arpa/inet.h>
#include <netinet/in.h>
#include <sys/socket.h>
#include <resolv.h>
#include "sqlite3.h"

int PORTNUMBER = 1024;

#define htons(a)
( ((a & 0x00ff) << 8) | ((a & 0xff00) >> 8))

void RecordHit(char * when)
{
  int rc;
  sqlite3 *db;
  char *zErrMsg = 0;
  char sql[200];
  rc = sqlite3_open("daytime_db.db",&db);
  if( rc )
  {
    printf( "Can't open database: %s\n", sqlite3_errmsg(db));
    sqlite3_close(db);
    return;
  }
  bzero(sql,sizeof(sql));
  sprintf(sql,"insert into hits values (DATETIME('NOW'),'%s');",when);
  rc = sqlite3_exec(db, sql, NULL, 0, &zErrMsg);
  if( rc!=SQLITE_OK )
  {
    printf( "SQL error: %s\n", zErrMsg);
  }

  sqlite3_close(db);
}

int main(int argc, char **argv)
{
int listenfd, connfd;
struct sockaddr_in servaddr;
char buf[100];
time_t ticks;
int done = 0;
int rc;
fd_set readset;
int result;
struct timeval tv;

  printf("Daytime Server\n");
  listenfd = socket(AF_INET,SOCK_STREAM,0);
  bzero(&servaddr,sizeof(servaddr));
  servaddr.sin_family = AF_INET;
```

1 Required headers

2 Listening port number

3 Define helpful macro

4 SQLite interaction

5 Set up and listen on socket

```
servaddr.sin_addr.s_addr = INADDR_ANY;
servaddr.sin_port = htons(PORTNUMBER);

rc = bind(listenfd, (struct sockaddr *) &servaddr,sizeof(servaddr));
if (rc != 0)
{
 printf("after bind,rc = [%d]\n",rc);
 return rc;
}
listen(listenfd,5);         ⑤ Set up and listen
while (!done)                  on socket
{
 printf("Waiting for connection\n");
 while (1)
 {
  bzero(&tv,sizeof(tv));
  tv.tv_sec = 2;
  FD_ZERO(&readset);
  FD_SET(listenfd, &readset);
  result = select(listenfd + 1, &readset, &readset, NULL, &tv);
  if (result >= 1)
  {
   printf("Incoming connection!\n");
   break;
  }
  else if (result == 0)
  {
   printf("Timeout.\n");
   continue;
  }
  else
  {
   printf("Error, leave.\n");
   return result;
  }
 }

 printf("Calling accept:\n");
 connfd = accept(listenfd,        ⑥ Accept socket
 (struct sockaddr *) NULL, NULL);   connection
 printf("Connecting\n");
 ticks = time(NULL);
 sprintf(buf,"%.24s",ctime(&ticks));
 printf("sending [%s]\n",buf);
 write(connfd,buf,strlen(buf));
 close(connfd);
 RecordHit(buf);       ⑦ Record activity
}
return 0;
```

As with many C language applications, a number of headers ❶ are required, including definitions and prototypes for time functions, SQLite functions, and of course a number of headers required for TCP sockets. Note that the sqlite3.h header file is not provided in the CodeSourcery tool chain. This file was acquired from a sqlite3 distribution, and the file was copied into the local directory along with daytime.c. This is why the include file is delimited with quotation marks rather than <>, which is used for finding include files in the system or compiler path. The htons function is typically implemented in the library named socket (libsocket.so). Android does not provide this library, nor was this found in any of the system libraries. Therefore htons is defined here as a macro ❸. This macro is required to get the network byte ordering correct. When the application is running, this port can be verified by running net-stat -tcp on the command line in the adb shell.

The standard TCP port for a daytime server is port 13. In ❷, application is using port 1024 because our application cannot bind to any port numbered 1023 or below. Only system processes may bind to ports below 1024.

In the RecordHit function, we see SQLite interaction ❹. The RecordHit() function is responsible for inserting a record into the SQLite database created for this application.

Jumping into the main function, we see the socket functions in use to listen on a socket for incoming connections ❺. When a connection is accepted ❻, the current system time is sent to the calling client. After this, the application makes a record of the transaction by calling the RecordHit function ❼.

That's all the code necessary to implement our Android/Linux Daytime Server application. Let's look next at the SQLite3 database interaction in more detail.

13.3.3   *The SQLite database*

This application employs a simple database structure created with the sqlite3 application. We interact with sqlite3 from the adb shell environment, as shown in figure 13.7.

```
C:\WINDOWS\system32\cmd.exe - adb shell

#

#

# sqlite3 daytime_db.db
sqlite3 daytime_db.db
SQLite version 3.5.0
Enter ".help" for instructions
sqlite> .databases
.databases
seq  name                 file
---  -------------------  -------------------------------------------------------
0    main                 /data/ch13/daytime_db.db
sqlite> .tables
.tables
hits
sqlite> .schema hits
.schema hits
CREATE TABLE hits (hittime date,hittext text);
sqlite> .header on
.header on
sqlite> .mode column
.mode column
sqlite> select * from hits;
select * from hits;
hittime              hittext
-------------------  -------------------------
2008-07-29 07:31:35  Tue Jul 29 07:31:35 2008
2008-07-29 07:56:27  Tue Jul 29 07:56:27 2008
2008-07-29 07:56:28  Tue Jul 29 07:56:28 2008
2008-07-29 07:56:29  Tue Jul 29 07:56:29 2008
2008-07-29 07:56:29  Tue Jul 29 07:56:29 2008
2008-07-29 07:56:29  Tue Jul 29 07:56:29 2008
2008-07-29 07:56:29  Tue Jul 29 07:56:29 2008
2008-07-29 07:56:29  Tue Jul 29 07:56:29 2008
2008-07-29 07:56:30  Tue Jul 29 07:56:30 2008
sqlite> .exit
.exit
#
```

Figure 13.7   Sqlite3 from the command line in the adb shell

The purpose of this database is to record some data each time Daytime Server processes an incoming request. From a data perspective this sample is a bit boring as it simply records the system time plus the text returned to the client, which is a ctime formatted time string. Though somewhat redundant from a data perspective, the purpose is to demonstrate the use of SQLite from our C application, utilizing the Android/Linux resident sqlite3 library, libsqlite.so.

The previous section of code outlined the syntax for inserting a row into the database; this section shows how to interact with the database using the sqlite3 tool. The sequence shown in figure 13.7 is broken out and explained in listing 13.9.

Listing 13.9   Interacting with a sqlite database

```
# pwd
pwd
/data/ch13                          ❶ Connect to our
# sqlite3 daytime_db.db    ◁─┘        database file
sqlite3 daytime_db.db
SQLite version 3.5.0
Enter ".help" for instructions
sqlite> .databases                                              ◁─┐
.databases
seq  name           file
---  -------------  ------------------------------------------------
0    main           /data/ch13/daytime_db.db        ❷ Examine database
sqlite> .tables                                           structure
.tables
hits
sqlite> .schema hits                                           ◁─┘
.schema hits
CREATE TABLE hits (hittime date,hittext text);   ◁──❸ The Create statement
sqlite> .header on
.header on
sqlite> .mode column
.mode column
sqlite> select * from hits;    ◁──❹ Select rows
select * from hits;
hittime             hittext
------------------  -----------------------
2008-07-29 07:31:35  Tue Jul 29 07:31:35 2008
2008-07-29 07:56:27  Tue Jul 29 07:56:27 2008
2008-07-29 07:56:28  Tue Jul 29 07:56:28 2008
2008-07-29 07:56:29  Tue Jul 29 07:56:28 2008
2008-07-29 07:56:30  Tue Jul 29 07:56:30 2008
sqlite> .exit
.exit
#
```

The SQLite database operates in a similar fashion to other, modern SQL-based environments. In listing 13.9 we see the output from an interactive session where the database for this chapter's sample application is opened ❶. A series of commands given at the sqlite> prompt ❷ display the contents of the database in terms of structure. The schema command dumps the Data Definition Language for a particular table. In this case, we see the CREATE TABLE instructions for the hits table ❸. Viewing the data is simple with the use of the familiar select statement ❹.

The SQLite database engine is known for its simplicity. This section displayed a simple interaction and just how easy it is to employ. In addition, the SQLite3 database may be pulled from the Android Emulator and used on the development machine, as shown in figure 13.8.

```
C:\WINDOWS\system32\cmd.exe

C:\software\sqlite-3.5.4>g:\tools\adb pull /data/ch13/daytime_db.db \temp\daytime_db.db
128 KB/s (0 bytes in 2048.000s)

C:\software\sqlite-3.5.4>sqlite3 \temp\daytime_db.db
SQLite version 3.5.4
Enter ".help" for instructions
sqlite> .databases
seq  name             file
---  ---------------  ----------------------------------------------------------------
0    main             C:\temp\daytime_db.db
sqlite> .tables
hits
sqlite> select * from hits;
2008-07-29 07:31:35|Tue Jul 29 07:31:35 2008
2008-07-29 07:56:27|Tue Jul 29 07:56:27 2008
2008-07-29 07:56:28|Tue Jul 29 07:56:28 2008
2008-07-29 07:56:29|Tue Jul 29 07:56:28 2008
2008-07-29 07:56:29|Tue Jul 29 07:56:29 2008
2008-07-29 07:56:29|Tue Jul 29 07:56:29 2008
2008-07-29 07:56:29|Tue Jul 29 07:56:29 2008
2008-07-29 07:56:29|Tue Jul 29 07:56:29 2008
2008-07-29 07:56:30|Tue Jul 29 07:56:30 2008
sqlite> .exit

C:\software\sqlite-3.5.4>
```

Figure 13.8   The SQLite database on the development machine

This feature makes Android a very compelling platform for mobile data collection applications because synching data can be as simple as copying a database file that is compatible across multiple platforms.

13.3.4   *Building and running Daytime Server*

To build this application we need to combine the components of the prior few sections. We know that our application requires a startup component and must also link against multiple libraries. Because the application interacts with the SQLite database, we must link against the sqlite library in addition to the c and android_runtime libraries. The full build script is shown in listing 13.10.

Listing 13.10   Daytime application build script

```
arm-none-linux-gnueabi-gcc -c daytime.c        ◁─❶ Compile daytime.c
arm-none-linux-gnueabi-gcc -c -o crt0.o crt.S  ◁─❷ Compile crt.S
arm-none-linux-gnueabi-ld --entry=_start --dynamic-linker /system/bin/linker -
    nostdlib -rpath /system/lib -rpath-link \android\system\lib -L
    \android\system\lib -l c -l android_runtime -l sqlite -o daytime daytime.o
    crt0.o                                            ◁
C:\software\google\<path to android sdk>\tools\adb       ❸ Link the application
        push daytime /data/ch13                 ◁
g:\tools\adb shell "chmod 777 /data/ch13/daytime"    ❹ Install application
```

The build script begins by compiling the main source file, daytime.c ❶. The next line compiles the crt.S file, which was introduced in listing 13.7 for our C runtime initialization ❷. The linker command contains a number of switches to create the desired application. Note the parameter to the linker in ❸ to include the sqlite library. Note also the inclusion of both daytime.o and crt0.o object files as inputs to the linker. Both are required to properly construct the Daytime Server application. The input files are found in local (to the development machine) copies of the libraries. adb is employed to push the executable file to the Android Emulator and to modify the permissions, saving a manual step ❹.

Running the Daytime Server application is the easy and fun part of this exercise. Figure 13.9 shows our Daytime Server running.

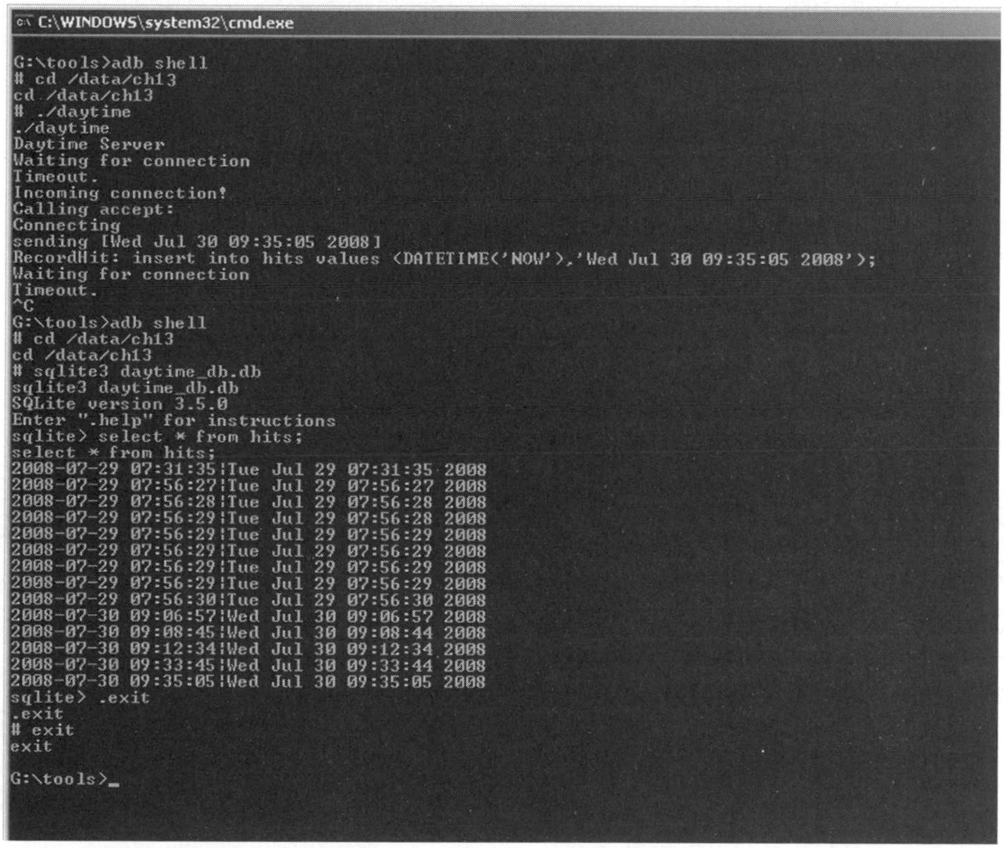

Figure 13.9 Daytime Server running in the shell

Here is a rundown of the sequence shown in figure 13.9:

1 Start the shell by running adb shell.
2 Change directories to /data/ch13, where our application resides, previously pushed there with an adb push command.

3 Run the ./daytime application.

4 The application binds to a port and begins listening for an incoming connection.

5 A timeout occurs prior to a connection being made. The application displays the timeout and returns to look for connections again.

6 A connection is detected and subsequently accepted.

7 The time string is constructed and sent to the client.

8 A record is inserted into the database with the shown sql statement.

9 We kill the application and restart the shell. Note that this is because we did not build a clean way of killing the Daytime Server. A proper version of the application would be to convert it to a daemon, which is beyond the scope of our interest here.

10 Run sqlite3 to examine the contents of our application's database.

11 Perform a select against the hits table, where we see the recently inserted record.

We have built an Android/Linux application that implements a variant of the traditional daytime server application as well as interacts with a SQL database. Not too shabby when you consider that this is a telephone platform! Let's move on to examine the Android/Java application used to exercise the Daytime Server, our Daytime Client.

13.4 *Daytime Client*

One of the stated objectives for this chapter is to connect the Java UI to our Daytime Server application. This section demonstrates the construction of a Daytime Client application, which communicates with our Daytime Server via TCP sockets.

13.4.1 *Activity*

The Daytime Client application has a single Activity, which presents a single Button and a TextView, as shown in figure 13.10.

When the Button is clicked, the Activity initiates the Daytime Server query and replaces the text of the TextView with the information received from the Daytime Server. Not much to it really, but that is fine, as all we are after in this sample is to demonstrate connectivity between the two applications. Listing 13.11 shows the onCreate method for this Activity.

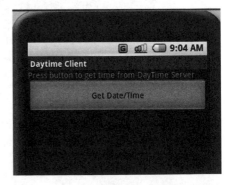

Figure 13.10   The Daytime Client app

Listing 13.11   UI elements of DaytimeClient.java

```
Handler h;                                  Declare and
@Override                               ❶  implement a Handler
public void onCreate(Bundle icicle) {
  super.onCreate(icicle);
```

```
setContentView(R.layout.main);

final TextView statuslabel = (TextView) findViewById(R.id.statuslabel);

h = new Handler() {                                          ❶ Declare and
    @Override                                                    implement a Handler
    public void handleMessage(Message msg) {
        switch (msg.what) {
            case 0:
                Log.d("CH13","data [" + (String) msg.obj + "]");
                statuslabel.setText((String) msg.obj);
                break;
        }
        super.handleMessage(msg);
    }
};

Button test = (Button) findViewById(R.id.testit);           ❷ Implement
test.setOnClickListener(new Button.OnClickListener() {           click listener
    public void onClick(View v) {
        try {
            Requester r = new Requester();    ◄──❸ Create a Requester instance
            r.start();
        } catch (Exception e) {
            Log.d("CH13 exception caught : ",e.getMessage())
        }
    }
});
}
```

This application is all about detecting the selection of a button ❷ and initiating an action based on that click. The action is the creation of an instance of the Requester class ❸, which we discuss in the next section. We handle the response from the socket server with the assistance of a Handler ❶. The Handler has a single role, which is to update the UI with textual data stored in the obj member of a Message object.

While the UI of this application is very simple, the more interesting side of this Activity is the interaction with the Daytime Server, which takes place in the Requester class, discussed in the next section.

13.4.2 *Socket client*

The Daytime Server application listens on a TCP port for incoming connections. In order to request the date and time, the Daytime Client must establish a client socket connection to the Daytime Server. It is hard to imagine a simpler TCP service than this—open a socket to the server and read data until the socket connection is closed. There is no additional requirement. Most of the networking examples in this book have focused on a higher-level protocol, HTTP, where the request and response are clearly defined with headers and a specific protocol to observe. In this example, the communications involve a lower-level socket connection, essentially raw, if you will, because there is no protocol associated with it beyond being a TCP stream (as opposed to UDP). Listing 13.12 demonstrates this lower-level socket communication.

Listing 13.12 `Requester` **class implementation**

```
public class Requester extends Thread {                 ①  Requester class extends
Socket requestSocket;                                       the Thread class
String message;
StringBuilder returnStringBuffer = new StringBuilder();
Message lmsg;
int ch;

public void run() {
    try {                                               ②  Socket
        requestSocket = new Socket("localhost", 1024);      communications
        InputStreamReader isr = new
InputStreamReader(requestSocket.getInputStream(),"ISO-8859-1");
        while ((ch = isr.read()) != -1) {
            returnStringBuffer.append((char) ch);
        }
        message = returnStringBuffer.toString();        ③  Create a
        lmsg = new Message();                               Message object
        lmsg.obj = (Object) message;
        lmsg.what = 0;                                  ④  Send the Message
        h.sendMessage(lmsg);                               to main thread
        requestSocket.close();
    } catch (Exception ee) {
        Log.d("CH13","failed to read data" + ee.getMessage());
    }
}
}
```

The `Requestor` ① class extends the `Thread` class by implementing the `run` method. Communications take place via an instance of the `Socket` class ②, which is found in the `java.net` package. Note the port number being used—1024, just like our socket server! A `Message` ③ is used to communicate back to the UI thread. Once the `Message` object is initialized, it is sent back to the calling thread ④.

With the Daytime Client now coded, it's time to test the application. In order for the Daytime Client to access a TCP socket, a special permission entry is required in the AndroidManifest.xml file: `<uses-permission android:name="android.permission.` `INTERNET"></uses-permission>`.

13.4.3 *Testing Daytime Client*

The first step in testing the Daytime Client is to ensure that the Daytime Server application is running, as described in section 13.3.4. Once you know the Daytime Server is running, you can run the Daytime Client.

NOTE If you are unclear on how to build and run the Daytime Client, refer to chapter 2 for information on properly setting up the Android development environment in Eclipse.

Figure 13.11 demonstrates the Daytime Client running, alongside a view of the Daytime Server. Note how the `TextView` of the Android application is updated to reflect the date and time sent by the Daytime Server.

Figure 13.11 Testing the Daytime Client

The Daytime Server is exercising both TCP socket functionality and SQLite database record insertions, all running in the Android Emulator. A production-ready Android/Linux application would need to be converted to run as a daemon, which is beyond our aim for this chapter.

13.5 Summary

This chapter wraps up this book with a topic that hopefully stretches your imagination for the kinds of applications possible with the versatile and open platform of Android. We had the goal of writing an application outside the Android SDK and demonstrating how that kind of application may be leveraged by a standard Android Java application. To write for the Android/Linux layer, we turned to the C programming language.

Developing C language applications for Android/Linux is a cross-platform compilation exercise using the freely available CodeSourcery tool chain. This chapter demonstrated using that tool set in conjunction with the adb utility provided in the Android SDK. The adb utility was vital because it enabled us to push our application to the Android Emulator for testing as well as to extract the Android system libraries, which were essential for linking our application with the Android resident libraries.

Of course, we used the adb shell to interact directly with the Android Emulator to run our C application.

C language mastery on this platform is powerful because much of the C language development process involves porting existing, open source Linux code to the ARM processor. This has the potential benefit of speeding up development for future functionality delivery to Android by leveraging existing code bases. A logical extension to this topic would be the development of a Java Native Interface (JNI) to bring many capabilities residing in C language libraries directly into the Java environment of Android.

Our sample application exercised TCP socket communications. The TCP communications capability proved to be a ready interface mechanism between the Android/Java layer and the Android/Linux foundation of the environment in the Daytime Client and Server applications, respectively. TCP socket communications may also take place from the Android/Linux environment to external, remote systems such as email servers or directory servers, opening up literally a world of possibilities.

The Daytime Server sample application also demonstrated the use of an Android resident library to manipulate a SQLite database used to store transaction data. The impact of this step should not be minimized as it satisfies three important development challenges. The first and most basic accomplishment of this functionality is that we have demonstrated linking against, and employing, an Android resident system library. This is significant because it shows how future applications may leverage Android functionality such as Open GL or media services. Second, using a device-resident database that is also accessible from the Java layer means we have an additional (and persistent) interface mechanism between the Java and Linux environments on the platform. Third, Android is a mobile platform. Anytime there is a mobile application, the topic of sharing and synching data bubbles up. We demonstrated in this chapter the ease with which an SQL-capable database was shared between the Android Emulator and a personal computer—and all without complex synchronization programming. Synchronization is, of course, a larger topic than this, but the capability of moving a single file between platforms is a welcome feature. There are only a few comparable solutions in the marketplace for other mobile environments, and that is after literally years of market penetration by these other platforms. Android gets it right from the start.

I trust that this chapter and this book will challenge you to dig deeper and that you may enjoy *Unlocking Android*.

appendix A:
Installing
the Android SDK

This appendix covers:
- Development environment requirements
- Obtaining the latest Android SDK
- Configuring the Android Development Tools for Eclipse

This appendix walks through the installation of Eclipse, the Android SDK, and the ADT plug-in for Eclipse. This appendix is meant to be a reference resource to assist in setting up the environment for Android application development. The topic of using the development tools is covered in chapter 2.

A.1 Development environment requirements

In order to develop Android applications, your computing environment must satisfy the minimum requirements. Android development is a quick-paced topic, with changes coming about very rapidly, so it is a good idea to stay in tune with the latest developments from the Android development team at Google. The latest information regarding supported platforms and requirements for Android development tools may be found at http://code.google.com/android/intro/installing.html#developmentrequirements.

The development environment used for the sample applications in this book includes:

- Windows XP/Vista, Mac OS X 10.4.8 or later (Intel x86 only), Linux
- Eclipse 3.3 (or later), including the JDT and Web Tools Platform, which are included in the Eclipse installation package
- JDK) and Java Runtime Environment (JRE) version 5
- ADT plug-in for Eclipse

A.2   *Obtaining and installing Eclipse*

A requirement for running the Eclipse IDE is the JRE version 5 or later. For assistance in determining the best JRE for your development computer, go to http://www.eclipse.org/downloads/moreinfo/jre.php. It is very likely that you already have an acceptable JRE installed on your computer. An easy way to determine what version (if any) you have is to run the following command from a command window or terminal session on your development computer:

```
java -version
```

This procedure checks to see if the JRE is installed and present in your computer's search path. If the command comes back with an error stating an invalid or unrecognized command, it is likely that the JRE is not installed and/or that it is not properly configured. Figure A.1 demonstrates using this command to check the version of the installed JRE.

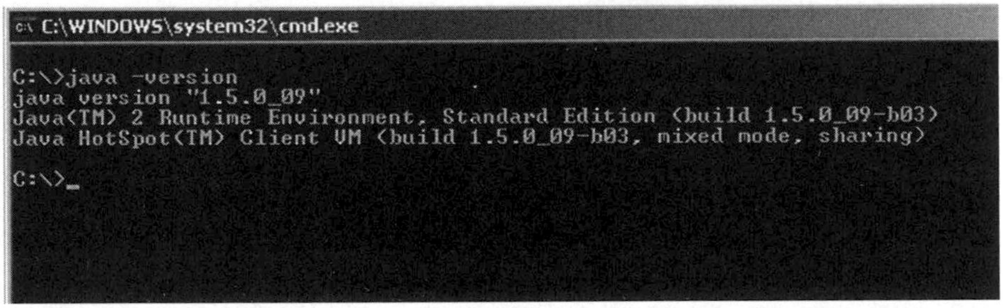

```
C:\WINDOWS\system32\cmd.exe

C:\>java -version
java version "1.5.0_09"
Java(TM) 2 Runtime Environment, Standard Edition (build 1.5.0_09-b03)
Java HotSpot(TM) Client VM (build 1.5.0_09-b03, mixed mode, sharing)

C:\>_
```

Figure A.1   The `java -version` command displays the version of Java installed on your computer.

Once your JRE is installed, the next step is to install the Eclipse IDE. Download the latest stable release from http://www.eclipse.org/downloads. You will want to download the version for Java developers. This distribution is described at the Eclipse website: http://www.eclipse.org/downloads/moreinfo/java.php. The Eclipse download is a compressed file. Once it is downloaded, extract the contents of the file to a convenient place on your computer. Because this download is simply a compressed file and not an installer, it does not create any icons or shortcuts on your computer.

To start Eclipse, run eclipse.exe (for Windows users) found in the Eclipse installation directory. You may want to make your own menu or desktop shortcut to eclipse.exe for convenience. This will start the IDE. Eclipse prompts for a workspace and suggests a default location such as C:\documents and settings\username\workspace. You may want to change that value to something Android specific to separate your Android work from other projects, as shown in figure A.2.

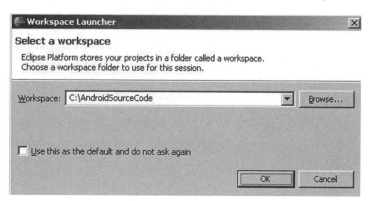

Figure A.2 Eclipse projects are stored in a workspace, which is a directory on your computer's hard drive.

Accept the suggested workspace location or specify an alternative workspace location, as desired. Once Eclipse is loaded, click the Workbench: Go to the Workbench icon on the main screen, as shown in figure A.3.

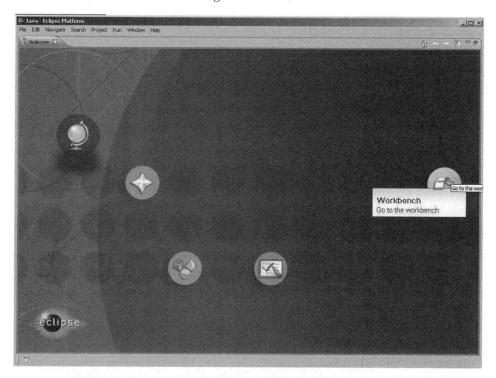

Figure A.3 Eclipse defaults to the home screen. Go to the workbench.

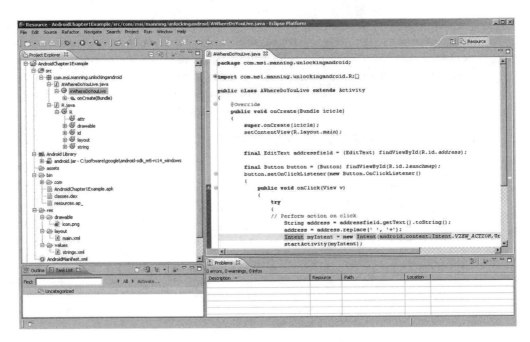

Figure A.4   Android development takes place in the Java Perspective.

Eclipse consists of many perspectives, the default being the Java Perspective. It is from this perspective that Android application development takes place. The Java Perspective is shown in figure A.4. Chapter 2 discusses in greater detail the use of the Eclipse IDE for Android application development.

For more information on becoming familiar with the Eclipse environment, visit the http://www.eclipse.org, where you can find online tutorials for building Java applications with Eclipse.

Now that Eclipse is installed, it's time to focus on the Android SDK.

A.3   *Obtaining and installing the Android SDK*

The Android SDK is available as a free download from a link on the Android home page, at http://code.google.com/android/download.html. SDK installation versions are available for multiple platforms, including Windows, Mac OS X (Intel x86 only), and Linux (i386). Select the latest version of the SDK for the desired platform.

> **TIP**   The Android SDK version shown in this appendix is marked 1.0_r1. The SDK will change from time to time as the Android team releases new versions. If you need to upgrade from one version to another, there will be an upgrade document on the Android website.

The Android SDK is a compressed folder download. Download and extract the contents of the compressed folder file to a convenient place on your computer. For example, you might install the SDK to C:\software\google\android-sdk-windows-1.0_r1, as shown in figure A.5.

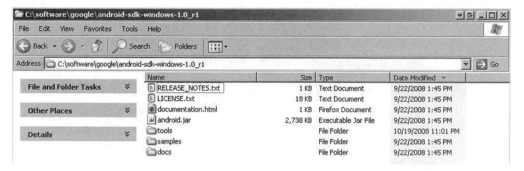

Figure A.5 The Android SDK installs into a directory on your hard drive.

As you can see from figure A.5, the installation footprint is rather simple. Opening the file documentation.html in your browser launches the SDK's documentation, which is largely a collection of Javadocs enumerating the packages and classes of the SDK; the complete documentation source is found in the docs folder. The file android.jar is the Android runtime Java archive. The samples folder contains a number of sample applications, each of which is mentioned in the documentation. The tools folder contains Android-specific resource compilers and the very helpful adb tool. These tools are explained and demonstrated in chapter 2 of this book.

Both Eclipse and the Android SDK are now installed. It's time to install the ADT plug-in for Eclipse to take advantage of the ADT's powerful features, which will assist in bringing your Android applications to life.

A.4 *Obtaining and installing the Eclipse plug-in*

The following steps demonstrate the installation of the Android plug-in for Eclipse, known as the ADT. The most up-to-date installation directions are available from the Android website. The first steps are somewhat generic for any Eclipse plug-in installation.

Here are the basic steps to install the ADT:

1 Run the Find and Install feature in Eclipse, found under the Help > Software Updates menu, as shown in figure A.6.

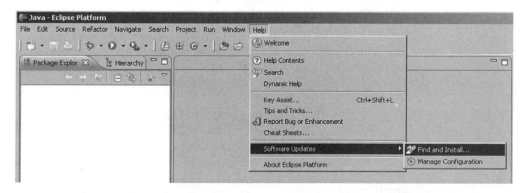

Figure A.6 The Eclipse environment supports an extensible plug-in architecture.

2   Select the Search for New Features to Install option, as shown in figure A.7. Click Next.

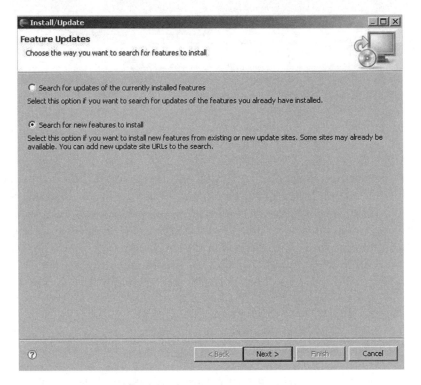

Figure A.7   Choose the new features option.

3   Select New Remote Site. Give this site a name, such as `Android Tools`, as shown in figure A.8. Use the following URL in the dialog: https://dl-ssl.google.com/ android/eclipse. Please note the https in the URL. Click OK.

Figure A.8   Create a new update site to search for Android-related tools.

4   A new entry is added to the list and is checked by default. Click Finish. The search results display the ADTs.

5 Select Android Tools and click Next, as shown in figure A.9.

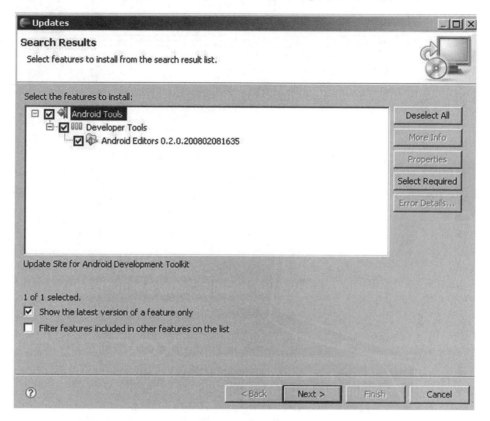

Figure A.9 You must select Android Tools for Eclipse to download and install.

6 After reviewing and accepting the license agreement, click Next.

7 Review and accept the installation location. Click Finish.

8 The plug-in is now downloaded and installed.

9 Restart Eclipse to complete the installation.

Congratulations! The ADT Eclipse plug-in is installed. Next step: configuration.

A.5 *Configuring the Eclipse plug-in*

Once Eclipse is restarted, it is time to connect the plug-in to the Android SDK installation. Select Preferences under the Window menu in Eclipse. Click the Android item in the tree view to the left to expand the Android settings. In the right-hand pane, specify the SDK installation location. For example, the value used for this appendix is C:\software\google\android-sdk-windows-1.0_r1, as shown in figure A.10.

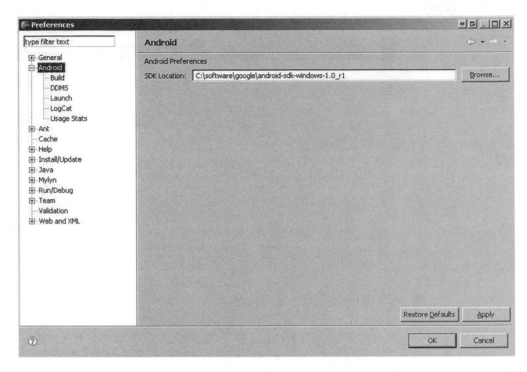

Figure A.10   You must select Android Tools for Eclipse to download and install.

Once the SDK location is specified, there are five other sections you may configure:

- *Build*—This section has options for automatically rebuilding resources. Leave this checked. The Build option can change the level of verbosity. Normal is the default setting.
- *DDMS*—This service is used for peering into a running virtual machine. These settings specify TCP/IP port numbers used for connecting to a running VM with the debugger and various logging levels and options. The default settings should be just fine.
- *Launch*—This section permits optional emulator switches to be sent to the emulator upon startup. An example of this might be the wipe-data option, which cleans the persistent file system upon launch of the emulator.
- *LogCat*—This is a log file created on the underlying Linux kernel. The font is selectable in this dialog. Adjust this as desired.
- *Usage Stats*—This optional feature sends your usage stats to Google to help the Android tools team better understand which features of the plug-in are actually used in an effort to enhance the toolset.

Your Android development environment is complete!

appendix B: Signing and installing applications on an Android device

This appendix covers:

- Using the adb tool to install and remove applications
- Using keytool and jarsigner
- Publishing applications to an android device
- Getting an application ready for distribution

After you get a handle on writing Android applications and working with the emulator, the next step is to digitally sign and install those applications on an actual device. Putting your applications on an actual device allows you to perform rigorous testing and lets you see practical results. You also have a bit more capability on an actual device (you can switch IP network types, use Bluetooth, use the real camera, and so on), so it is of course the first step on the road to publishing your application to a broader audience. In this appendix we provide concise information about how to get your applications ready for release and how to work with a real device to sign and install applications.

B.1 Recapping the Android Debug Bridge

Although we covered the Android Debug Bridge (adb) in chapter 2, a recap is in order as background for signing and installing applications and working with Android devices.

The adb is a client/server program that lets you interact with the Android SDK in various ways, including pushing and pulling files, installing and removing applications, issuing shell commands, and more. The adb tool comprises three components: a development machine–based server, a development machine client for issuing commands, and a client for each emulator or device in use. (Other Android tools, such as the DDMS tool, also create clients to interact with the adb.)

You can make sure your local adb server is running by issuing the adb start-server command. Similarly, you can stop your server with adb kill-server and then restart it, if necessary (or just to get familiar with the process). When you start the Eclipse/ADT environment, it automatically starts an adb server instance.

Once you are sure your adb server is running, you can tell if any devices or emulators are connected by issuing the adb devices command. The output of this command with an emulator running and a physical device attached via a USB cable is shown here:

```
#$ adb devices
List of devices attached
emulator-5554    device
HT845GZ49611     device
```

There are many more adb commands and uses than we are addressing here, of course, and obviously adb is very important in terms of developing Android applications (it is the chassis of the entire SDK), but it's important to understand that it supports *both* the emulator *and* any connected physical devices. The first step in getting your applications onto an actual device is to connect your device and make sure it is recognized by the adb and then run the applications from the SDK (to make the process as simple as possible, close down any running emulators and restart your adb server, then connect your device so that it is the only option present).

B.2 Digital signatures

When you are running your applications using the adb, you are running in debug mode. In debug mode your applications are automatically digitally signed by the SDK using a self-signed debug key that is stored in the debug.keystore file (this file is in the .android subdirectory of the user's home directory by default).

The Android platform requires digital signatures on every .apk package (every application archive file). Without a digital signature, an .apk is not allowed to run. The debug key and store are conveniences included for you, so that you do not have to worry about digital signatures while developing applications using the SDK. When you are ready to go beyond debug mode and run outside the adb, you need to sign your application with a non-debug key (the debug key is not allowed outside debug mode).

Here we are going to cover basic examples of using the Java to create your own key and keystore. We will also include an example of using such a key to sign your .apk files with the Java tool. These are standard Java tools included with the Sun Java SDK; for specific information about these tools, see the Sun documentation for your platform: http://java.sun.com/javase/6/docs/technotes/tools/index.html - security.

B.2.1 Keytool

An example of using the keytool command to create your own self-signed private key is the following:

```
keytool -genkey -v -keystore my-release-key.keystore -alias my_key -keyalg
➥ RSA -validity 10000
```

This command generates a key (-genkey) in verbose mode (-v) using a keystore file named my-release-key.keystore and an alias of my_key with the RSA cryptographic algorithm and a validity period of 10000 days. Every key in a keystore requires an alias. We will use the alias next when referring to the key within the keystore while demonstrating how to sign an .apk file. Also note that we are using a very long time period for the key. The Android documentation recommends at least a 25-year key life, and the Android Market currently requires a key that does not expire until after October 22, 2033.

The keytool command will prompt you for a key password and organizational information when creating a key. You should use accurate information (it is possible for your users to view this later), and you should use a strong password. Once you create your key, you also need to be very careful to store it securely and keep the password private. (If your key is lost or compromised, your identity can be misused, and the trust relationships to your key via your applications can be abused.)

B.2.2 Jarsigner

Once you have a private key, you can use it to sign your application files. Signing your files is done using the jarsigner tool. Before you can use the jarsigner tool, you need to export your project as an *unsigned* .apk archive. To export your project using the Eclipse/ADT environment, right-click and select the Android Tools > Export Unsigned Application Package option, as shown in figure B.1.

Once you have an unsigned archive file, then you can use the jarsigner tool to sign it with your key, as shown here:

```
jarsigner -verbose -keystore my-release-key.keystore RestaurantFinder.apk
➥ my_key
```

This command tells the jarsigner tool to use the previously defined keystore file (my-release-key.keystore) for the particular .apk, using the specified key (designated by the key alias my_key).

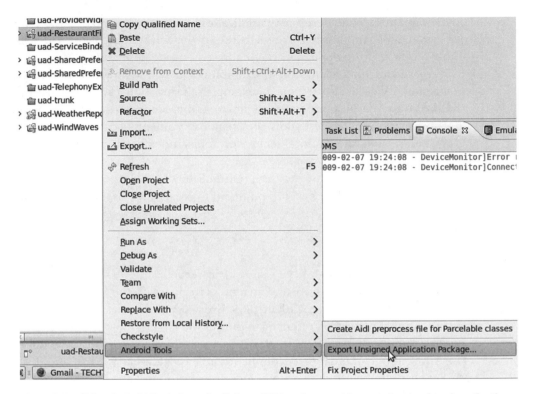

Figure B.1   Using Android Tools from the Eclipse/ADT environment to export an unsigned application archive package

Once you enter this command and use the correct password, jarsigner will create a few metadata files (a manifest, for example) and will digitally sign each file in the archive with your key, as shown here:

```
Enter Passphrase for keystore:
****************
   adding: META-INF/MANIFEST.MF
   adding: META-INF/TOTSP_KE.SF
   adding: META-INF/TOTSP_KE.RSA
  signing: res/anim/scaler.xml
  signing: res/drawable/no_review_image.png
  signing: res/drawable/restaurant_icon.png
  signing: res/layout/review_criteria.xml
  signing: res/layout/review_detail.xml
  signing: res/layout/review_list.xml
  signing: res/layout/spinner_view.xml
  signing: res/layout/spinner_view_dropdown.xml
  signing: AndroidManifest.xml
  signing: resources.arsc
  signing: classes.dex
```

Jarsigner is the last step; after your archive is signed with your key, it's ready to be installed on a device and tested outside debug mode. You can use the adb tools to install a signed .apk archive (`adb install [path_to_apk]`), or you can optionally use the very handy APK Installer application that is available in the Android Market (http://www.android.com/market/).

The APK Installer tool lets you install archives that are copied onto your SD card, as opposed to using the adb. Once you plug your device in via USB, you can elect to mount the device (following the on-device screen instructions) and copy files to it. This works like any USB drive, and you can drag your .apk onto your phone. With an .apk archive on your SD card, you can then browse to it from the APK Installer and select Install—it will take care of the rest.

The streamlined process we have outlined here, creating a key and signing your applications with it, is the bare minimum that you need to install an application on an Android device in non-debug mode. For more detailed information you should review the Android documentation in this area (http://code.google.com/android/devel/sign-publish.html - signing).

Once you are familiar with signing your applications, the next thing you need to do is perform some final cleanup before actual distribution to end users.

B.3   *Cleaning up for distribution*

Getting an Android application cleaned up to go to distribution is straightforward. You generally need to remove any extraneous code, such as log statements, and anything else debug-specific, such as the `android:debuggable="true"` attribute, if present, in the manifest. You should also use common sense and do things like making sure that any local data stores are cleaned up and cleaned out before packaging (don't include your test data). Along with that, you need to provide a few required manifest elements, you should test on an actual device, and you may want to add data import and export support or provide an End User License Agreement (EULA).

B.3.1   *Important manifest elements: label, logo, version, SDK level*

Your application needs to have several key manifest elements before you consider distribution.

You should include an appropriate label and icon using the `android:label` and `android:icon` attributes within the `<application>` element of the manifest. Make the icon and the label text the right size so that they are not cut off on the device or devices you are targeting. (Smaller amounts of text are better for labels, in general.)

Every application should also include the `android:versionCode` and `android:versionName` attributes in the `<application>` element of the manifest as well. The `versionCode` is an integer value that can be checked programmatically (and is typically incremented at each release), and the `versionName` is what is displayed to users. Android provides solid documentation on these elements as well (http://code.google.com/android/devel/sign-publish.html - versioning).

Along with the label, icon, and versions, it is also important to specify the `android:minSdkVersion` attribute. Without this attribute, the application is assumed to be compatible with all versions of the Android SDK. If your application works with 1.0r2 or 1.1 but not 0.9, then you should provide this attribute (and this attribute will likely be even more important in the future when more versions are available in the wild).

B.3.2 *Test, test, then test again*

Once you think your application is streamlined and ready, with logo and versions and so on, you should put it through some paces in non-debug mode on an actual device as a testing step. Here we are talking about acceptance-style testing, actually using the application to see how it performs (unit tests are also a good idea, as is the Monkey exerciser that Android provides at http://code.google.com/android/reference/monkey.html, but those are a different level of tests that should generally come well before distribution time arrives).

Make sure to run your application under as many conditions as you can (with Wi-Fi on and off, network (GPRS, EDGE, 3G) on and off, GPS on and off, and so on), and make sure it responds as you expect (even if the response is just a context-sensitive message to users that data is not available, if that is what you expect). Pay extra attention to how your application responds to being stopped and restarted; for example, if your device supports it, change the screen orientation at each activity back and forth (this stops and starts the current `Activity`, which may cause problems if you have not used `onCreate`/`onStart`/`onPause` and the other lifecycle methods appropriately).

Along with making sure your application works on an actual device in as many conditions as possible, you may want to consider a few additional touches.

B.3.3 *An End User License Agreement*

Your own EULA is recommended. Everyone is familiar with these types of agreements, from so frequently encountering them and *not* reading them in everyday life. Even though users often blaze past these, it is a good idea to have one to define terms and to potentially protect yourself from liabilities. (You should consult a lawyer about all legal matters, including drawing up a EULA.)

It is common to require a EULA to be shown as an `Alert` the first time your application is started and then not show it again on subsequent launches (you can do this with a single saved `boolean` as a preference). As well as showing the EULA the first time out, it is also a good idea to include a setting to allow users to get back to it and view it if they choose to.

B.3.4 *Nice extra: data import and export*

As an extra step, if your application saves any state using any local form (files, preferences, database, and the like) you may want to implement an import/export data–type `Activity`. This `Activity` should allow the user to save the data out to the SD card (in XML format, for example) and should also allow the user to read data back in and populate the local stores. This can make application upgrades easier in some cases, and it can make switching to a new device possible without losing all local data (something your users will appreciate).

Once you are convinced that everything is in place, data import/export included or not, you are then ready to take your wares to the Android Market.

B.4   Publishing to the Market

The Android Market (http://market.android.com) is the built-in application that comes with the Android platform that allows users to browse and install applications with just a few clicks. The significant point to keep in mind is that governance (terms that developers must agree to) is included with Android devices. There are no outside steps required for a user to install your application if it is on the Market—direct from service to device.

B.4.1   The Market rules

Before you put your application on the Market, you should carefully read the developer terms (http://www.android.com/us/developer-distribution-agreement.html) and the content guidelines (http://www.android.com/market/terms/developer-content-policy.html).

The Market terms cover pricing and payments, returns, license grants, takedowns, and many other important topics that you should be familiar with. The content guidelines further define what is acceptable in terms of subject matter and media (again, there are rules; it's not an entirely open system).

If the Market terms are amenable to you and you plan to post applications, you need to register (which can be done online at the Market website) and have a Google account. There is a small fee to register, but this is minimal and probably worthwhile to allow the Market to associate an identity with an account using an actual payment method (which has contact information).

Once you are set up, you can begin placing your applications in the Market for users to download and install directly.

B.4.2   Getting your application in the Market

Registered Market developers simply use an online form to upload applications. When uploading applications, you can define the different Market locations that are supported, pricing and terms, as well as a category and description and other options.

B.4.3   Automatic Market updates

Currently the Android Market is in beta form, and it does not support automatically alerting your users about updates to installed applications. Because of this, the Android documentation has a section titled "Publishing Upgrades on Android Market" that details how you can create your own automatic update support.

Basically, this process boils down to hosting a web service that your application should poll periodically to check for application updates. If an update is found, you can have your application programmatically invoke the Market application (which supports its own rich set of intents) and direct the user to the new version.

B.4.4   *Why the Market matters*

In short, the Android Market matters because it's built in and it's open.

We touched on this in chapter 1, but the open nature of Android itself—and of the Market—is an important advantage to Android developers and Android users. There is no arbitrary inclusion or exclusion process that an individual or company holds over the Market. Anyone who joins and agrees to the terms can put applications on the Market. Some applications will do better than others, of course (and users can rate them and comment on them), but anyone can join.

The Android Market is a merit-based system; impress your users and they will rate your application well and compliment you; do the opposite and they will do the opposite (survival of the fittest, if you will). Some pundits have panned this as a potentially negative aspect of the overall Android experience, purporting that without more control too many bad (or even rogue) applications will appear. Although some abuse is probably inevitable, we think the reality is that the Market will be very healthy (it does have sensible terms of use), and that the open nature will reveal itself as invaluable in the long term (creating an environment where better applications are created and rewarded, in the end greatly benefiting users).

B.5   *Other distribution means*

The last thing to be aware of with regard to distributing your application and the Android Market is the fact that there are other means.

Various third-party sites offer distribution channels too. These sites have different agreement types and different payment models, so you should research them carefully before using them, but you should know that they are available.

These services include:

- http://andappstore.com
- http://slideme.org/
- http://www.androidfreeware.org/

You may want to distribute your application only in the official Market or on third-party services, or you may decide to use a combination. If you do use third-party services, keep in mind that these, while growing in popularity, are not as accessible to users as the built-in Market. (Users have to find the third-party service and generally then have to install applications on their own or at least bootstrap the service with an application specifically designed to use it.)

Lastly, you can deliver your .apk file on your own as well. Normal end users should not be expected to use the shell to install applications, of course, but you can point them to the APK Installer (which itself is in the Market), and they can install any archive you can deliver them. The more means you have at your disposal to get your applications into the hands of users, obviously, the better.

index